GCSE

SCIENCE

EDUCATIONAL

Letts Educational
Aldine Place
London W12 8AW
Tel: 020 8740 2266
Fax: 020 8743 8451
e-mail: mail@lettsed.co.uk

First published 1993
Reprinted 1994, 1995 (twice)
Revised 1997
Reprinted 1999 (twice), 2000

British Library Cataloguing-in-Publication Data
A CIP record for this book is available from the British Library

ISBN 1 85805 440 0

Printed and bound in Great Britain by Bath Press Colourbooks, Glasgow

Letts Educational Ltd, a division of Granada Learning Ltd. Part of the Granada Media Group.

Acknowledgements
I am grateful to the following Examining Groups for permission to reproduce questions from recent examinations and sample assessment material.

Midland Examining Group (MEG)
Northern Examinations and Assessment Board (NEAB)
Northern Ireland Council for the Curriculum Examinations and Assessment (NICCEA)
Scottish Examination Board (SEB)
Southern Examining Group (SEG)
EDEXCEL, formerly University of London Examinations and Assessment Council (ULEAC)
Welsh Joint Education Committee (WJEC)

The answers and workings given are my own and in no way the responsibility of the Examining Groups.
    In preparing this revision guide, I am indebted to my wife, Elizabeth, for her improvements to the text and illustrations and the care with which she turned my initial manuscript into an accurate typescript. I must also thank the staff of Letts Educational, particularly Wayne Davies, for their support and encouragement throughout the project.

Graham Hill 1997

The author and publishers are grateful to the following for permission to reproduce photographs:
The Ancient Art & Architecture Collection 14.1; Bruce Coleman Ltd 9.9 (right); Holt Studios Ltd/Frank Lane Picture Agency 1.1, 7.6, 9.9 (left); Retna Pictures Ltd 9.1; Science Photo Library 6.3, 6.5, 9.10, 11.2, 22.6, 25.3

Contents

Starting points

Introduction   1
How to use this book   1
The National Curriculum and the GCSE   2
Standard Grade in Scotland   4

Syllabus checklists   5
MEG   5
NEAB   7
NICCEA   8
SEG   10
EDEXCEL (formerly ULEAC)   12
WJEC   13
SQA (formerly SEB)   13
Double award study checklist   14
Single award study checklist   15
Scottish Standard Grade study checklist   16

Studying and revising   17
Hints for revision   17
The examination   18

AT2 Life processes and living things

1   Living things and populations   21
1.1   The variety of living things   21
1.2   Characteristics of living things   22
1.3   Classification of living things   22
1.4   Naming living things   24
1.5   Ecosystems as habitats and
        communities   24
1.6   Interactions in ecosystems –
        food chains   25
1.7   Food chains and food webs   26
1.8   The growth of populations   28
1.9   The human population   29
1.10   Food production and ecosystems   29
1.11   Important cycles and energy chains   30
        Summary   32
        Quick test 1   33

2   Photosynthesis   35
2.1   Cells – building blocks for living
        things   35
2.2   From atoms to ecosystems   36
2.3   The movement of substances into
        and out of cells   37
2.4   Plants – the source of all food   39
2.5   What chemicals do plants use to
        produce starch?   40

2.6   What happens in photosynthesis?   41
2.7   Photosynthesis and transpiration   42
2.8   Essential elements for plants   43
        Summary   44
        Quick test 2   45

3   Food and diet – nutrition   47
3.1   Different kinds of food   47
3.2   Carbohydrates, fats and proteins   48
3.3   Vitamins   49
3.4   Minerals   49
3.5   Diet and health   50
        Summary   51
        Quick test 3   51

4   Digestion   53
4.1   What happens to food after we eat it?   53
4.2   How is food digested?   54
4.3   Using the absorbed foods   54
4.4   Problems in the digestive system   56
        Summary   56
        Quick test 4   57

5   The blood system   58
5.1   What is blood?   58
5.2   The functions of blood   59
5.3   Blood vessels   60
5.4   Circulation of blood   60
5.5   Diseases of the circulation system   62
5.6   Getting rid of waste   63
5.7   Kidney failure   64
        Summary   64
        Quick test 5   65

6   Respiration   67
6.1   Introduction   67
6.2   Breathing   67
6.3   Gas exchange in the lungs   68
6.4   Smoking or health   70
6.5   Cellular respiration   71
6.6   Respiration in all living things   71
6.7   Living without oxygen   73
6.8   Brewing and breadmaking   73
6.9   Anaerobic respiration in our muscles   74
        Summary   75
        Quick test 6   76

7   Senses and responses   78
7.1   Detecting changes and responding   78

7.2 Detecting light – the eye 79
7.3 Detecting sound and balancing – the ear 81
7.4 Detecting smell and taste – the nose and mouth 81
7.5 Detecting temperature and touch – the skin 82
7.6 The nervous system 83
7.7 Reflex and conscious actions 84
7.8 The effect of drugs on the CNS 85
7.9 Hormones and hormonal control 86
7.10 Plant hormones 87
7.11 Homeostatic control 88
Summary 89
Quick test 7 90

8 Reproduction 92
8.1 Sexual and asexual reproduction 92
8.2 Asexual reproduction – cloning 92
8.3 Sexual reproduction in animals 94
8.4 Human reproduction 94
Summary 95
Quick test 8 96

9 Genetics and evolution 98
9.1 Introduction 98
9.2 Chromosomes and cell division 98
9.3 Sexual reproduction and meiosis 100
9.4 Genes and genetics 101
9.5 Why is genetics important? 103
9.6 Evolution 104
9.7 How has evolution occurred? 105
Summary 108
Quick test 9 109

10 Our effect on the environment 112
10.1 Waste and its disposal 112
10.2 Agricultural practices 113
10.3 Pollution 114
10.4 Air pollution 115
10.5 The finite Earth – depleting the Earth's resources 115
10.6 Conservation of wildlife and the countryside 116
Summary 117
Quick test 10 117

AT3 Materials and their properties

11 Earth science 120
11.1 Origins of the Earth and atmosphere 120
11.2 Weathering 121
11.3 Rocks in the Earth's crust 122
11.4 Plate tectonics 123

11.5 The theory of plate tectonics 124
Summary 125
Quick test 11 126

12 Materials, elements and compounds 128
12.1 Raw materials 128
12.2 Classifying materials by their properties 128
12.3 Separating mixtures 130
12.4 Chromatography 132
12.5 Testing for pure substances 133
12.6 Elements – building blocks for all substances 133
12.7 Elements and compounds 134
12.8 Mixtures 135
12.9 Air – an important mixture 135
12.10 Reactions with oxygen 136
Summary 136
Quick test 12 137

13 Particles 139
13.1 Introduction 139
13.2 Evidence for moving particles 139
13.3 Particles in motion – the kinetic theory 140
13.4 Changes of state 141
13.5 Gas pressure 142
13.6 Temperature scales 143
13.7 Atoms and molecules 144
13.8 Symbols and formulas 145
13.9 Chemical equations: word equations and symbolic equations 146
13.10 Measuring atoms 147
13.11 How much? 148
Summary 149
Quick test 13 150

14 Metals and alloys 152
14.1 Introduction 152
14.2 Reactions of metals 152
14.3 Summarising the reactions of metals 154
14.4 Alloys and their uses 155
14.5 Extracting iron 156
14.6 Rusting 157
14.7 Redox 157
14.8 Extracting metals 158
14.9 The structure of metals 159
14.10 Explaining the properties of metals 160
Summary 161
Quick test 14 162

15 Electricity and electrolysis 164
15.1 Electric currents 164
15.2 Conduction of electricity by solids and liquids 165
15.3 Explaining electrolysis 166

15.4	Charges on ions	167
15.5	Electrolysis in industry	168
15.6	Ionic compounds	169
15.7	Molecular compounds	171
15.8	Comparing different structures	172
	Summary	173
	Quick test 15	174

16	Acids, bases and salts	176
16.1	Acids in everyday life	176
16.2	Measuring acidity	177
16.3	The properties of acids	178
16.4	Bases and alkalis	179
16.5	Neutralisation	180
16.6	Alkalis in industry	181
	Summary	182
	Quick test 16	182

17	The chemical industry	184
17.1	Choosing an industrial site	184
17.2	Sulphuric acid – an important industrial acid	185
17.3	Manufacturing sulphuric acid	186
17.4	Ammonia – an important industrial alkali	187
17.5	Manufacturing ammonia	187
17.6	Fertilisers from ammonia	188
17.7	The nitrogen cycle	189
17.8	Reaction rates and industrial processes	190
17.9	How fast?	190
17.10	Factors affecting reaction rates	192
17.11	The effect of temperature on the rate of enzyme-catalysed reactions	194
	Summary	194
	Quick test 17	195

18	Energy, fuels and plastics	197
18.1	Burning and fuels	197
18.2	Fuels for various processes	197
18.3	Measuring the energy from fuels	199
18.4	Fossil fuels – coal, oil and natural gas	199
18.5	Alternative energy sources	200
18.6	Crude oil	201
18.7	Chemicals in crude oil – alkanes	202
18.8	Alkenes	203
18.9	Plastics	205
18.10	Ethanol	207
	Summary	208
	Quick test 18	209

19	The periodic table and atomic structure	211
19.1	Mendeléev's periodic table	211
19.2	Modern periodic tables	212
19.3	Atomic structure	214
19.4	Atomic number and mass number	215
19.5	Relative atomic mass and isotopes	215
19.6	Electron structures and the periodic table	217
19.7	Group I – the alkali metals	218
19.8	Group VII – the halogens	219
19.9	The transition metals	221
19.10	Group 0 – the noble gases	222
19.11	Chemical bonding	223
	Summary	224
	Quick test 19	224

AT4 Physical processes

20	Force and motion	226
20.1	Forces	226
20.2	Force, weight and mass	226
20.3	Stretching forces	227
20.4	Frictional forces	229
20.5	Turning forces	230
20.6	Force and pressure	231
20.7	Pressure in liquids	232
20.8	Distance and displacement	233
20.9	Speed and velocity	234
20.10	Distance–time graphs	234
20.11	Average speed	235
20.12	Changing speed – acceleration	236
20.13	Speed–time graphs	236
20.14	Newton's laws of motion	237
20.15	Falling under gravity	239
	Summary	241
	Quick test 20	242

21	Energy transfers	244
21.1	Doing work and using energy	244
21.2	Forms of energy	245
21.3	Efficiency of energy conversions	247
21.4	Power	248
21.5	Energy transfers in a power station	249
21.6	How do we use our sources of energy?	250
21.7	Heat as a form of energy	251
21.8	Heat transfer	251
21.9	Preventing heat transfer	252
	Summary	254
	Quick test 21	255

22	Sound and waves	256
22.1	Introduction	256
22.2	Sound waves	256
22.3	Hearing sounds	257
22.4	Echoes – the speed of sound in air	258
22.5	Echoes and ultrasound waves	259
22.6	Describing waves	260
22.7	Measuring sounds	262
22.8	Reflection and refraction of waves	264
22.9	Transverse and longitudinal waves	265

22.10	Evidence for the Earth's layered structure	267
22.11	Electromagnetic waves	268
22.12	Diffraction	269
	Summary	271
	Quick test 22	271

23	Light and colour	273
23.1	Laser beams and light rays	273
23.2	Reflecting light	273
23.3	Refracting light	275
23.4	Total internal reflection	277
	Summary	279
	Quick test 23	279

24	Electricity and electric currents	281
24.1	Introduction	281
24.2	Electric currents and circuits	281
24.3	Measuring current and charge	283
24.4	Voltage and potential difference	284
24.5	Resistance and resistors	285
24.6	Measuring resistance – Ohm's law	286
24.7	Voltage and energy	288
24.8	Electricity in the home	289
24.9	Safety in electrical circuits	291
24.10	Power ratings	293
24.11	Electricity bills	294
24.12	Electric charges	294
24.13	The dangers and uses of elctrostatic charges	295
	Summary	296
	Quick test 24	297

25	Motors and generators	300
25.1	Magnets and magnetic poles	300
25.2	North and south poles	300
25.3	Permanent and temporary magnets	301
25.4	Magnetic fields	301
25.5	The Earth's own magnetic field	302
25.6	The magnetic effects of electric currents	303
25.7	Uses of electromagnets	304

25.8	Electric motors	305
25.9	Electromagnetic induction	306
25.10	The a.c. generator (alternator)	307
25.11	Transformers	309
25.12	Transmitting electricity	310
	Summary	311
	Quick test 25	312

26	Radioactivity and nuclear energy	314
26.1	Radioactivity	314
26.2	Alpha, beta and gamma radiation	314
26.3	Nuclear reactions	315
26.4	Detecting radioactivity	316
26.5	Half-life	316
26.6	Uses of radioactive materials	317
26.7	Dangers from radiation	318
26.8	Nuclear energy	318
	Summary	321
	Quick test 26	321

27	The Earth's place in the universe	323
27.1	Introduction	323
27.2	What are stars?	323
27.3	The Sun	324
27.4	Planets and the solar system	325
27.5	Gravity and gravitational forces	325
27.6	The origin of the solar system	326
27.7	The Earth and its Moon	327
27.8	Our exploration of space	329
27.9	The life cycle of stars	330
27.10	The evolution of the universe	330
	Summary	332
	Quick test 27	332

Questions and answers

Longer exam questions	334
Answers to longer questions	351
Answers to quick tests	358
Coursework	366
Index	369

Introduction

How to use this book

This book is specially written to help you in preparing for GCSE and Scottish Standard Grade Science exams. It will help you to revise and contains the following:

- Hints on **how to use this book** during your preparation and revision for the exam.
- Information about the **GCSE** (**Key Stage 4** and the **National Curriculum**) in England, Wales and Northern Ireland and the **Standard Grade** in Scotland.
- Tables explaining what your syllabus requires in the **Syllabus checklists**. Advice on how to use these tables is given below. This book covers all GCSE and Standard Grade Science syllabuses, both single and double award.
- **Twenty-seven chapters of text**, broken down into topic units, covering all the requirements for Standard Grade and GCSE (i.e. Key Stage 4 of the National Curriculum). These chapters are concise, clear and easy to read. A lot of information is summarised in easy-to-revise tables and diagrams.
- A **summary** at the end of each chapter that picks out the key facts and ideas.
- A **quick test** at the end of each chapter that covers the material in the chapter. These tests contain objective and short-answer structured questions. The questions are similar to those used in module tests and external GCSE and Scottish exams. The quick tests are an ideal preparation for module tests.
- **Longer questions** from sample assessment materials and from recent examinations. These provide further practice in answering questions (pages 334–350). Longer question 1 should be attempted after Chapter 1, longer question 2 after Chapter 2, and so on.
- **Answers** to all the quick test questions (pages 358–367) and the longer questions (pages 351–357).
- Information on how to prepare for, plan, carry out and write up your **coursework** (pages 366–368).

Using the syllabus tables

Turn to pages 5–13 and find the Examining Group, the syllabus and tier which relate to your science course and exams. (If you are not sure which syllabus and tier you are taking, check with your teacher.) The syllabus tables show you:

- which grades correspond to your tier.
- the number of examination papers you will be required to sit and their length.
- the percentage of the total mark awarded to the external exam, module tests (if these are used) and teacher (internal) assessment.
- the types of questions used on the examination papers.

If you are preparing for **double award science** at the **higher tier** you need to study all the units in the book. If you are preparing for double award science at the **foundation tier** then you do not need to study the units listed in the 'Higher tier only' column of Table 1 (page 14).

If you are preparing for **single award science** you need to refer to Table 2 (page 15). Again, some of the units are required for the **higher tier** only and do not need to be studied if you are entering at the **foundation tier**.

Table 3 (page 16) is for you if you are preparing for Scottish Standard Grade. Sections listed in the 'Required units' column must be revised and understood. Sections listed in the 'Recommended units' column are required, but with reservations; for example, 'less detail than this is required' or 'this topic illustrates important ideas and issues in the syllabus but is not specifically mentioned' or 'only an appreciation of the ideas in the section are required'. If a unit is not listed, or the entry for a chapter is blank, then it means that the topic is not in the Scottish syllabus.

The most up-to-date syllabuses and National Curriculum documents have been used to compile the tables but, if you write to your Examining Group for the syllabus and for copies of past exam papers (using the addresses given), you will be able to judge the requirements of your syllabus more precisely. Your teacher will also be able to advise you.

Using the chapters, quick tests and longer questions

In order to succeed in the examination, you need to plan and organise your revision carefully. The chapters, quick tests and longer questions in this book will help you to revise and prepare for the exam.

You should plan a revision timetable well before the exam. Decide how much you need to revise and how long before the exam you should start. The following list shows how to revise the topics in this book chapter by chapter.

1. Decide which chapter you will revise.
2. Study the units relevant to you in this chapter, and also study your class notes which relate to them.
3. Make lists, summaries, diagrams, etc., to help your understanding (see 'Hints for revision', page 17).
4. Answer the 'Quick test' questions at the end of the chapter.
5. Check your answers to the 'Quick test' questions. Make sure you agree with the right answer.
6. After covering the chapter, answer the longer question with the same number as the chapter.
7. Check your answer to the longer question. Make sure that you agree with the right answer.

The National Curriculum and the GCSE

The National Curriculum provides a course which all students in State schools in England and Wales must follow. A similar arrangement applies in Northern Ireland. In Scotland, the curriculum arrangements are somewhat different and these are described on page 4.

The National Curriculum deals with the period of compulsory education, i.e. from age 5 to 16, in four Key Stages. At the end of each Key Stage (i.e. at ages 7, 11, 14 and 16) attainments in specified subjects are measured. At the end of Key Stage 4 (KS4), assessment is made through single and double award science courses for the GCSE. The overall arrangements for the National Curriculum and GCSE at KS4 are shown in Fig. 1.

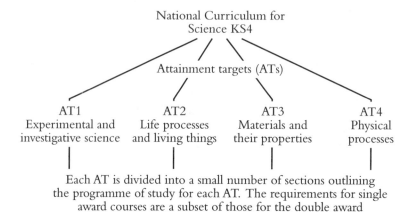

Fig. 1 Overall arrangements for the National Curriculum and GCSE at Key Stage 4

Attainment Targets (ATs)

The knowledge, understanding and skills which you are expected to have acquired at the end of each Key Stage are identified under broad areas of study known as Attainment Targets (ATs). In Science there are four ATs, each of which carries 25% of the marks in your overall GCSE assessment.

- AT1 Experimental and Investigative Science (also known as Sc1).
  This AT assesses your scientific skills in planning experimental and investigative work, in obtaining evidence (i.e. observations and measurements) and in considering the evidence. It will be assessed by your teacher (see pages 366–368).
- AT2 Life Processes and Living Things (Sc2).
- AT3 Materials and their Properties (Sc3).
- AT4 Physical Processes (Sc4).

AT2, AT3 and AT4 cover the knowledge and understanding associated with the key areas of science – biology, chemistry, physics, earth science, astronomy and other associated sciences. These attainment targets will be assessed by external written exams at the end of the course and possibly also by module tests during the course.

Programmes of Study

Each attainment target is divided into a small number of sections of related knowledge, understanding, concepts and skills. For example, AT4, Physical Processes, is divided into the following six sections:

1. Electricity and magnetism,
2. Forces and motion,
3. Waves,
4. The Earth and beyond,
5. Energy resources and energy transfer,
6. Radioactivity.

Each of these sections is described in terms of a **Programme of Study**. These Programmes of Study set out the key ideas, concepts, skills, facts and information which you should be taught.

Single and double awards

Before starting your GCSE studies in science, you will have to choose whether to take a double award course (equivalent to two GCSE subjects) or a single award course.

If you choose a **double award** course, your GCSE science studies will cover the whole of Sc1 together with all of the sections in Sc2, Sc3 and Sc4.

If you choose a **single award** course, your GCSE science studies will cover the whole of Sc1 together with a reduced programme of study for Sc2, Sc3 and Sc4.

Table 2 (page 15) lists the units in this book that are required for single award courses. The ⟨D⟩ symbol is used in the main text to indicate units that are required for double award courses only.

GCSE results in double award science courses are shown on certificates as a pair of identical grades, e.g. BB. In single award courses, GCSE results will be shown on certificates as one grade.

Tier of entry

Besides choosing either a double award or a single award science course, you will also (with the help and advice of your teacher) have to decide the tier at which you take the written examinations. There are two tiers of entry for almost all GCSE science exams. Each tier covers only a limited range of grades.

In general:
- the foundation tier covers grades G to C,
- the higher tier covers grades D to A★.

Tables 1 and 2 (pages 14 and 15) list the units, for both single and double award courses, that will be examined at the higher tier only.

Standard Grade in Scotland

Scottish Standard Grade is not part of the National Curriculum that covers England, Wales and Northern Ireland, but the topics for it are covered in this book (see Table 3, page 16).

Aims

The main aims of standard grade are:
- to indicate the contribution that science can make to society, and
- to develop knowledge, understanding and practical abilities and the use to which these can be put in problem-solving activities.

Course content

Standard grade consists of:
- **four** compulsory topics, occupying approximately three-quarters of the course, and
- **one** or **two** additional topics, occupying about one-quarter of the course.

The compulsory topics are:
1 Healthy and safe living,
2 An introduction to materials,
3 Energy and its uses,
4 A study of environments.

Schools are free to devise their own additional topics.

Levels

Standard grade is offered at Foundation, General and Credit levels. It is designed to challenge the most able students and also provide support and allow success for those of lower ability. Candidates may attempt papers at one or two levels in the external examination. Information about grades and papers at the three different levels is given on page 13.

Grades

Certificates show an overall award on a 7-point scale of grades, grade 1 being the highest. In the overall grade, equal weighting is given to:
- knowledge and understanding } assessed by external exam
- problem solving
- practical abilities – internally assessed by your teacher.

Syllabus checklists

You should be able to find your examining group and syllabus in the following tables. This will then give you details about the course, the exam papers you will be sitting and the type of questions set.

Unlike the syllabuses for the separate subjects of Biology, Chemistry and Physics, the syllabuses for double science and single science courses are dictated entirely by the National Curriculum for science. So, all double science syllabuses are the same, although they may be set out and ordered differently. In the same way, all single science syllabuses are also the same.

Checklists are available for double award (Table 1, page 14), single award (Table 2, page 15) and Scottish Standard Grade (Table 3, page 16). Tables 1 and 2 also indicate which material is only needed for higher tier study.

Midland Examining Group (MEG)

1 Hills Road, Cambridge, CB1 2EU   Tel: 01223 553311

Science (co-ordinated): Double and single award

Type of syllabus/course. Co-ordinated approach in which areas of biology (Sc2), chemistry (Sc3) and physics (Sc4) form separate sections of a unified course. Either a 'traditional' or a 'Nuffield' approach can be adopted.

	Double						Single					
Tiers	Foundation			Higher			Foundation			Higher		
Grades available	GG–CC			DD–A★A★			G–C			D–A★		
End of course exam												
Paper numbers	1	3	5	2	4	6	1	3	5	2	4	6
Times in hours	$1\frac{1}{2}$	$1\frac{1}{2}$	$1\frac{1}{2}$	$1\frac{3}{4}$	$1\frac{3}{4}$	$1\frac{3}{4}$	$\frac{3}{4}$	$\frac{3}{4}$	$\frac{3}{4}$	1	1	1
% of overall assessment	25	25	25	25	25	25	25	25	25	25	25	25
ATs covered	Sc2	Sc3	Sc4	Sc2	Sc3	Sc4	Sc2	Sc3	Sc4	Sc2	Sc3	Sc4
Types of questions												
Short answer	✓			✓			✓			✓		
Structured	✓			✓			✓			✓		
Extended prose	✓			✓			✓			✓		
Is there any choice of question?	No			No			No			No		
Teacher (internal) assessment of coursework (Sc1)	Paper 7 – 25% on both awards for both foundation and higher tiers (see 'Coursework', pages 366–368)											
Modular arrangements	None available. All papers 1–6 are externally set and marked at the end of the course.											

Science (Salters): Double and single award

Type of syllabus/course. Co-ordinated, integrated or topic-based to suit individual schools. Each topic is introduced through everyday materials, phenomena or issues. Applications and implications of scientific ideas are emphasised.

	Double				Single		
Tiers	Foundation		Higher		Foundation	Higher	
Grades available	GG–CC		DD–A★A★		G–C	D–A★	
End of course exam							
Paper numbers	1	3	2	4	1	2	
Times in hours	1¾	1¾	2¼	2¼	1¾	2¼	
% of overall assessment	37.5	37.5	37.5	37.5	75	75	
ATs covered	All papers Sc2 Sc3 Sc4				All papers Sc2 Sc3 Sc4		
Types of questions							
Short answer	✓		✓		✓	✓	
Structured	✓		✓		✓	✓	
Extended prose	✓		✓		✓	✓	
Is there any choice of question?	No		No		No	No	
Teacher (internal) assessment of coursework (Sc1)	Paper 5 – 25% on both awards for both foundation and higher tiers (see 'Coursework', pages 366–368)						
Modular arrangements	None available. All papers 1–4 are externally set and marked at the end of the course.				None available. Both papers 1 and 2 are externally set and marked at the end of the course.		

Science (Suffolk): Double and single award

Type of syllabus/course. Co-ordinated approach in which areas of biology (Sc2), chemistry (Sc3) and physics (Sc4) form separate sections with emphasis on the applications and implications of science. The course units are arranged in two phases, corresponding to year 10 and year 11. In each phase, there are 3 units in each subject area (Sc2, Sc3 and Sc4) making a total of 18 units. In each unit, the content is divided into 3 levels – credit, merit and special. Credit and merit levels relate to the foundation tier. Merit and special levels relate to the higher tier. Each unit for the single award is part of one of the units for the double award.

	Double						Single					
Tiers	Foundation			Higher			Foundation			Higher		
Grades available	GG–CC			DD–A★A★			G–C			D–A★		
End of course exam												
Paper numbers	1	3	5	2	4	6	1	3	5	2	4	6
Times in hours	1¼	1¼	1¼	1¼	1¼	1¼	⅔	⅔	⅔	⅔	⅔	⅔
% of overall assessment	16.6	16.6	16.6	16.6	16.6	16.6	16.6	16.6	16.6	16.6	16.6	16.6
ATs covered	Sc2	Sc3	Sc4	Sc2	Sc3	Sc4	Sc2	Sc3	Sc4	Sc2	Sc3	Sc4
Types of questions												
Short answer	✓			✓			✓			✓		
Structured	✓			✓			✓			✓		
Extended prose	✓			✓			✓			✓		
Is there any choice of question?	No			No			No			No		
Teacher (internal) assessment of coursework (Sc1)	Paper 7 – 25% on both awards for both foundation and higher tiers (see 'Coursework', pages 366–368)											
Periodic examination	Paper 8, 9 or 11 (1½ hrs) taken at end of year 10 or year 11. These test year 10 work only (25%)			Paper 8, 10 or 12 (1½ hrs) taken at end of year 10 or year 11. These test year 10 work only (25%)			Paper 8 or 9 (50 mins) taken at end of year 10 or year 11. These test year 10 work only (25%)			Paper 8 or 10 (50 mins) taken at end of year 10 or year 11. These test year 10 work only (25%)		
Modular arrangements	None available. All terminal and periodic written papers are set and marked externally.											

Northern Examinations and Assessment Board (NEAB)

12 Harter Street, Manchester, M1 6HL   Tel: 0161 953 1170

Science (Modular): Double and single award

Type of syllabus/course. Content is organised in a range of modules, which vary in the extent to which the different subject areas (Sc2, Sc3 and Sc4) are co-ordinated or integrated.

	Double		Single	
Tiers	Foundation	Higher	Foundation	Higher
Grades available	GG–CC	DD–A★A★	G–C	D–A★
End of course exam				
Paper numbers	1F 2F	1H 2H	F	H
Times in hours	1½ 1½	1½ 1½	1½	1½
% of overall assessment	25 25	25 25	50	50
ATs covered	Both papers cover Sc2, Sc3 and Sc4	Both papers cover Sc2, Sc3 and Sc4	Sc2, Sc3 and Sc4	Sc2, Sc3 and Sc4
Types of questions				
Objective	In the module tests only		In the module tests only	
Short answer				
Structured	✓	✓	✓	✓
Extended prose	✓	✓	✓	✓
Is there any choice of question?	No	No	No	No
Teacher (internal) assessment of coursework (Sc1)	25% on both awards for both foundation and higher tiers (see 'Coursework', pages 366–368)			
Modular arrangements	Candidates take 12 modules for the double award and 6 modules for the single award. An equal number of modules cover Sc2, Sc3 and Sc4. Each single award module is made up from parts of two of the double award modules. Half of the modules (6 for double and 3 for single) are assessed by module tests (each of 30 mins) and the other half in the terminal exam. Module tests make up 25% of the assessment. All exam papers and module tests are set and marked externally.			

Science (Co-ordinated): Double and single award

Type of syllabus/course. Co-ordinated approach in which the separate areas of science (Sc2, biology, Sc3, chemistry, and Sc4, physics) form distinct sections of a unified course. Emphasis is placed on the applications of science and the nature of scientific ideas.

	Double						Single					
Tiers	Foundation			Higher			Foundation			Higher		
Grades available	GG–CC			DD–A★A★			G–C			D–A★		
End of course exam												
Paper numbers	1F	2F	3F	1H	2H	3H	1F	2F	3F	1H	2H	3H
Times in hours	1½	1½	1½	1½	1½	1½	¾	¾	¾	¾	¾	¾
% of overall assessment	25	25	25	25	25	25	25	25	25	25	25	25
ATs covered	Sc2	Sc3	Sc4	Sc2	Sc3	Sc4	Sc2	Sc3	Sc4	Sc2	Sc3	Sc4
Types of questions												
Short answer	✓			✓			✓			✓		
Structured	✓			✓			✓			✓		
Extended prose	✓			✓			✓			✓		
Is there any choice of question?	No			No			No			No		
Teacher (internal) assessment of coursework (Sc1)	25% on both awards for both foundation and higher tiers (see 'Coursework', pages 366–368)											
Modular arrangements	All written papers are set and marked by the board. Modular arrangements are *not* available.											
Other points to note	Some questions on all the written exam papers will be common to the double and single awards. A data book, with which candidates should be familiar, is provided for papers 2F and 2H.											

Northern Ireland Council for the Curriculum Examinations and Assessment (NICCEA)

Clarendon Dock, 29 Clarendon Rd, Belfast, BT1 3BG   Tel: 01232 261200

Science (Non-modular): Double and single award

Type of syllabus/course. Co-ordinated approach in which areas of biology (Sc2), chemistry (Sc3) and physics (Sc4) are clearly and separately laid out in the syllabus with emphasis on the applications and implications of science.

	Double						Single					
Tiers	Foundation			Higher			Foundation			Higher		
Grades available	GG–CC			DD–A★A★			G–C			D–A★		
End of course exam												
Paper numbers	1	2	3	1	2	3	1	2	3	1	2	3
Times in hours	1½	1½	1½	2	2	2	1	1	1	1½	1½	1½
% of overall assessment	25	25	25	25	25	25	25	25	25	25	25	25
ATs covered	Sc2	Sc3	Sc4	Sc2	Sc3	Sc4	Sc2	Sc3	Sc4	Sc2	Sc3	Sc4
Types of questions												
Short answer	✓			✓			✓			✓		
Structured	✓			✓			✓			✓		
Extended prose												
Is there any choice of question?	No			No			No			No		
Teacher (internal) assessment of coursework (Sc1)	25% – All NICCEA science syllabuses at KS4 use a common scheme for the assessment of coursework (Sc1 – Exploring and Investigating in Science). There are three equally weighted assessment categories (skill areas): A Planning 8.33% B Carrying out 8.33% C Interpreting and evaluating 8.33% Internal assessment of a candidate's performance is made as part of normal class practical work and is then moderated across a wider range of schools.											
Modular arrangements	None available – all the written exam papers are set and marked externally.											

Science (Modular): Double award only

Type of syllabus/course. Co-ordinated modular approach in which areas of biology (Sc2), chemistry (Sc3) and physics (Sc4) form separate sections of the syllabus in clearly designated modules. The course emphasises the applications and implications of science.

	Double					
Tiers	Foundation			Higher		
Grades available	GG–CC			DD–A★A★		
End of course exam						
Paper numbers	1	2	3	1	2	3
Times in hours	1	1	1	1½	1½	1½
% of overall assessment	16.66	16.66	16.66	16.66	16.66	16.66
ATs covered	Sc2	Sc3	Sc4	Sc2	Sc3	Sc4
Types of questions						
Short answer	In the module tests only					
Structured	✓			✓		
Extended prose	✓			✓		
Is there any choice of question?	No			No		
Teacher (internal) assessment of coursework (Sc1)	25% as on NICCEA science (non-modular) double and single award					
Modular arrangements	Module test (8.33%) ½ hr at foundation and ¾ hr at higher tier, after each of the first 3 modules (total – 25%). These 3 modules are: Living Things and the Processes of Life, Using Materials and Understanding Reactions, Forces and Energy. The module tests consist of short answer questions.					

Science (Modular): Single award only

Type of syllabus/course. Modular course (foundation tier only) based on the 'Science at work' series published by Longman, with emphasis on the applications of science.

	Single
Tiers	Foundation only
Grades available	G–C
End of course exam	
Paper numbers	1
Times in hours	2
% of overall assessment	25
ATs covered	8.33% on Module 6 – Chemical reactions 16.66% on Modules 1–5 (see below)
Types of questions	
Short answer	✓
Structured	✓
Extended prose	
Is there any choice of question?	No
Teacher (internal) assessment of coursework (Sc1)	25% – as on NICCEA science (non-modular) double and single award
Modular arrangements	There are six modules to the course, five of these modules are assessed through end of module tests (each ¾ hr) as follows. 1 Staying alive (Sc2) – 10% 2 Materials (Sc3) – 10% 3 Energy and space (Sc4) – 10% 4 Maintaining the species (Sc2) – 10% 5 Light, forces and energy (Sc4) – 10% The module tests are composed of short answer questions, externally set and marked.

Southern Examining Group (SEG)

Stag Hill House, Guildford, GU2 5XJ   Tel: 01483 506506

Science: Double and single award

Type of syllabus/course. Combined, co-ordinated or integrated to suit individual schools, but with an assessment arrangement in which the different attainment targets (Sc2, biology, Sc3, chemistry, and Sc4, physics) are assessed separately.

	Double						Single					
Tiers	Foundation			Higher			Foundation			Higher		
Grades available	GG–CC			DD–A★A★			G–C			D–A★		
End of course exam												
Paper numbers	2	3	4	5	6	7	2	3	4	5	6	7
Times in hours	1½	1½	1½	1½	1½	1½	1	1	1	1	1	1
% of overall assessment	25	25	25	25	25	25	25	25	25	25	25	25
ATs covered	Sc2	Sc3	Sc4	Sc2	Sc3	Sc4	Sc2	Sc3	Sc4	Sc2	Sc3	Sc4
Types of questions												
Short answer	✓			✓			✓			✓		
Structured	✓			✓			✓			✓		
Extended prose	✓			✓			✓			✓		
Is there any choice of question?	No			No			No			No		
Teacher (internal) assessment of coursework (Sc1)	Component 1 – 25% on both awards for both foundation and higher tiers (see 'Coursework', pages 366–368)											
Modular arrangements	Modular arrangements are *not* available. All papers are set and marked externally by the Exam Group.											
Other points to note	Questions on the single award papers are identical to those assessing the same subject content on the double award paper.											

Science (Modular): Double and single award

Type of syllabus/course. Modular course based on the 'Science at work' series published by Longman. The modules can be taught by specialist teachers or as an integrated scheme in whichever order is felt to be appropriate.

	Double			Single	
Tiers	Foundation	Higher		Foundation	Higher
Grades available	GG–CC	DD–A★A★		G–C	D–A★
End of course exam					
Paper numbers	2 3	4 5		2	3
Times in hours	1½ 1½	2 2		1½	2
% of overall assessment	25 25	25 25		50	50
ATs covered	All papers cover Sc2, Sc3 and Sc4			All papers cover Sc2, Sc3 and Sc4	
Types of questions					
Objective	in module tests only			in module tests only	
Short answer	✓	✓		✓	✓
Structured	✓	✓		✓	✓
Extended prose	✓	✓		✓	✓
Is there any choice of question?	No	No		No	No
	End of course exam papers 2 and 4 for the double award are the same as papers 2 and 3 for the single award				
Teacher (internal) assessment of coursework (Sc1)	Component 1 – 25% on both awards for both foundation and higher tiers (see 'Coursework', pages 366–368)				
Modular arrangements	Candidates take 9 modules (1 to 9) for the double award and 5 modules (1 to 5) for the single award. 1 Maintenance of life (Sc2) 6 Vital exchanges (Sc2) 2 Maintenance of the species (Sc2) 7 Bonding and materials (Sc3) 3 Structure and changes (Sc3) 8 Using power (Sc4) 4 Force and transfers (Sc4) 9 Universal changes (Sc3 & Sc4) 5 Energy sources (Sc3 & Sc4) 9 module tests (each 20 mins) for the double award = 25% 5 module tests (each 20 mins) for the single award = 25% Each test consists of 18 multiple choice questions. The tests are externally set and marked and can be taken in any order.				

EDEXCEL: London Examinations (formerly ULEAC)

Stewart House, 32 Russell Square, London, WC1B 5DN   Tel: 0171 331 4000

Science (Combined): Double and single award

Type of syllabus/course. Combination of three sections – essentially biology (Sc2), chemistry (Sc3) and physics (Sc4) – with emphasis on the applications and implications of science.

	Double						Single					
Tiers	Foundation			Higher			Foundation			Higher		
Grades available	GG–CC			DD–A★A★			G–C			D–A★		
End of course exam												
Paper numbers	1F	2F	3F	4H	5H	6H	1F	2F	3F	4H	5H	6H
Times in hours	1½	1½	1½	1½	1½	1½	1	1	1	1	1	1
% of overall assessment	25	25	25	25	25	25	25	25	25	25	25	25
ATs covered	Sc2	Sc3	Sc4	Sc2	Sc3	Sc4	Sc2	Sc3	Sc4	Sc2	Sc3	Sc4
Types of questions												
Short answer	✓			✓			✓			✓		
Structured	✓			✓			✓			✓		
Extended prose	✓			✓			✓			✓		
Is there any choice of question?	No			No			No			No		
Teacher (internal) assessment of coursework (Sc1)	Paper 7 – 25% on both awards for both foundation and higher tiers (see 'Coursework', pages 366–368)											
Modular arrangements	None available. All the written exam papers set and marked externally.											

Science (Modular): Double and single award

Type of syllabus/course. Modular scheme based on the 'Science at work' approach, emphasising everyday applications of science including sport, environment, forensic science, the home and communications.

	Double				Single	
Tiers	Foundation		Higher		Foundation	Higher
Grades available	GG–CC		DD–A★A★		G–C	D–A★
End of course exam						
Paper numbers	1F	2F	1H	2H	1F	1H
Times in hours	1½	1½	2	2	1½	2
% of overall assessment	25	25	25	25	50	50
ATs covered	All papers cover Sc2, Sc3 and Sc4				Both papers cover Sc2, Sc3 and Sc4	
Types of questions						
Objective	in module tests only				in module tests only	
Short answer	✓		✓		✓	✓
Structured	✓		✓		✓	✓
Extended prose	✓		✓		✓	✓
Is there any choice of question?	No		No		No	No
Teacher (internal) assessment of coursework (Sc1)	25% on both awards for both foundation and higher tiers (see 'Coursework', pages 366–368)					
Modular arrangements	Candidates take 10 modules (1 to 10) for the double award and 5 modules (1, 2, 6, 8 and 10) for the single award. 1 Body maintenance 6 Chemical patterns 2 Inheritance and survival 7 Science in sport 3 Understanding ecosystems 8 Electricity and waves in the home 4 Chemistry and the Earth 9 Applications of sound and electricity 5 Materials chemistry 10 Energy and gravitation 10 module tests (each 20 mins) for the double award = 25% 5 module tests (each 20 mins) for the single award = 25% Each test consists of 20 multiple choice questions. The tests are externally set and marked.					

Welsh Joint Education Committee (WJEC)

245 Western Avenue, Cardiff, CF5 2YX   Tel: 01222 265000

Science: Double and single award

Type of syllabus/course. Co-ordinated approach in which the separate areas of science (Sc2, biology, Sc3, chemistry, and Sc4, physics) form distinct and discrete sections of a unified course.

	Double						Single					
Tiers	Foundation			Higher			Foundation			Higher		
Grades available	GG–CC			DD–A★A★			G–C			D–A★		
End of course exam												
Paper numbers	1	2	3	4	5	6	1	2	3	4	5	6
Times in hours	$1\frac{1}{3}$	$1\frac{1}{3}$	$1\frac{1}{3}$	$1\frac{2}{3}$	$1\frac{2}{3}$	$1\frac{2}{3}$	$\frac{3}{4}$	$\frac{3}{4}$	$\frac{3}{4}$	$\frac{3}{4}$	$\frac{3}{4}$	$\frac{3}{4}$
% of overall assessment	25	25	25	25	25	25	25	25	25	25	25	25
ATs covered	Sc2	Sc3	Sc4	Sc2	Sc3	Sc4	Sc2	Sc3	Sc4	Sc2	Sc3	Sc4
Types of questions												
Short answer	✓			✓			✓			✓		
Structured	✓			✓			✓			✓		
Extended prose	✓			✓			✓			✓		
Is there any choice of question?	No			No			No			No		
Teacher (internal) assessment of coursework (Sc1)	25% on both awards for both foundation and higher tiers (see 'Coursework', pages 366–368)											
Modular arrangements	Modular arrangements are *not* available.											
Other points to note	For both double and single award, all question papers will comprise two sections, A and B, with section B of the foundation tier paper becoming section A of the corresponding higher tier paper. Questions concerning the applications and implications of science will make a significant contribution to the total marks available in the written exam papers.											

Scottish Qualifications Authority (formerly SEB)

Ironmills Road, Dalkeith, Midlothian, EH22 1LE   Tel: 0131 663 6601

Science (Integrated): Single award only

Type of syllabus/course. Co-ordinated or integrated to suit individual schools.

	Single		
Tiers	Foundation	General	Credit
Grades	6–5	4–3	2–1
End of course exam			
Paper numbers	1	1	1
Times in hours	1	$1\frac{1}{4}$	$1\frac{3}{4}$
% of overall assessment	67	67	67
Types of questions			
Short answer	✓	✓	✓
Structured	✓	✓	✓
Extended prose	✓	✓	✓
Teacher (internal) assessment of coursework	33%	33%	33%
Other points to note	Grade 7 is awarded if a candidate completes the course but fails to reach Grade 6. Questions in the end of course exam will relate to the 4 compulsory topics.		

Table 1 Double award study checklist

	Topic	Reference	Higher tier only	Target finish date	✓
1	Living things and populations	1.1–1.11	–		
2	Photosynthesis	2.1–2.8	2.3		
3	Food and diet – nutrition	3.1–3.5	3.2		
4	Digestion	4.1–4.4	4.3		
5	The blood system	5.1–5.7	–		
6	Respiration	6.1–6.9	–		
7	Senses and responses	7.1–7.11	7.2, 7.7, 7.11		
8	Reproduction	8.1–8.4	–		
9	Genetics and evolution	9.1–9.7	9.2–9.7		
10	Our effect on the environment	10.1–10.6	–		
11	Earth science	11.1–11.5	11.4, 11.5		
12	Materials, elements and compounds	12.1–12.10	–		
13	Particles	13.1–13.11	13.9, 13.11		
14	Metals and alloys	14.1–14.10	14.9, 14.10		
15	Electricity and electrolysis	15.1–15.8	15.5–15.8		
16	Acids, bases and salts	16.1–16.6	–		
17	The chemical industry	17.1–17.10	17.7		
18	Energy, fuels and plastics	18.1–18.10	18.8–18.10		
19	The periodic table and atomic structure	19.1–19.11	19.5, 19.6, 19.9, 19.11		
20	Force and motion	20.1–20.15	20.13–20.15		
21	Energy transfers	21.1–21.9	–		
22	Sound and waves	22.1–22.12	22.7, 22.10, 22.12		
23	Light and colour	23.1–23.4	–		
24	Electricity and electric currents	24.1–24.13	24.3, 24.7, 24.10, 24.11, 24.13		
25	Motors and generators	25.1–25.12	25.8–25.12		
26	Radioactivity and nuclear energy	26.1–26.8	26.3–26.5		
27	The Earth's place in the universe	27.1–27.10	27.6, 27.9		

Table 2 Single award study checklist

	Topic	Reference	Higher tier only	Target finish date	✓
1	Living things and populations	1.1–1.6, 1.8, 1.9	–		
2	Photosynthesis	2.1, 2.2, 2.4, 2.6–2.8	–		
3	Food and diet – nutrition	3.1, 3.2, 3.4	3.2		
4	Digestion	4.1, 4.2	–		
5	The blood system	5.1–5.3, 5.6	–		
6	Respiration	6.1–6.6	–		
7	Senses and responses	7.1, 7.2, 7.5–7.9, 7.11	7.2, 7.7, 7.11		
8	Reproduction	8.1, 8.3, 8.4	–		
9	Genetics and evolution	9.1–9.5, 9.7	9.2–9.5, 9.7		
10	Our effect on the environment	10.1, 10.4	–		
11	Earth science	11.2, 11.3	–		
12	Materials, elements and compounds	12.1–12.10	–		
13	Particles	13.1–13.9	13.9		
14	Metals and alloys	14.1–14.8	–		
15	Electricity and electrolysis	–	–		
16	Acids, bases and salts	16.1–16.6	–		
17	The chemical industry	17.2, 17.4, 17.9, 17.10	–		
18	Energy, fuels and plastics	18.1, 18.2, 18.4–18.9	18.8, 18.9		
19	The periodic table and atomic structure	19.1–19.4, 19.6–19.8, 19.10	19.6		
20	Force and motion	20.1–20.6, 20.8–20.13, 20.15	20.13, 20.15		
21	Energy transfers	21.1–21.3, 21.5–21.9	–		
22	Sound and waves	22.6–22.8, 22.11	22.7		
23	Light and colour	23.1–23.4	–		
24	Electricity and electric currents	24.1, 24.2, 24.4–24.6, 24.8, 24.9, 24.11	24.11		
25	Motors and generators	25.1–25.4, 25.6, 25.9, 25.10	25.9, 25.10		
26	Radioactivity and nuclear energy	26.1–26.7	26.3–26.5		
27	The Earth's place in the universe	27.1–27.6, 27.8	27.6		

Table 3 Scottish Standard Grade study checklist

	Topic	Required units	Recommended units	Target finish date	✓
1	Living things and populations	1.2, 1.5–1.11	1.1		
2	Photosynthesis	2.3–2.6	2.1, 2.2, 2.7, 2.8		
3	Food and diet – nutrition	3.1, 3.2, 3.5	3.3, 3.4		
4	Digestion	–	–		
5	The blood system	5.1–5.5	5.6		
6	Respiration	6.1–6.5	6.6		
7	Senses and responses	7.5, 7.8	7.1, 7.4, 7.6, 7.9, 7.11		
8	Reproduction	–	–		
9	Genetics and evolution	–	–		
10	Our effect on the environment	10.1–10.6	–		
11	Earth science	–	–		
12	Materials, elements and compounds	12.1, 12.2, 12.6–12.8, 12.10	12.3–12.5, 12.9		
13	Particles	13.3	13.1, 13.2, 13.4		
14	Metals and alloys	14.4, 14.6	14.1–14.3, 14.7		
15	Electricity and electrolysis	15.1, 15.2, 15.5	15.3, 15.4		
16	Acids, bases and salts	16.1, 16.2	–		
17	The chemical industry	17.1, 17.4, 17.7	17.5, 17.6		
18	Energy, fuels and plastics	18.1, 18.2, 18.4–18.9	18.10		
19	The periodic table and atomic structure	–	–		
20	Force and motion	20.3, 20.4	20.1		
21	Energy transfers	21.2, 21.3, 21.5, 21.7–21.9	21.1, 21.4, 21.6		
22	Sound and waves	–	–		
23	Light and colour	–	–		
24	Electricity and electric currents	24.1, 24.2, 24.4, 24.7–24.12	24.3, 24.5, 24.6, 24.13		
25	Motors and generators	–	–		
26	Radioactivity and nuclear energy	26.1, 26.5, 26.7, 26.8	26.2, 26.6		
27	The Earth's place in the universe	–	–		

Studying and revising

Hints for revision

The most important aim of GCSE Science examinations is to assess **what you know**, **what you understand** and **what you can do**. The key to all this is to ensure that you *understand* what you have studied. If you understand a topic it is much easier to revise and remember key facts. In order to understand a topic, you must do more than just read your notes or read the sections in this book.

Your learning and revision must be *active* rather than passive. Here are some activities which will help you to keep your learning active and interesting. By revising in this way, you will practise the skills needed to show the examiner what you can do.

- **Underline or highlight important words and sentences**
- **Make lists of key words or key facts**
- **Write out and learn important definitions**
  Writing notes will help you to remember key points.
- **Draw diagrams to summarise important topics**
  Label the diagrams and write notes at the side. Diagrams are a very powerful way of reinforcing your memory and your understanding of something. Most people find it easier to remember things from pictures than from words alone.
- **Summarise important ideas and explanations**
  Sometimes it is helpful to make a flow chart to summarise a sequence of events or ideas. The flow chart is simply a series of short statements connected by arrows.
- **Keep your lists, notes, diagrams and summaries** so that you can look at them again and again. Diagrams and summaries that you have made yourself will jog your memory and your understanding very quickly. If your notes are disorganised, you will not gain much. But with concise notes, clear summaries and good diagrams similar to those in this book, you will increase your long-term knowledge and understanding significantly.
- **Try to copy your summaries and diagrams from memory**
  This won't be easy at first. You will need to look at the original to refresh your memory, but don't be discouraged. Spending time in testing yourself on work revised in previous sessions is an important part of exam preparation.
- **Answer the 'quick tests' and the 'longer questions'** in this book and check the answers. Answering examination-type questions is one of the best ways to prepare for an examination.
- **Ask your teacher if you still don't understand something**. Your teacher wants you to succeed just as much as you do. He or she will be delighted to help you with your revision particularly if your motivation and commitment are clear.

Keeping fit and well during revision

Keeping fit and well during revision and the exam period is just as important as keeping fit and well when training for a sports event.

- Don't overdo your revision. Set aside a realistic time for revision each day.
- Decide on a regular time for studying each day and try to stick to it.
- During revision sessions, study for 30 to 40 minutes, then take a break for 5 to 10 minutes. Continue revising for another 30 to 40 minutes, followed by another short break.
- During your breaks, try to take your mind off revision.
- While you are revising, avoid distractions from friends, family, radio and television.
- Make sure that you have regular meals, that you get enough sleep and that you take some exercise.
- Don't try to do much revision the evening before an exam. Just read through the notes and summaries you have already made to reassure yourself.

The examination

Short answer questions

Short answer questions are very common on GCSE papers. Large numbers of short answer questions can be used to cover the whole syllabus. There are several types of short answer questions. The required answer may be a single word, several words or a sentence, or you may be asked to complete a diagram. Short answer questions may also form part of a longer structured question.

Structured questions

Structured questions are the most common questions on GCSE papers. Usually, a structured question consists of some introductory information followed by a series of questions based on or related to that information. Sometimes, the information concerns social, environmental, industrial or economic aspects of science. It is always important to read the information carefully before starting to answer the question(s).

In structured questions, spaces are usually left for the answers on the question paper itself. Very often, the marks for each part of the question are also given. The space left and the marks given are a guide to the length of the answer required and the time you should spend. Don't feel you have to fill the space, but if your answer is much too short, think again. On the other hand, if you have average-sized writing and feel you have not been given enough space, your answer is probably more detailed than necessary.

There are examples of structured questions in the 'Quick tests' at the end of each chapter in this book.

Extended prose questions

Extended prose questions can be used on their own or as part of longer structured questions. In these questions, you are expected to compose three, four or even five or six sentences. There are examples of extended prose questions in the longer questions printed at the end of this book (pages 334–350), followed by model answers (pages 351–357).

Objective (multiple choice) questions

Objective (multiple choice) questions are used in the module tests of *some* GCSE syllabuses (check the syllabus table for your Exam Board in this book), *but they are not used in the end of course exams.* Objective questions ask you to choose the correct answer from four or five alternatives. They usually require only a single letter for the answer.

Example:
A sparrow is
A a reptile.   B a mammal.   C a bird.   D an amphibian.
Answer. C

At first sight, these questions seem easy because they involve simply choosing one answer from the four or five alternatives. But don't be deceived! Many objective questions are carefully designed to test difficult ideas. You should prepare just as thoroughly for a module test involving objective questions as you would for one involving longer questions.

Read the question carefully and never leave an objective question unanswered. If necessary, make an intelligent guess. You do not lose marks for a wrong answer.

Preparing for the exam

Success in an exam often depends on good examination technique.
1 **Arrive for the exam in plenty of time** – avoid any worry over missing the start.
2 **Come fully equipped** with pen, pencil, rubber, ruler, calculator, watch and coloured pens or pencils.

3 **Read the exam instructions carefully**.

4 **Plan your time sensibly**. If you have four questions to do in 1 hour, then you should not spend more than 15 minutes on any one question. If you are stuck on part of a question, leave it and come back to it at the end.

5 **Answer all the questions**. Usually, exams allow you plenty of time to complete all the questions. Check that you have answered all the questions and that you have not missed any.

6 **Keep your answers relevant**. Answer the question that has been asked. Don't twist the examiner's words into a different question. Don't waffle: this will only waste time and gain no marks.

7 **Plan your answer** if you have to write more than two or three sentences.
- Jot down in rough the key points.
- Decide the order in which to present these points before starting to write the answer.
- Use *short*, clear sentences.

8 **Use diagrams where appropriate**. Make sure they are drawn clearly and labelled neatly.

9 **If a graph is required**, make sure that you
- label the axes,
- show scales on the axes,
- include the units for quantities plotted along the axes,
- show the points clearly and neatly,
- draw the 'line or curve of best fit' smoothly.

10 **If a calculation is required**, make sure that you
- explain your calculation, stating the principle you are using in words or with an equation,
- write the correct units with your numerical answer, for example, an electric current must be 2 amps, not simply 2.

11 **Keep your work neat and legible**. Illegible answers gain no marks.

12 **Check your spelling, punctuation and grammar**. These may affect your marks and final grade.

Chapter 1
Living things and populations

1.1 The variety of living things

There are a vast number of living things in the world. These comprise animals, plants and microorganisms. The study of these living things is called **biology**. Living things are often described as **organisms**.

Living things are found everywhere in the world – on land, in the air, in the sea and underground. Different organisms live in different places. The place where an organism lives is called its **habitat**. The habitat of a fly might be a greenhouse, a goldfish's habitat might be its tank or bowl. The Earth provides millions of different habitats – some hot, some cold, some dry, some wet. The conditions in a habitat make up the **environment**.

In general, living things prefer a moderate environment with warm temperatures, water and a supply of food. This is why there are many different organisms in Britain, but very few organisms in hot deserts and cold Arctic regions.

The differences in physical factors, such as temperature, humidity and daylight hours, between localities are often reflected in the organisms found there. For example, animals which live in water often have streamlined bodies and those that live in very cold climates often have thick fur or layers of fat. We can sum this up by saying that many organisms are **adapted** to the habitat in which they live.

Fig. 1.1 These foxes are each well adapted to their very different environments. The fennec fox (left) is a native of the Sahara Desert. It has short fur (pale gold in colour, blending in with its sandy surroundings) and its large ears radiate heat. The Arctic fox (right) is insulated so well by its long, thick fur that it can sit comfortably in snow at -40 °C. Its small ears retain heat.

1.2 Characteristics of living things

There are thousands of different chemical reactions occurring in even the smallest animals and plants. These reactions are essential for life. If they stop, the organism dies. All the chemical processes in an organism are called its **metabolism**.

There are seven important characteristics or life processes common to *all* plants and animals.

1 **They grow**. Plants grow all their lives, but animals usually stop growing once they are adult. Even when growth stops, the materials in an animal's body are being replaced by substances from its food. In an adult human being, all the chemicals in the body are replaced over a period of seven years.

2 **They feed**. Organisms must feed in order to grow. Food is needed for growth, for energy and to replace worn-out parts. Animals and plants feed in different ways.

Plants take in simple substances like carbon dioxide and water. They use these simple substances to make more complex substances which can be used as food. In order to do this, plants need energy which they get from sunlight. This process of making food is called **photosynthesis** (see Chapter 2).

Animals eat plants or other animals. They then break down the complex chemicals in their food into simpler substances. These simpler substances are then used for growth or energy (see Chapters 3 and 4).

3 **They need energy**. Living things need energy to grow, to replace worn-out parts and to move. They get this energy from their food. The process of breaking down food and gaining energy is called **respiration** (see Chapter 6).

4 **They get rid of waste products**. Organisms are like factories. Materials are constantly being taken in and used to produce other materials. Some of the products are useless, others are poisonous. The waste products of metabolism must not be allowed to collect in an organism or they will poison it. So the organism must get rid of them – this process is called **excretion** (see 5.6 and 6.3).

5 **They produce offspring**. Organisms must produce offspring in order for the species to survive. This process is called **reproduction** (see Chapter 8). Usually reproduction involves the union of a male and a female of the same species. This is called **sexual** reproduction. Some organisms can reproduce on their own without needing both a male and a female. This is called **asexual** reproduction.

6 **They move**. Animals can move parts of their body or even their whole body from one place to another. Plants cannot move themselves from one place to another, but they can move parts of their structure. For example, leaves may turn towards the sunlight and roots may grow towards moisture (see 7.10).

7 **They respond to stimuli**. If someone tickles you, you will probably draw back. The tickling is a **stimulus**, your drawing back is a **response** (see Chapter 7). The main stimuli to which organisms respond are heat, light, sound, touch and chemicals which have tastes and smells. In general, plants respond to stimuli much more slowly than animals.

Examiner's tip

The mnemonic 'MR GREEF' will help you to remember the seven important life processes common to plants and animals:

Movement
Response
Growth
Reproduction
Energy need
Excretion
Feeding

1.3 Classification of living things

There are more than one million different organisms. Studying them would be impossible without sorting them into groups. These groups are then divided into smaller groups, and so on. The members of a group have similar features.

Living things are first divided into **kingdoms**. These include the animal kingdom and the plant kingdom (Fig. 1.2).

Kingdoms are then divided into **phyla** (singular, *phylum*). For example, there are two phyla in the animal kingdom – vertebrates (animals with backbones) and invertebrates (animals without backbones). Each phylum is split into **classes**. For example, there are five different classes of vertebrates. Look at Fig. 1.2 and identify them. Some important characteristics of the five classes of vertebrates are shown in Fig. 1.2.

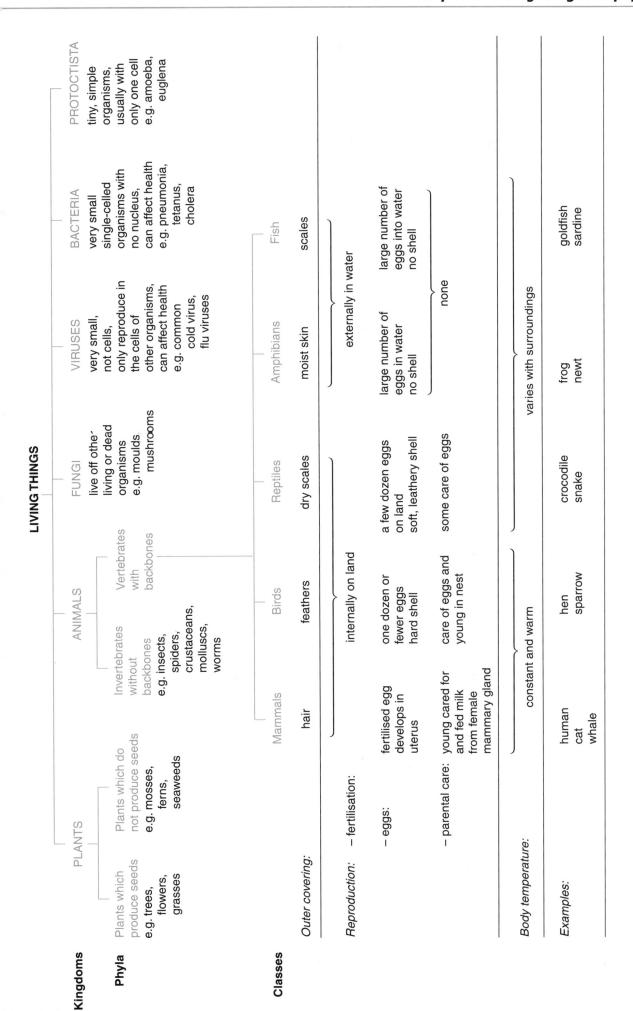

Fig. 1.2 The classification of living things into kingdoms, phyla and classes

In turn, classes are divided into **orders**, orders into **families**, families into **genera** (singular, *genus*) and genera into **species**. Orders, families, genera and species are not shown in Fig. 1.2.

1.4 Naming living things

In 1735, Carl Linnaeus suggested a method of naming living things which we still use today. He used *two words* to describe each organism so his method is called the **binomial system**. The words used are often derived from Latin names.

Linnaeus used the *genus* and the *species* of an organism to name it. This name is called the **proper name** of the organism because it identifies it precisely. **Common names** like cat, frog and buttercup can be confusing because the same name is sometimes used for several different organisms. Some examples of this system are given in Table 1.1.

Table 1.1 Naming organisms

Common name (like a nickname)	Proper name	
	Genus (like a surname, but written first)	*Species* (like a forename, but written second)
Human	*Homo*	*sapiens*
Cat (domestic)	*Panthera*	*catus*
Lion	*Panthera*	*leo*
Meadow buttercup	*Ranunculus*	*acris*
Creeping buttercup	*Ranunculus*	*repens*
	↑ starts with a capital letter	↑ starts with a small letter

1.5 Ecosystems as habitats and communities

Look under a stone or in a pond. Notice that organisms exist in groups rather than as individuals. There might be several woodlice under the stone or several sticklebacks in the pond. Groups of organisms of the *same species* which are found in one particular area are called **populations**. For example, we might talk about the population of humans in Liverpool, the population of woodlice under a stone or the population of daisies in a garden lawn.

Usually there will be populations of many different species within a given area. For example, under a stone there may be woodlice, mosses, fungi and ants. *Different populations* living together in an area are called a **community**. The area in which the community lives is called its **habitat**. Habitats can be very large, like a forest or a city, much smaller, like a garden or a pond, or tiny, like a small stone or a puddle. Different habitats support different plants and animals.

In any habitat there are many different interactions between the organisms in the community and the habitat itself. These interactions include finding and providing food, water and shelter. In fact, each organism depends upon the habitat and the community for its survival.

The combination of a habitat and a community is called an **ecosystem**. The study of ecosystems is called **ecology**. For example, the soil, the rotting vegetation and the trees in a wood together with all the plants and animals which live in the wood make up a woodland ecosystem.

xaminer's tip

The key words and ideas used in this chapter so far are summarised in Fig. 1.3 which shows a simple ecosystem in an aquarium.

Ecosystems are not usually isolated. They interact with each other. For example, flies and insects from other ecosystems may settle and feed on the surface of the aquarium in Fig. 1.3. Even ecosystems as far apart as Africa and Europe are linked by migrating birds, e.g. swallows, which feed in both areas at different times of the year.

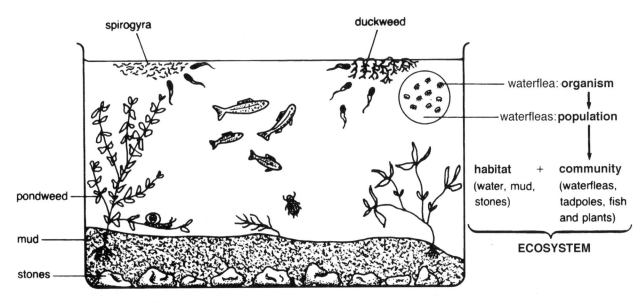

Fig. 1.3 A simple ecosystem in an aquarium

1.6 Interactions in ecosystems – food chains

Some of the most important interactions in any ecosystem involve feeding patterns. Plants are the only living things which can photosynthesise and produce their own food. They are called **producers**. All other living things depend on plants for their food. They *consume* the food which plants have produced or animals which have eaten plants. They are called **consumers**. Fig. 1.4 shows an example of the relationship between producers and consumers.

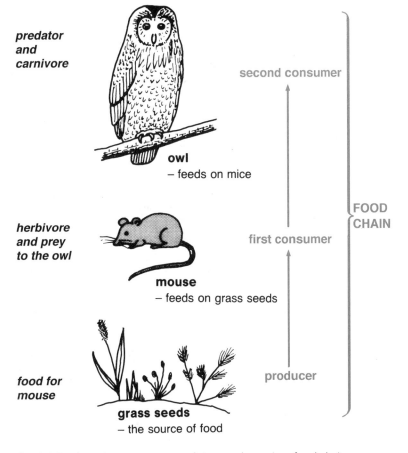

Fig. 1.4 Producers, consumers, predators and prey in a food chain

Table 1.2 shows more examples of producer/consumer combinations. Notice that producers are always plants. Very often, the first consumers are **herbivores** – animals that eat *plants only*. The second and third consumers are either **carnivores** – animals that eat *meat only* – or **omnivores** – animals that eat *both plants and animals*.

Table 1.2 Producers and consumers

Producer	First consumer	Second consumer	Third consumer
grass	cow	human	–
algae	waterflea	stickleback	pike
seaweed	crab	seagull	–

Sequences of producers to consumers, such as

grass seeds → mice → owls

are examples of **food chains**. A food chain has a minimum of three organisms. It always begins with a producer (a green plant) and the subsequent links in the chain are all consumers. Carnivores, such as owls, which hunt and eat other animals, are called **predators**. The animals which they eat, such as mice, are the predator's **prey**. A food chain always ends with an animal, such as an owl, which has no predator.

1.7 Food chains and food webs

In an ecosystem, feeding patterns are not usually as simple as those shown in Table 1.2 and Fig. 1.4. For example, mice will eat fruit and small insects as well as grass seed. The owl will also eat other prey. In any community of plants and animals, complex patterns will emerge. Many food chains will exist and some of these will be interlinked. These interlinked food chains are described as a **food web**. A food web for a simple pond community is shown in Fig. 1.5.

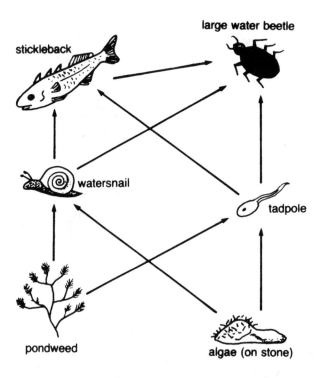

Fig. 1.5 A food web for a simple pond community

Pyramids of numbers

As you pass along a food chain, the number of each type of organism usually gets less. An illustration of this is shown in Fig. 1.6. Along a stretch of river there may be only six herons. These herons feed on thousands of small fish in the river, which in turn are supported by tens of thousands of tadpoles. The tadpoles feed on millions of algae growing on the stones of the river bed. Diagrams like that in Fig. 1.6 are called pyramids of numbers.

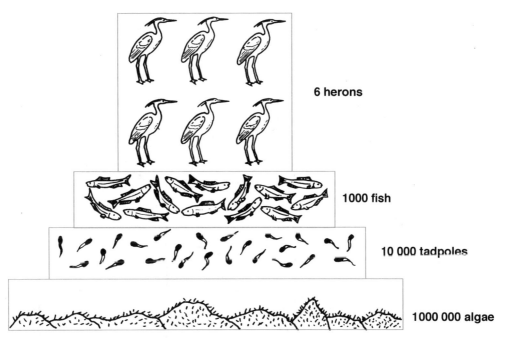

6 herons

1000 fish

10 000 tadpoles

1 000 000 algae

Fig. 1.6 A pyramid of numbers for a food chain in a river

Sometimes, the numbers in a pyramid are converted to masses. This shows the reduction in the *mass of living material* (**biomass**) at each stage along the food chain. The result is a **pyramid of biomass** like that in Fig. 1.7.

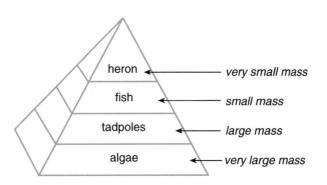

heron — *very small mass*

fish — *small mass*

tadpoles — *large mass*

algae — *very large mass*

Fig. 1.7 A pyramid of biomass

Pyramids like these can be drawn for all food chains. They help to explain why:

- top carnivores like herons, eagles and foxes are rare;
- the biomass of each species is ultimately limited by the ability of green plants at the bottom of the pyramid to produce food;
- there is a great waste of energy along a food chain. For example, only a small percentage of the energy in the algae eventually helps the heron grow. Most of the energy in the algae is lost along the food chain as heat, in urine and in faeces. Less energy is wasted if the food chain is short. This explains why humans can get more energy from cereals by eating them directly than by feeding the cereals to cattle and then eating meat.

Examiner's tip

Make sure that you understand food webs and food chains and the meaning of the terms producers, consumers, predators and prey.

1.8 The growth of populations

If a species is well adapted to a habitat, the population will start to grow. Look at Table 1.3. This shows the number of mice which inhabited a newly built barn. The results are plotted on a graph in Fig. 1.8.

Table 1.3 The number of mice which inhabited a newly built barn

Time/weeks	0	5	10	15	20	25	30	35	40
Number of mice	2	7	17	35	66	94	99	100	100

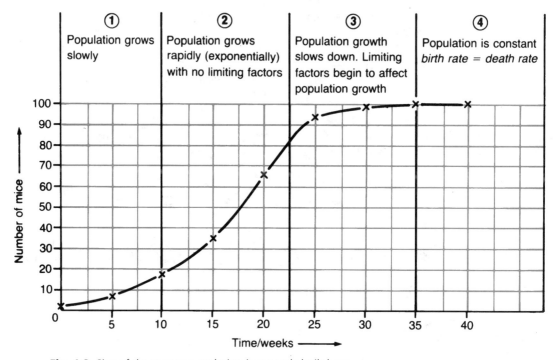

Fig. 1.8 Size of the mouse population in a newly built barn

Notice (from the graph) that the number of mice increases slowly at first and then very rapidly. For the first 20 weeks, the population of mice seems to double every four or five weeks. This is called **exponential growth**. Fortunately for the farmer, this does not go on forever. The growth rate slows down after about 23 weeks and the number in the population becomes steady after 35 weeks. All populations grow in a similar way to the mice in the barn. Growth occurs in four distinct phases as outlined at the top of Fig. 1.8.

Factors affecting population growth

The size of a population of organisms may be affected by various factors. These include:

- **food supplies**
- **water supplies**
- **space**
- **waste products** from the organisms which produce poisonous (toxic) materials and cause pollution
- **disease**
- **predators**
- **climate**, which may become too cold or too wet
- **light**, which is particularly important for plants so that they can photosynthesise, grow and reproduce

Organisms which compete successfully for resources, such as food and water, in their environment will contribute more offspring to the next generation. When the number of organisms in a population reaches a constant value, the rate at which new organisms are born (**birth rate**) equals the rate at which organisms are dying (**death rate**).

1.9 The human population

Fewer factors limit the human population than limit the populations of other organisms. Although space, food and water supplies are a problem in some parts of the world, they are not so in many places. Medicines, particularly antibiotics, have reduced the problems caused by many diseases. Predators are no real problem to humans and extremes of climate can be counteracted with appropriate shelter and clothing.

The improvements in hygiene, diet and medical care that began in the nineteenth century have enabled people in most parts of the world to live longer. At the same time, the birth rate has increased because there are more healthy men and women able to reproduce. This has brought about a dramatic increase in the world population since 1850 (see Fig. 1.9).

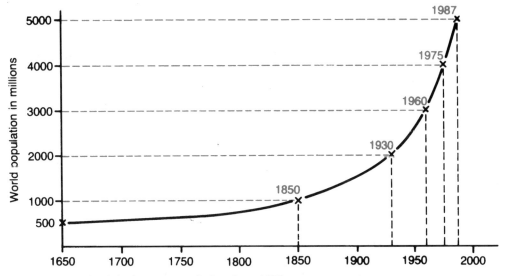

Fig. 1.9 Growth of the human population since 1650

Population growth varies from one country to another. In many developed countries, such as Britain, France and the USA, methods of birth control have almost brought the population to a steady level. But in the developing countries of Africa and Asia, the population continues to grow and grow. The world population growth is still exponential. Notice how the human population graph (Fig. 1.9) resembles the first two phases of the mouse population graph in Fig. 1.8.

The human population graph has not begun to level off yet, but the population explosion cannot go on forever. Eventually one of the limiting factors listed earlier will make it level off – shortage of food, overcrowding, pollution or, perhaps, disease. Many people believe that the only way to avoid these disasters is to introduce reliable methods of birth control throughout the world.

1.10 Food production and ecosystems

Food production often involves the *careful management of ecosystems*. For example, in taking fish from the sea or from rivers, we must ensure that stocks do not fall below acceptable levels. Otherwise, the fish population may not be able to maintain its numbers and this would disrupt the network of food chains and food webs. Similar situations arise when we kill other wild animals, such as deer or pheasants, for food.

Food production may also involve *the creation of artificial ecosystems*. Examples of this are fish farms, arable farms, dairy farms and market gardens. In these examples, the ecosystems are not in balance. Very often there are far more animals or plants per hectare than would normally be the case and any predators are held at bay. This might involve fencing in animals or destroying the insects that feed on the plants. These artificial ecosystems place additional demands on farmers and gardeners. They need to:

- provide adequate supplies of food,
- provide adequate supplies of water,
- remove waste products such as manure and dead plants,
- prevent diseases in their animals and plants.

These arrangements show how food production can be managed to improve the efficiency of energy transfer. This may involve improving the efficiency in turning the energy in sunlight into chemical energy in plants or improving energy transfer from plants to animals (see 1.11).

1.11 Important cycles and energy chains

As plants photosynthesise and plants and animals respire, die and decay, there is a continual recycling of materials. The recycled materials include carbon, nitrogen, water and minerals. This recycling of materials helps to maintain a balance of the materials in any biological community.

The recycling of materials is also affected by the activities of humans. For example, we add fertilisers to the soil which affects the balance of nitrogen compounds. We also burn fuels and produce carbon dioxide which disturbs the balance of carbon compounds.

The carbon cycle

The recycling of carbon compounds through the air, plants, animals and decaying remains is usually called the **carbon cycle**. This is shown in more detail in Fig. 1.10. Notice the following points:

- Photosynthesis (Chapter 2) and respiration (Chapter 6) play an important part in the carbon cycle. Plants gain carbon through photosynthesis and lose it through respiration. Animals gain carbon by eating plants and lose it through respiration.
- Carbon dioxide is removed from the atmosphere by photosynthesis and returned to the atmosphere by respiration, combustion and the decomposition of dead plants and animals. These processes in the carbon cycle help to maintain the balance of carbon dioxide in the atmosphere.
- The decomposition of dead plants and animals is speeded up by bacteria and fungi. They play an important role in breaking down compost and in sewage disposal as they feed on the decaying organic materials. For this reason they are called **decomposers**. They help to recycle carbon, nitrogen, minerals and water by releasing carbon dioxide and nitrogen into the air and nitrogen compounds, water and minerals into the soil.
- Under natural circumstances, the amount of carbon dioxide in the atmosphere would stay about the same. Unfortunately, the carbon dioxide balance is being disturbed by the activities of human beings. This is leading to problems such as the 'greenhouse effect' (see 10.3).

The recycling of nitrogen compounds through plants and animals is discussed more fully in 17.7.

The recycling of carbon, nitrogen and water through an ecosystem provides important materials for the growth of animals and plants. Fig. 1.11 shows how carbon, nitrogen, water and minerals are cycled through plants, animals and decaying remains. It also shows how energy is transferred through an ecosystem. The source of energy for every ecosystem is, of course, the Sun. Energy from sunlight allows green plants (producers) to photosynthesise at the start of food chains. When this happens, the Sun's energy is converted into chemical energy in carbohydrates, fats and proteins in plants. The energy in these foods is then passed along the food chains to animals (consumers) in the ecosystem. Eventually, the energy is lost from the food chain when the plants and animals die. But it is retained by the ecosystem because the plants and animals decay, forming water, minerals and nitrogen compounds in the soil and carbon dioxide and nitrogen in the air, and the cycle starts all over again.

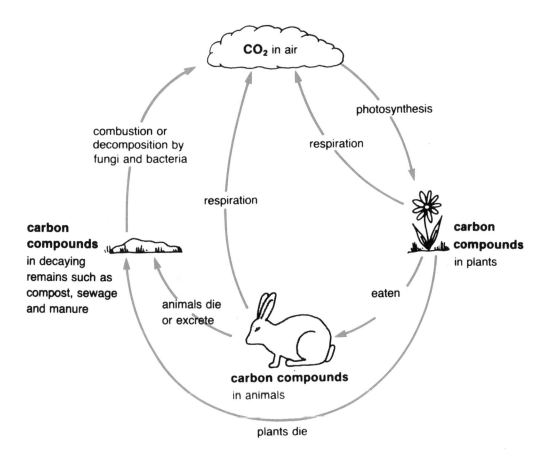

Fig. 1.10 The carbon cycle

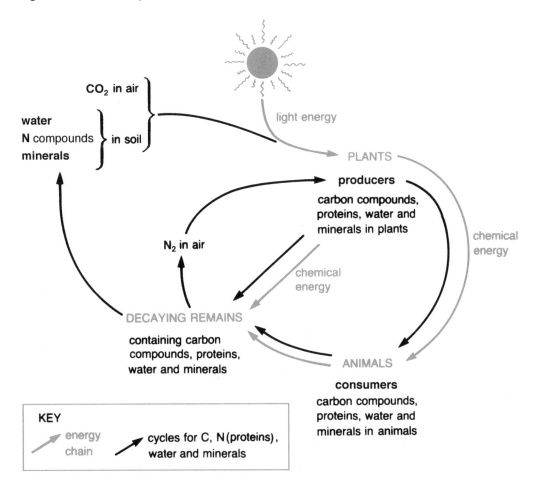

Fig. 1.11 The transfer of carbon, nitrogen, water, minerals and energy through an ecosystem

Summary

1   Living things are often described as **organisms**.

2   A **habitat** is the place where an organism lives. Different habitats support different plants and animals. Some organisms are specially adapted to survive daily and seasonal changes in their habitat.

3   The conditions in a habitat make up the **environment**.

4   There are seven important life processes common to all plants and animals: **growth**, **feeding**, **respiration** (energy need), **excretion**, **reproduction**, **movement** and **response**.

5   Although living things have common names, they are also named precisely using **proper names**. Proper names use the **genus** (capital letter) and **species** (small letter) of an organism, e.g. a human is *Homo sapiens*.

6   A group of organisms of the same species which live together in one area is called a **population**.

7   Different populations living together in an area make up a **community**.

8   The combination of a community and its habitat is called an **ecosystem**.

9   Important interactions in any ecosystem involve feeding patterns. Plants, the only organisms which produce their own food, are called **producers**. Other organisms are called **consumers**.

10 Sequences of producers to consumers, showing which organisms eat which others, are called **food chains**.

11 In any community, several food chains will have species in common. These interlinked food chains are called **food webs**.

12 The number of each type of organism in a food chain can be shown as a **pyramid of numbers**. Alternatively, the numbers in a pyramid can be converted to masses in order to show a **pyramid of biomass**.

13 Various factors affect the size of populations. These include: competition for resources (food, water and space), disease, predators, climate and light.

14 Food production often involves the creation and careful management of artificial ecosystems, e.g. fish farms, arable farms. These artificial ecosystems often involve a more efficient transfer of energy in food production.

15 As plants and animals grow, die and decay, there is a continual recycling of carbon, nitrogen, water and minerals.

16 In the carbon cycle, carbon from carbon dioxide in the air passes to carbon compounds in plants by photosynthesis and then to carbon compounds in animals which eat plants. These carbon compounds reform as carbon dioxide in the air when plants and animals respire or when their remains are either burnt or decay.

17 As various elements and compounds are being recycled through animals and plants, energy is transferred along a chain from sunlight to chemical energy in plants, then to chemical energy in animals, then to chemical energy in the remains of animals and plants, and finally to heat when these remains decay or burn.

Quick test 1

Questions 1 to 5

Complete the following table for goldfish.

Ordinary name	man	goldfish
Scientific name	*Homo sapiens*	*Carassius auratus*
Name of species	*sapiens*	1
Name of genus	*Homo*	2
Name of class	mammals	3
Name of phylum	animals with backbones	4
Name of kingdom	animals	5

Questions 6 and 7

Dolphins and whales are mammals that live in the sea.

A They have hairless skin.
B They have a constant body temperature.
C They give birth to their young.
D They have fins and a tail, but no legs.
E They feed their young on milk from mammary glands.

From the characteristics A, B, C, D and E above, choose

6 those which are unusual for mammals.
7 those which are possessed *only* by mammals.

Questions 8 to 10

A earthworm   D ladybird
B trout   E lizard
C frog

Which of the organisms above
8   has an exoskeleton (external skeleton)?
9   is cold blooded with a dry scaly skin?
10 has no skeleton?

Questions 11 to 13

Living things have seven important characteristics. Which characteristic is the most important to
11 someone looking through a microscope?
12 an athlete running a 100 m race?
13 a sick person taking glucose tablets?

Questions 14 to 16

The graph below shows the number of yeast cells in a vat of beer during fermentation.

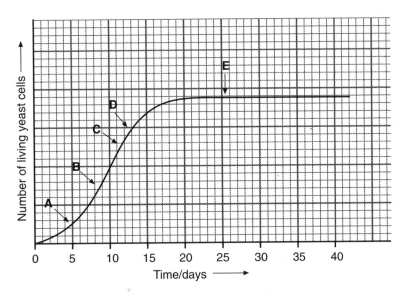

Which letter, A–E, identifies the time when
14 the yeast cells are dying at the same rate as they are being produced?
15 the yeast cells are multiplying at the fastest rate?
16 there are half as many cells as there are after 13 days?

Questions 17 to 22

The diagram below shows how different living things depend on others.

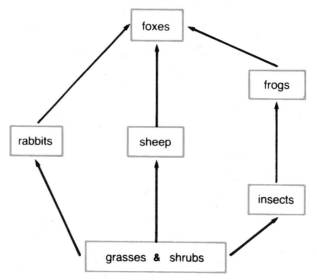

17 What is the name or term given to this type of diagram?
18 Which group would contain the smallest number of individual living things?
19 Which group would contain the greatest total weight of living things?
20 Which box contains the primary producers?
21 Where do these primary producers get their energy from?
22 If the rabbit population was killed off by disease, what two effects could this have on sheep farming in the area?

(WJEC)

Questions 23 to 27

The diagram represents the flow of energy through a food chain.

23 Where does the energy in the system come from?
24 Explain why grass is called the primary producer.
25 How much energy is passed on to
    (a) the grasshopper?
    (b) the chicken?
    (c) the human?
26 At each step energy is lost. Give *two* examples of how it is lost.
27 Use the diagram to explain why meat (animal food) is more expensive to produce than vegetables (plant food). *(ULEAC)*

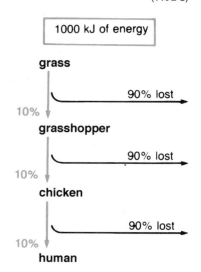

Chapter 2
Photosynthesis

2.1 Cells – building blocks for living things

All living things are made of cells. Cells are the building blocks for organisms in the same way that bricks are the building blocks for houses.

Looking at cells

Your body contains about one hundred million, million cells. Each cell is about one hundredth of a millimetre wide (1/100 mm). You cannot see them with your naked eye, but they can be seen under a microscope. The cells are sometimes stained with a dye so that different parts show up more clearly (see Fig. 2.1).

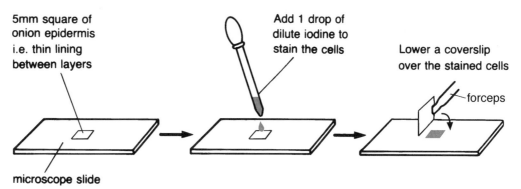

Fig. 2.1 Staining and mounting cells for examination under a microscope

Typical cells

Fig. 2.2 shows a typical animal cell (e.g. a cheek cell or a liver cell) side by side with a typical plant cell (e.g. a leaf cell). The diagram emphasises the similarities and differences between animal cells and plant cells.

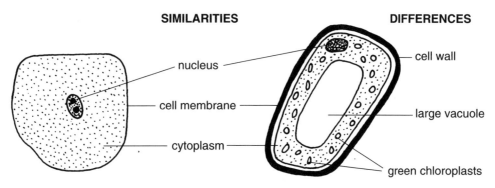

Fig. 2.2 Comparison of an animal cell and a plant cell

All living cells contain *three common features*:

① A **nucleus** which contains thread-like structures called **chromosomes**. The chromosomes are composed of DNA. This chemical controls all the reactions inside the cell and plays an important part when the cell divides.

② **Cytoplasm** in which all the life processes take place. The cytoplasm is a jelly-like liquid containing smaller parts of the cell called **organelles**. These look like little dots under the microscope. They include **mitochondria**, which produce energy, and small granules of stored food.

③ A **cell membrane** which forms the boundary of the cell. The cell membrane is a very thin protein layer which allows food and water to pass into the cell and waste products to pass out.

In addition to these common features, *plant cells have three other features*:

① A **cell wall** outside the cell membrane. The cell wall is made of cellulose which is much tougher than the thin cell membrane. Even so, the cell wall is porous to various substances. The main function of the cell wall is to support and protect the cell.

② **Chloroplasts** are small bodies containing the green pigment **chlorophyll**. Chlorophyll has an essential role in photosynthesis.

③ A **vacuole** in the centre of the cell containing a watery liquid. The vacuole occupies a large volume of the cell and is separated from the cytoplasm by a thin membrane. The vacuole has two main functions:
(a) It can act as a storage space for dissolved foods and chemicals such as sugars and salts.
(b) The liquid in the vacuole creates a pressure on the cell wall which helps to keep the cell wall rigid.

During the 1930s, electron microscopes were invented. These use beams of electrons instead of beams of light and are much more powerful than light (optical) microscopes. Light microscopes can magnify one thousand times, but electron microscopes can magnify one million times. Electron microscopes have enabled scientists to study cells in much greater detail and to identify even smaller features than the six shown in Fig. 2.2.

Examiner's tip

Learn the similarities and differences between animal cells and plant cells.

Examiner's tip

As you read the following chapters, you will see how different cells in animals and plants (e.g. blood cells, sperm cells, nerve cells and pallisade cells) are adapted to their specific functions.

2.2 From atoms to ecosystems

Fig. 2.3 shows how living things are built up from atoms and how organisms themselves group to form a whole ecosystem. Notice also that **cells** are grouped together as **tissues**

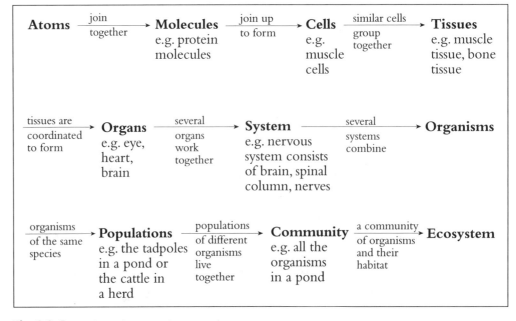

Fig. 2.3 From atoms to ecosystems

and then coordinated to form **organs**. In animals and plants, it is these organs (e.g. eye, heart, lungs) that enable life processes, such as respiration and reproduction, to take place. In fact, organs and organ systems are usually adapted for their specific roles in life processes.

2.3 The movement of substances into and out of cells

Water is the main component of all cells. Water in the cytoplasm and in cell sap contains many dissolved substances. The water and other substances enter and leave cells through the cell membrane. The cell membrane allows certain particles to pass through it, but it blocks the passage of others. Because of this, it is described as a **partially permeable membrane**.

Particles enter and leave cells by three processes:
❶ **Diffusion** (see 13.2)
❷ **Active transport**
❸ **Osmosis**.

Diffusion

Diffusion occurs because of the free movement of particles in a liquid or a gas from a region of high concentration to a region of low concentration.

The process happens simply because of the random motion of the particles and the difference in concentration. The difference in concentration creates a **concentration gradient** from high to low. Examples of diffusion in living things include:
● small molecules of digested food diffusing from the gut into blood capillaries (4.1)
● oxygen diffusing from air sacs in the alveoli into blood capillaries (6.3).
Substances made up of small molecules, for example water, oxygen and carbon dioxide, will usually diffuse through a cell membrane and down a concentration gradient. Substances with larger particles, such as sugar molecules, diffuse much more slowly through membranes because of the partially permeable properties of the membrane.

Active transport

Sometimes an organism needs to move dissolved substances from a region where they are in *low* concentration to a region where the dissolved substances are at a *higher* concentration. This process is, of course, opposite to the direction in which the particles would normally move by diffusion. An example of this occurs when plants obtain minerals, such as nitrates, from the soil. These salts are usually at a lower concentration in the soil than in the roots of the plant. Therefore, the plant has to move (transport) the dissolved substances in the opposite direction to normal diffusion. This transport requires energy which must be supplied by the plant. The process is therefore called **active transport**.

When organisms employ active transport, the energy for the process comes from respiration. Because of this, the cells capable of active transport usually have more mitochondria, in which respiration takes place, than other cells (6.5 and 6.6). Notice that:
● Active transport involves *selective* movement of certain particles, whereas diffusion is *non-selective*;
● Active transport involves movement of particles *against* a concentration gradient, whereas diffusion takes place *down* a concentration gradient;
● Active transport requires *energy*, whereas diffusion requires *no energy*.

Osmosis

Fig. 2.4 shows an experiment to illustrate osmosis. Visking tubing is a partially permeable membrane, like a cell membrane. It has tiny, invisible holes that allow water particles, which are small, to pass through, but not sugar particles, which are larger. When the Visking bag containing sugar solution is placed in pure water, water passes into the bag and the liquid rises in the capillary tube.

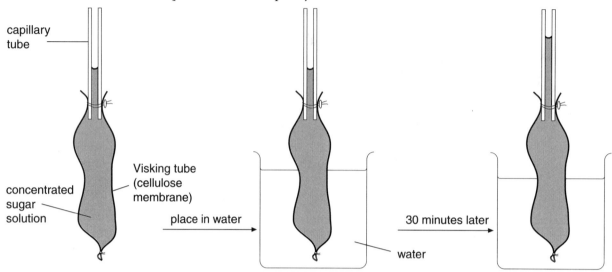

Fig. 2.4 Osmosis through a partially permeable membrane

Water molecules have moved from a region of high water concentration in pure water through the Visking bag to a region of lower water concentration. This is an example of **osmosis**.

Osmosis is a special case of diffusion in which water molecules diffuse from a high water concentration through a partially permeable membrane to a lower water concentration.

Osmosis can be explained using the kinetic theory (13.3). Molecules of water and sugar are continually moving and bombarding the partially permeable membrane (Fig. 2.5). Occasionally, a water molecule passes through one of the tiny holes from one side of the membrane to the other. If pure water occupied both sides of the membrane, equal numbers of water molecules would pass in both directions and there would be no overall change. But, in the sugar solution, large sugar molecules impede the movement of water molecules and block their passage through the holes. So, more water molecules flow from the pure water to the sugar solution than the other way. The overall effect is that water flows through the membrane and into the solution.

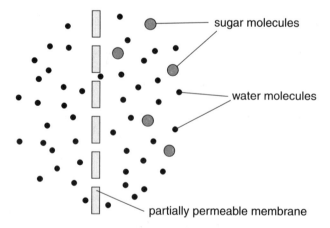

Fig. 2.5 Explaining how osmosis occurs

Osmosis is very important in living organisms. Cell cytoplasm contains a solution of various substances, such as salts, sugars, proteins, etc., in water. These substances must be kept at reasonable concentrations all the time if body processes are to occur successfully. Because of this, water must be able to pass into and out of cells easily. This happens by osmosis through the cell membrane and the whole process is called **osmo–regulation**.

2.4 Plants – the source of all food

One of the important differences between plants and animals is that plants make their own food. Animals cannot make their own food. They obtain their food by eating plants or by eating animals which have fed on plants. So humans and other animals rely on plants for their food. The process by which plants make their own food is called **photosynthesis**.

The production of starch during photosynthesis

Plants cannot grow well in the dark. Because of this, very few plants grow in caves or in the shade of a large tree. Plants need light to photosynthesise.

We can show this by using two similar potted plants such as geraniums. Before the experiment, both plants must be *de-starched* by keeping the plants in the dark for several days. This uses up all the starch stored in their leaves. When the experiment starts, one plant is left in the dark and the other is placed in the light. After a few days, a leaf is taken from each plant and tested for starch using iodine (see Fig. 2.6). If starch is present, a dark blue colour forms with iodine.

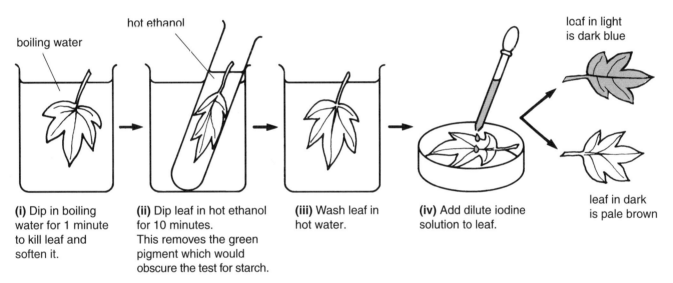

(i) Dip in boiling water for 1 minute to kill leaf and soften it.

(ii) Dip leaf in hot ethanol for 10 minutes. This removes the green pigment which would obscure the test for starch.

(iii) Wash leaf in hot water.

(iv) Add dilute iodine solution to leaf.

leaf in light is dark blue

leaf in dark is pale brown

Fig. 2.6 Testing for starch using iodine

The leaf which has been in the light is stained dark blue by the iodine solution. This shows that:

Starch (biomass) forms during photosynthesis.

In fact, the presence of starch in the leaves of a plant is used as evidence for photosynthesis.

The leaf which is kept in the dark is stained brown by the iodine. There is no starch in this leaf. This shows that:

Light is necessary for photosynthesis.

Light affects plants in their natural surroundings. On a bright, sunny day, plants photosynthesise faster than on a dull day. Plants in an open meadow photosynthesise faster than those in the shade.

The role of chlorophyll in photosynthesis

Fig. 2.7 shows the result when a variegated leaf with green and white patches is tested for starch. The green part of the leaf is coloured by a pigment called **chlorophyll**. After testing, the green part of the leaf is stained a dark blue colour showing that starch is present in this area. The white part of the leaf turns pale brown showing that it contains no starch. This experiment shows that:

Chlorophyll is needed for photosynthesis.

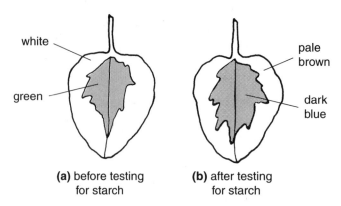

Fig. 2.7 Testing a variegated leaf for starch using iodine

2.5 What chemicals do plants use to produce starch?

We have already shown that both light and chlorophyll are needed for the production of starch during photosynthesis. What chemicals are used to make the starch? Starch is a *carbohydrate*. Therefore, it contains *carbon*, *hydrogen* and *oxygen* which might come from carbon dioxide and water.

Do plants need carbon dioxide to make starch?

An experiment designed to answer this question is illustrated in Fig. 2.8. Both plants must be de-starched before the experiment. Plant A, on the left, is deprived of carbon dioxide which is absorbed by the damp soda lime. Plant B, on the right, has plenty of carbon dioxide which is provided by the slow decomposition of the sodium hydrogencarbonate.

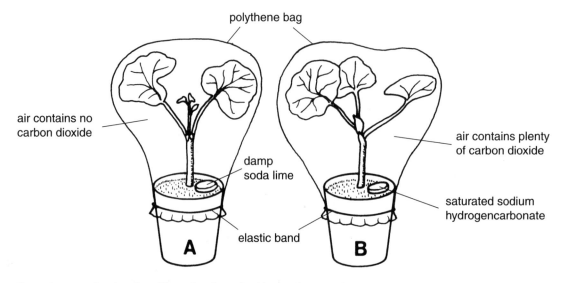

Fig. 2.8 Investigating the effect of carbon dioxide on photosynthesis

When the experiment starts, both plants are placed side by side in a well lit room. After two or three days, a leaf from each plant is tested for starch. The leaf from plant A goes brown, that from plant B goes dark blue. These results show that:

Carbon dioxide is needed for photosynthesis.

Experiments show that plants photosynthesise faster if the air surrounding them contains more carbon dioxide. Carbon dioxide is sometimes pumped into greenhouses or produced from a burner to make plants grow faster.

Do plants need water to make starch?

There are no simple experiments that we can carry out to answer this question. We cannot deprive the plant of all water – this would kill it. The role of water in starch production has been investigated using water containing the heavy oxygen isotope (oxygen-18, $^{18}_{8}O$). If plants are fed with water containing this heavier oxygen isotope, oxygen-18 is found in starch in the plant's leaves. This shows that:

Water plays an important part in photosynthesis.

Plants photosynthesise more slowly if their supply of water is insufficient. However, plants need water for other processes besides photosynthesis, so the effect of water shortage on photosynthesis is not clear.

2.6 What happens in photosynthesis?

The experiments described in this chapter so far tell us that:

Plants need carbon dioxide, water, light and chlorophyll in order to make starch by photosynthesis.

If a plant is deprived of any one of these essentials, it cannot photosynthesise.

Experiments show that the first product of photosynthesis is *glucose*. The glucose molecules then link together to form starch. Experiments similar to the one shown in Fig. 2.9 show that *oxygen* is produced during photosynthesis as well as sugar (glucose) and starch.

When the apparatus is kept in the light, the pondweed produces bubbles of gas. After a few days enough gas collects in the test tube to be able to test for oxygen.

Although photosynthesis is a complicated process, we can summarise the overall reaction as:

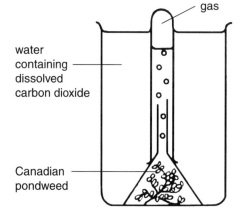

Fig. 2.9   Investigating the production of oxygen during photosynthesis

Examiner's tip

Learn the equation opposite which summarises photosynthesis.

$$\text{carbon dioxide} + \text{water} \xrightarrow[\text{chlorophyll}]{\text{light and}} \text{glucose} + \text{oxygen}$$

$$6CO_2 + 6H_2O \longrightarrow C_6H_{12}O_6 + 6O_2$$

During photosynthesis, chlorophyll absorbs light energy. This energy is used to turn carbon dioxide and water into glucose. So the overall result of photosynthesis is to turn the energy in sunlight into chemical energy in glucose.

How do plants use glucose?

The glucose which plants make by photosynthesis has three main uses. These are summarised in Fig. 2.10.

1 Glucose is converted to **starch** and **stored** for future use. This is why the leaves of plants usually contain starch as a result of photosynthesis.

2 Glucose is converted to **cellulose**, which is needed to support the plant as it **grows**.

3 Glucose is used to produce **energy** for the plant by **respiration** (see Chapter 6).

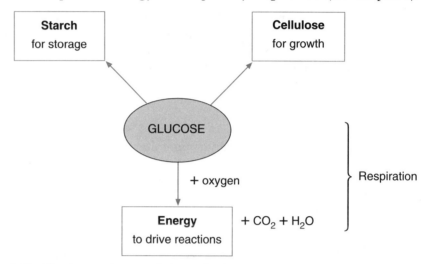

Fig. 2.10 The three main uses of glucose in plants

Looking at Fig. 2.10, notice the overall effect of respiration is the reverse of photosynthesis. The energy produced in respiration is used to drive the other reactions which go on in plants. These reactions include the conversion of glucose to starch and cellulose.

What factors affect the rate of photosynthesis?

There are four factors that strongly influence the rate of photosynthesis:

1 light intensity (see 2.4)
2 concentration of carbon dioxide (see 2.5)
3 water supply (see 2.5)
4 temperature.

Plants photosynthesise faster in warm weather. Roughly speaking, the rate of photosynthesis doubles if the temperature rises by 10 °C. This explains why plants thrive in warm conditions in a greenhouse or in a sheltered garden. Although plants thrive when there is warmth, there is a limit to the temperature at which they can survive. The rate of photosynthesis increases until the temperature reaches about 40 °C. Above 40 °C, photosynthesis slows down and then stops. This is because some important chemicals in plants are destroyed above 40 °C. These important chemicals are called **enzymes**. Enzymes are catalysts (see 17.10 and 17.11). They speed up the reactions in all living things.

2.7 Photosynthesis and transpiration

In order to live and grow, plants must transport materials from one part of themselves to another. The substances transported within plants are required for support, growth and reproduction.

- Water must be transported from the roots to the leaves for photosynthesis and for support.
- Sugars which are produced in the leaves by photosynthesis must be transported to other parts of the plant.
- Minerals (salts) such as nitrates and phosphates must be absorbed from the soil by the roots and transported to different parts of the plant.

Materials such as sugars and minerals can only be moved around a plant if they are in solution. The movement of these solutions round the plant requires a transport system connecting the roots, stem and leaves. This is called the plant's **vascular system**.

The vascular system in a plant can be compared to the blood system in animals (Chapter 5). When the stem of a plant is cut, liquid oozes out. This is sap escaping from the cut vascular system.

Look at Fig. 2.11. This shows an experiment to investigate the uptake of water by a plant. The volume of water in the measuring cylinder was recorded over a few days. The results are shown in Table 2.1.

Table 2.1 Investigating the uptake of water by a plant

Time after start of experiment/days	Volume of water/cm³
0	90
1	88
2	85
3	83
4	81

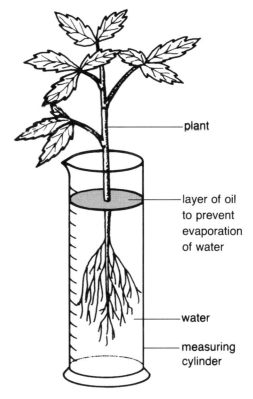

Fig. 2.11   Investigating the uptake of water by a plant

The results in Table 2.1 show that water was taken up by the plant through the root hairs. Some of this water is used in photosynthesis. Most of it evaporates from the leaves, escaping through tiny holes in the leaves called **stomata**. As water is lost from the leaves, it is replaced by more water from the measuring cylinder. This is drawn up from the roots to the leaves through the vascular system.

The evaporation of water from the leaves of a plant is called **transpiration**. The continuous flow of water (sap) through the plant from roots to leaves is called the **transpiration system**.

Water is also important in enabling plants to support themselves. If plant cells are filled with water the cell membrane presses tightly, so the cell wall and the plant can support itself fully. If, however, water is lost from the cells, the cell wall is no longer tight and the plant will flop over (wilt).

2.8 Essential elements for plants

Plants need certain elements in order to grow. These elements are therefore called **essential elements** (see Table 2.2).

Ten of the essential elements are known as **major elements** because they are needed in quite large amounts. The most important essential elements are carbon, hydrogen and oxygen. These are obtained mainly from water and from carbon dioxide in the air.

The seven other major elements are *calcium, potassium, magnesium, iron, nitrogen, phosphorus* and *sulphur*. These seven elements are present in the soil as soluble compounds

Table 2.2 Essential elements for plants

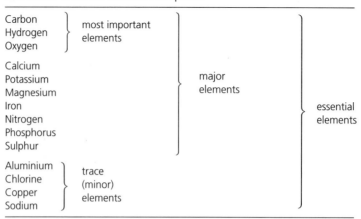

and as minerals, such as calcium phosphate and potassium nitrate. Plants absorb these through their roots (see 2.7). Essential elements are needed by plants for important structures and functions. For example, nitrogen is used to synthesise DNA (**d**eoxyribo-**n**ucleic **a**cid). Chlorophyll contains magnesium and the enzymes which make chlorophyll contain iron. So, if the plant lacks either magnesium or iron, it cannot make chlorophyll and its leaves will turn yellow. This is called **chlorosis**.

Trace elements

In addition to the ten major elements, plants also require other elements in tiny amounts. These elements are therefore called **minor elements** or **trace elements**. They include *zinc, copper, sodium, chlorine, aluminium* and *manganese*. Trace elements are also absorbed from the soil through the roots of plants. The important point about trace elements is that they are only needed in small amounts. Too much of a trace element can be more damaging to a plant than too little.

Summary

1 All living things are made up of **cells**. Different cells and organs are adapted for their different roles in life processes.

2 All living cells contain a **nucleus, cytoplasm** and a **cell membrane**. In addition to these, plant cells also have a **cell wall, chloroplasts** and a **vacuole**.

3 Plants are capable of making their own food by **photosynthesis**. Animals cannot photosynthesise.

4 Experiments show that:

● Plants need carbon dioxide, water, light and chlorophyll in order to photosynthesise. During the process oxygen and glucose are produced, i.e.

$$\text{carbon dioxide} \ + \ \text{water} \xrightarrow[\substack{\text{absorbed by chlorophyll} \\ \text{in chloroplasts}}]{\text{energy in sunlight}} \text{glucose} \ + \ \text{oxygen}$$

$$6CO_2 \ + \ 6H_2O \longrightarrow C_6H_{12}O_6 \ + \ 6O_2$$

● The glucose which is produced during photosynthesis is either
(i)   converted to starch and stored as food,
(ii) converted to cellulose which supports the plant as it grows, or
(iii) used to produce energy for the plant by respiration.

5   The rate of photosynthesis is affected by
   ● intensity of light
   ● concentration of carbon dioxide
   ● water supply
   ● temperature

6   All chemical processes in living things, such as photosynthesis, are speeded up by chemicals called **enzymes**. Enzymes act as biological catalysts.

7   All plant cells which contain chlorophyll can photosynthesise. These cells are mainly in the leaves.

8   Carbon dioxide needed for photosynthesis enters plants through **stomata** on the underside of leaves. Water needed for photosynthesis enters plants through their roots. This water is then transported from the roots to the leaves.

9   Water containing dissolved substances for growth and reproduction can move through a plant via its **vascular system**. The vascular system in a plant can be compared to the blood system in animals.

10   The continuous flow of water (sap) through a plant from roots to leaves is called the **transpiration system**. The evaporation of water from the leaves of a plant is called **transpiration**.

11   Plants need certain elements in order to grow. These are called **essential elements**. These essential elements are obtained from carbon dioxide in the air and from water and minerals in the soil.

12   Ten of the essential elements for plants are known as **major elements** because they are needed in quite large amounts. Other elements which plants require in tiny amounts are called **trace elements**.

Quick test 2

Questions 1 to 6

A cell wall
B cytoplasm
C nucleus
D chloroplast
E cell membrane

From the list A to E above, choose the part of a cell which contains

1 chromosomes.
2 cellulose.
3 chlorophyll.

4 mitochondria.
5 DNA molecules.
6 starch granules.

Questions 7 to 10

Choose the option, A to D, which correctly completes the sentence.

7   Photosynthesis
   A is essential to all life on Earth.
   B uses up oxygen.
   C takes place only in darkness.
   D is not important to animals.

8   There is no starch in the white part of a variegated ivy leaf because that part of the leaf
   A is dead.
   B is too cold.
   C contains no chloroplasts.
   D has been in the shade.

9   Carbon dioxide enters plants through holes in the leaves called
   A air spaces.   C cuticles.
   B chloroplasts. D stomata.

10 The metal present in chlorophyll is
   A calcium.   C magnesium.
   B iron.   D potassium.

11 The volume of oxygen produced per hour by a sample of duckweed was measured over a 12 hour period. Which letter on the graph represents 12.00 noon?

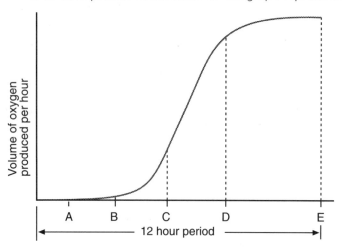

Questions 12 to 14

A carbon
B cobalt
C magnesium
D nitrogen
E phosphorus

Choose, from A to E above, the essential element which

12 would improve the colour of grass.
13 would be provided by ammonium salts.
14 is required in only trace quantities.

Questions 15 and 16

The diagram below shows four test tubes labelled A to D. Each tube contains the organisms shown in river water. The tubes were left in sunlight for six hours.

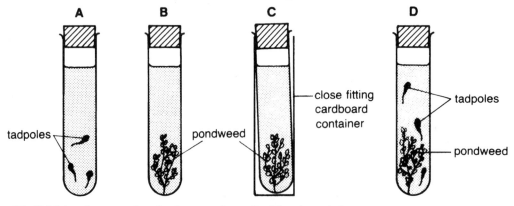

15 Which tube contains the least carbon dioxide after six hours?
16 In which tube or tubes will photosynthesis occur?

Questions 17 and 18

A market gardener found that the average mass of a lettuce grown in an ordinary greenhouse was 80 g, whereas the average mass of a lettuce grown in a greenhouse where the atmosphere contained added carbon dioxide was 115 g.

17 Why is there a difference in the average mass of the lettuces?
18 State three other ways in which the gardener could increase the mass of the lettuces.

Questions 19 and 20

19 Name the two products of photosynthesis.
20 What energy conversion takes place during photosynthesis?

Chapter 3
Food and diet – nutrition

3.1 Different kinds of food

The food that we eat and drink each day makes up our **diet**. We need different foods for different purposes. We require three types of food:

1 **energy foods** which give us the energy to move and keep warm. These energy foods are sometimes called *body fuels*. The main energy foods are **carbohydrates** and **fats**. Carbohydrates include starch in bread, potatoes and rice. Fats include cream, margarine and cooking oil.

2 **body-building foods** which provide the important chemicals we need to grow and to repair the worn-out parts of our bodies. The main body-building foods are **proteins**. Meat, fish, milk, cheese and eggs are rich in proteins.

3 **maintenance foods** which are needed in small amounts to control our metabolism and keep our bodies running smoothly. The key maintenance foods are **vitamins** (e.g. vitamin C in oranges) and **minerals** (e.g. sodium in salt).

In addition to these three types of food, we also need **water** and **fibre**.

Most people can survive several weeks without food, but only a few days without water. We take in most of our water by drinking, but most solid food also contains water. For example, meat contains about 60% water and cabbage is about 90% water. Even so, we need to drink at least one cubic decimetre (1 dm³ = 1000 cm³) of water everyday.

Fibre is important in the diet as **roughage** (see 3.5).

To summarise, a balanced diet must include the following seven constituents:

carbohydrates
fats
proteins
vitamins   These essential requirements in our
minerals   diet are called **nutrients**.
fibre
water

3.2 Carbohydrates, fats and proteins

Table 3.1 Comparison of carbohydrates, fats and proteins

	Carbohydrates	Fats	Proteins
Elements present	C, H and O with H and O in the ratio 2:1	C, H and O, but ratio H:O is very high (i.e. very little O)	C, H, O and N
Examples	The main carbohydrates are: **glucose** ($C_6H_{12}O_6$) and **fructose** in fruit; **sugar** (sucrose) in sugar cane and sugar beet; **starch** in bread, potatoes, rice and cereals; **cellulose** (fibre) in the cell walls of plants in leaves, stems and wood.	Beef fat ($C_{57}H_{110}O_6$), butter, margarine, cooking oil.	Milk, eggs, meat and fish contain a high percentage of protein.
Units (monomers) and polymers	Simple **monosaccharides** (monomers), e.g. glucose (G) and fructose (F), join together to form **disaccharides**, e.g. sucrose (G)—(F), and **polysaccharides** (polymers), e.g. starch and cellulose	Fats are made by a reaction between **glycerol** and **fatty acids**: glycerol + fatty acids fats	Proteins are synthesised from 23 different **amino acids**. Amino acids (monomers) join together in long chains to form proteins (polymers): amino acids protein Certain amino acids can be made by our bodies so we do not need them in our diet. Others cannot be made by our bodies, so they must be in our diet – these are called **essential amino acids**.
Function	1 Carbohydrates are important **energy foods** (fuels). During *respiration* (see 6.5) they release energy in order to maintain the body's activity and also keep warm. 2 Excess carbohydrates can be stored as *starch* in plants or as *glycogen* in animals and used as energy foods at a later date. Starch and glycogen are therefore **energy stores**. 3 *Cellulose* is an important **structural substance** in the cell walls of plants. It acts as *fibre* (**roughage**) in our diet because it is not broken down in humans. Roughage keeps food moving through the gut and prevents constipation.	1 Fats are also **energy foods** (fuels). They produce about twice as much heat per gram during metabolism as carbohydrates and proteins. 2 Fats are stored under the skin (*subcutaneous fat*) in humans and other animals. This acts as **insulation**. 3 Subcutaneous fat also acts as an **energy store**.	1 Proteins form the main structures of our body. So proteins are **body-building foods**. We need them for growth and the repair of damaged tissues. Muscles, skin, hair and nails are nearly 100% protein. Bone is partly protein. 2 *Enzymes* are proteins. Enzymes catalyse the reactions in living things and help to **control the rate of metabolism**. 3 Proteins give us **energy**, but they are not as important in this role as carbohydrates and fats.
Effects and dangers of excess or lack	Excess carbohydrate of any kind can cause a person to become overweight. This can lead to heart disease. Too much sugar can cause tooth decay.	Too much fat is unhealthy. It causes a person to become overweight and may cause heart disease.	In some parts of the world, protein is very scarce. A severe lack of protein leads to a disease called **kwashiorkor**.

3.3 Vitamins

Vitamins are an essential part of our diet. They help to control the chemical reactions in our bodies. Without vitamins many of these reactions cannot take place. Most vitamins are complex chemicals. They do have chemical names, but they are usually known simply by letters of the alphabet.

We need only tiny amounts of vitamins, but without them people suffer from illnesses known as **deficiency diseases**. Table 3.2 summarises the sources of some important vitamins, their functions and the deficiency diseases associated with them.

Table 3.2 Some important vitamins

Vitamin	Good sources	Function	Deficiency disease
A (retinol)	green vegetables, carrots, liver	helps us to see in the dark, protects the surface of our eyes	poor vision in the dark or in dim light – *night blindness*
B₁ (thiamine)	bread, cereals (especially in the seed husks)	helps us to produce energy from foods	stomach ache, diarrhoea, vomiting, muscular weakness – *beriberi*
B₂ (riboflavin)	green vegetables, eggs, fish	helps us to produce energy from foods	dry sores on the skin and around the mouth, poor growth
C (ascorbic acid)	green vegetables, black-currants, citrus fruits	helps to heal wounds and form strong skin	bleeding from the gums and the stomach – *scurvy*
D (calciferol)	liver oil, eggs (also made by the skin in sunlight)	helps us to form strong, hard bones and teeth	weak bones, deformed bones – *rickets*

3.4 Minerals

We must have certain elements in our diet. The main elements in our bodies are carbon, hydrogen, oxygen and nitrogen. There is a good supply of these elements in the carbohydrates, fats, proteins and water in our diet.

In addition to these elements, we need many other elements in smaller quantities. These elements are usually present in the **minerals** which occur in small amounts in our food. Minerals are sometimes called **salts**. Perhaps the best example of a mineral (salt) is sodium chloride (common salt). Common salt provides us with essential small amounts of sodium. Table 3.3 shows some important minerals, their sources, their function and the effects of deficiency.

Table 3.3 Some important minerals

Mineral	Good sources	Function	Effect of deficiency
Sodium	common salt (table salt)	helps nerves and muscles to work smoothly	pains in muscles – *cramp*
Calcium	milk, cheese, bread	hardens bones and teeth	soft and deformed bones – *rickets*
Iron	red meat, liver, kidney, green vegetables, dried fruit	needed to form *haemoglobin* in red blood cells	tiredness, lack of energy – *anaemia*
Iodine	sea foods, table salt	needed to make the hormone *thyroxine* which controls metabolism	thyroid gland in neck swells – *goitre*

Examiner's tip

Examiners are keen on questions related to diet and health. Read section 3.5 carefully.

3.5 Diet and health

A **balanced diet** is one that maintains our health and provides the necessary amounts of carbohydrates, fats, proteins, vitamins, minerals, water and fibre. No single food contains all these nutrients, so we need to balance our diet by eating a wide variety of different foods. Table 3.4 shows the recommended amounts of energy, protein and iron needed by different people for a balanced diet.

Table 3.4 Daily amounts of energy, protein and iron recommended by the Department of Health

Person	Energy needed/kJ	Protein needed/g	Iron needed/mg
Baby under 1 year	3300	20	6
Child, 5 years	7500	45	8
Boy, 15–17 years	12600	75	15
Girl, 15–17 years	9600	58	15
Adult male (moderately active)	12600	75	10
Adult female (moderately active)	9200	55	12

The requirements of a balanced diet depend on:
- *age* (growing children need more of each type of food, relative to their weight, than adults),
- *sex* (generally, males need more food than females),
- *occupation* (people in some jobs need more energy and more water (to replace sweat) than those in other jobs),
- *climate* (in hot countries the amounts of energy required to keep warm and amount of water to replace sweat will be different from what is required in cold countries).

The dangers of overeating

Most people enjoy food. This is healthy and natural, but it is easy to eat too much and put on weight. Some people become obese (very overweight). The reason for being overweight is not simply eating too much. It is often caused by eating too much of the wrong foods, in particular sugary and fatty foods. Being overweight can cause other health problems. People who are overweight tend to suffer more from high blood pressure, diabetes, heart disease and strokes (cerebral haemorrhages).

For health reasons, it is important to eat a balanced diet. This does not mean cutting down on all foods, but choosing a diet which is low in sugar and fat. In this way you are much less likely to suffer from weight problems. Regular exercise will also help you to keep fit and healthy.

High-fibre diets

High-fibre diets include wholemeal bread, wholegrain rice, muesli, brown pasta, vegetables and fruit. These foods are good sources of carbohydrate and fibre. By eating them, people cut down their intake of fats and sugars which are the main causes of obesity (being overweight). Fibre acts as **roughage** in the diet. This helps **peristalsis** (the movement of food through the gut) and prevents constipation.

Vegetarian diets

Some people prefer not to eat meat or fish. They are called **vegetarians**. The main constituents in their diet are vegetables, fruit, cereals, rice, nuts, milk, eggs and cheese. The proteins in plants do not usually contain the right balance of amino acids for humans. So milk, eggs and cheese are very important in a vegetarian's diet (see Table 3.1).

Some vegetarians also prefer not to eat animal products such as eggs or dairy (milk-based) products. They are called **vegans**. By carefully combining pulses (beans, peas and lentils) and cereals, they can obtain the necessary balance of amino acids.

Summary

1   Our diet must include three types of food:
    - **Energy foods** which act as body fuels and allow us to move and keep warm. The main energy foods are **carbohydrates** and **fats**.
    - **Body-building foods** which provide the chemicals we need for growth and repair. The main body-building foods are **proteins**.
    - **Maintenance foods** which are needed in small amounts to control our metabolism. These include **vitamins** and **minerals**, such as sodium in salt.

2   In addition to these three types of food, we also need **water** and **fibre**. So, a balanced diet must include seven essential constituents: carbohydrates, fats, proteins, vitamins, minerals, fibre and water.

3   Carbohydrates contain carbon, hydrogen and oxygen with hydrogen and oxygen atoms in the ratio of 2:1 as in water. The main carbohydrates are glucose, sugar (sucrose), starch and cellulose. Starch and cellulose are polymers which are made up from glucose monomers.

4   Fats contain carbon, hydrogen and oxygen, but their proportion of oxygen is very low compared to that in carbohydrates. Butter, margarine, cream and cheese contain a high proportion of fat.

5   Proteins contain carbon, hydrogen, oxygen and nitrogen. They are polymers made up from different amino acids (monomers). Milk, eggs, nuts and fish contain a high percentage of protein.

6   Vitamins help to control the chemical reactions in our bodies. Without vitamins certain reactions cannot take place. We need only tiny amounts of vitamins, but without them people suffer from **deficiency diseases**, e.g. lack of vitamin C leads to scurvy.

7   In order to maintain good health, we need a **balanced diet**. This provides all six nutrients plus **fibre**. Fibre acts as roughage which helps the movement of food through the gut and prevents constipation.

Quick test 3

Questions 1 to 7

These refer to the information below which comes from the label on a can of baked beans.

Constituent	Average amount per 100 g
carbohydrate	9.3 g
fibre	7.3 g
protein	5.2 g
added sugar	2.0 g
added salt	0.8 g
fat	0.4 g

1   Which constituent of the beans provides a good source of amino acids?
2   Which constituents of the tinned beans were not present in the freshly picked beans?
3   Which constituent of the beans is good for digestion because it helps food to pass through the gut?
4   Which constituent of the beans provides an important mineral nutrient?
5   One constituent listed on the label is 'carbohydrate'. Which of the other constituents are also carbohydrates?
6   In a 100 g sample, what is the total mass of the constituents shown on the label?
7   What major constituent in the baked beans is not shown on the label?

Questions 8 to 12

Jane's meal consisted of: a glass of water, roast beef, boiled potatoes and carrots followed by cheese and an apple. Assuming she eats the same mass of each food, which food will provide:

8   the least energy?
9   the most protein?
10   both calcium and fat?
11   the most iron?
12   vitamin A?

Questions 13 to 16

The table below shows the amount of energy a human being needs at different ages just to stay alive (breathe, keep warm, grow, etc.).

	Mass/kg	Energy (kJ) needed each day For each kg	Total
Infant, 1 year old	10	210	2100
Child, 7 years old	25	170	4250
Adult, 20 years old	60	100	

13   How much energy does a 7-year-old child need each day for each kilogram of body mass?
14   What is the total energy needed each day by a 20-year-old adult of mass 60 kg?
15   How does the total daily energy requirement of humans change as they grow from infants to adults?
16   How does the energy needed per kilogram of body mass change as humans grow from infants to adults?

Chapter 4
Digestion

4.1 What happens to food after we eat it?

A cheese sandwich contains carbohydrates, fats and proteins – carbohydrates in the bread, fats and proteins in the cheese and butter. All these foods are solids. After we eat them, they pass into the **digestive system**. The digestive system is like a long, coiled tube which runs from the mouth to the anus. It is usually called the **gut** or the **alimentary canal**.

The main purpose of digestion is to break food down into smaller particles. These smaller particles are soluble in water and they can pass through the wall of the gut into the bloodstream (Figs. 4.1 and 4.2). Once in the bloodstream, the smaller particles can be carried to other parts of the body where they are needed. Food which cannot be broken down stays in the gut. This passes out of the body, through the anus, as **faeces**.

Digestion involves two distinct sets of processes:

1 **Physical processes** which simply divide the food pieces. These include *chewing* in the mouth and *churning* in the stomach.

2 **Chemical processes** which break down chemicals in the food into smaller molecules. These chemical processes are reactions involving the food we eat and *digestive enzymes*. Digestive enzymes are produced by glands which open into the gut.

Enzymes are biological catalysts (see 17.10 and 17.11). They are proteins which are affected by changes in temperature and pH (acidity level). Almost all the chemical reactions in your body are catalysed by enzymes. Every cell in your body contains dozens of different enzymes and each enzyme catalyses a different reaction.

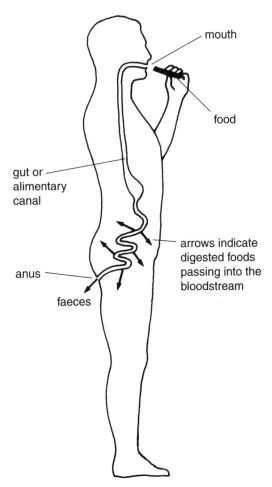

mouth

food

gut or alimentary canal

arrows indicate digested foods passing into the bloodstream

anus

faeces

Fig. 4.1 A simple plan of the human digestive system

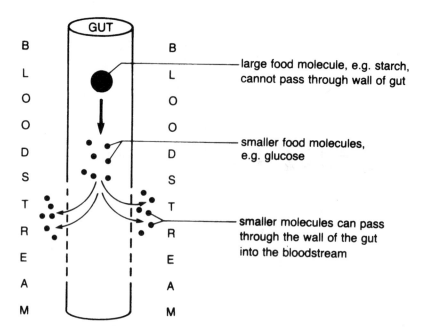

Fig. 4.2 Digestion involves breaking down large food molecules into smaller ones. These smaller molecules pass through the wall of the gut into the bloodstream.

4.2 How is food digested?

Although we said that the alimentary canal is like a long, coiled tube, it has distinctly different parts. Each part has a different role in digestion. Fig. 4.3 shows the main parts of the alimentary canal (gut) as they are arranged in the human body. The role of each part of the gut is summarised on the diagram.

Notice that there are digestive enzymes in saliva in the mouth, in the gastric juice of the stomach, in pancreatic juice and in the small intestine. These enzymes break down large molecules to form simpler units (e.g. glucose and amino acids). These can then be absorbed into the body through the lining of the small intestine. They pass into the capillaries and are carried away in the blood.

Food which cannot be broken down (waste material) is excreted through the anus.

4.3 Using the absorbed foods

Soluble food molecules are absorbed into the blood capillaries of the small intestine. From the small intestine the blood flows first to the liver. The liver acts as a food processing factory for the absorbed foods:

● Glucose (i) travels in the blood to muscles to provide energy.
        (ii) Excess glucose is stored in the liver as glycogen.
● Amino acids (i) travel in the blood to other organs to form protein for growth and repair.
        (ii) Some amino acids are processed in the liver to form blood proteins, e.g. fibrinogen for blood clotting.
        (iii) Excess amino acids are broken down, giving energy.
● Vitamins are stored in the liver and released into the bloodstream when required.

xaminer's tip

Fig. 4.3 provides an excellent summary of digestion and the whole digestive system. Make sure you understand this.

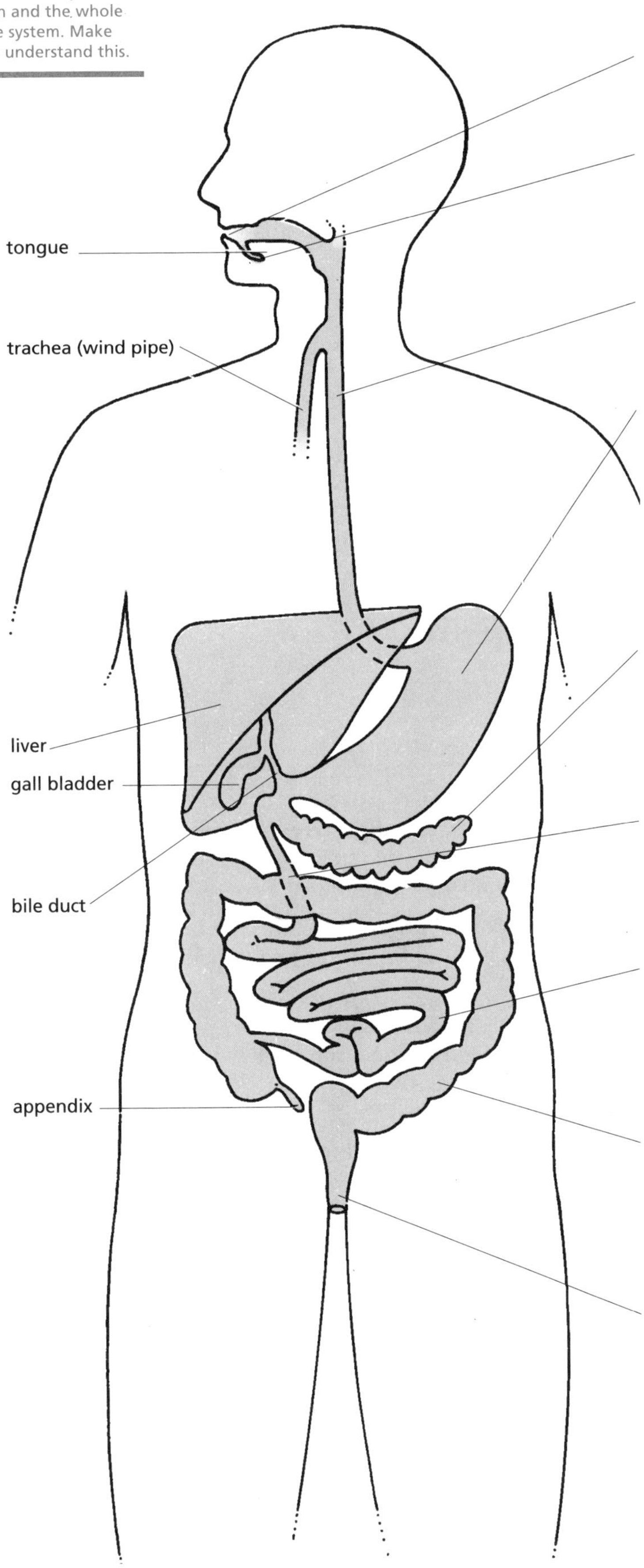

tongue

trachea (wind pipe)

liver

gall bladder

bile duct

appendix

Mouth: Food chewed by teeth. This chops the food into small pieces and increases the surface area. Enzymes can then react with the food more quickly.

Salivary glands produce saliva ('spit') containing:
- *mucus* which makes food slippery and easy to swallow
- *amylase*, an enzyme which catalyses the reaction which breaks down starch.

Gullet (oesophagus): The gullet has muscles in its wall. These muscles contract behind the food and push it along the gut (peristalsis).

Stomach: The stomach wall is thick and muscular. Muscular contractions churn up the food. Glands in the walls of the stomach (gastric glands) produce *gastric juice*. This contains *pepsin*, an enzyme which catalyses the reaction which breaks down proteins to form smaller molecules called *peptides*.
The gastric glands also produce *hydrochloric acid* which helps to break down proteins and kill germs in the stomach.

Pancreas produces *pancreatic juice* which contains enzymes. These enzymes enter the duodenum and cause the breakdown of:
- starch to sugars,
- proteins to peptides,
- fats to fatty acid and glycerol.

Duodenum: The **liver** produces a liquid called *bile* which is stored in the **gall bladder**. Bile enters the duodenum after a meal. It breaks up the fat in food into small droplets which can then mix with other watery liquids. This is called *emulsification*.

Ileum: Glands in the ileum produce more enzymes. These break down
- sugars to glucose and
- peptides to amino acids.
Small molecules of digested food are absorbed through the walls of the ileum into the bloodstream.

Colon: By this stage, digestible foods have been broken down and absorbed into the blood. Indigestible foods, such as roughage (fibre), and water remain. In the colon, water is absorbed into the blood so the undigested material becomes more solid.

Rectum: Semisolid matter (waste material) collects in the rectum as *faeces* which pass out, once or twice a day, through the **anus**.

- small intestine { duodenum
ileum

- large intestine { colon
appendix
rectum

Fig. 4.3 The main parts of the human alimentary canal

4.4 Problems in the digestive system

Most of the time, our digestive system works smoothly and comfortably. Problems can occur when we develop bad eating habits. The most common problems, their causes and their cures are summarised in Table 4.1.

Table 4.1 Some common problems in the digestive system

Problem	Cause	Cure
Indigestion – stomach ache	Eating too quickly – gastric glands produce excess acid. If the person belches, acid comes up the gullet giving a burning sensation ('heartburn').	Indigestion tablets which contain a mild alkali to neutralise the excess acid.
Stomach ulcer	Worry and stress which cause a constant excess of acid in the stomach. The acid attacks the stomach wall making it raw and sore.	Reduce stress and worry. Indigestion tablets.
Constipation	Not going to the toilet regularly. Faeces remain in the rectum too long and more water is removed from them. This makes them hard, dry and difficult to pass out.	Regular, daily, toilet habits. Roughage in the diet helps to keep materials moving through the gut. Take laxatives.
Diarrhoea – can lead to dehydration	Bacteria irritate the gut which produces too much mucus. Faeces move through the gut and are expelled from the anus before the colon can absorb water from them.	A short period without food allows the harmful bacteria to be expelled with the watery faeces. Drink plain water to prevent dehydration.

Summary

1   After we have eaten, our foods pass into the **digestive system**. The digestive system is like a long, coiled tube running from the mouth to the anus. It is often called the **gut** or the **alimentary canal**.

2   During digestion, food is broken down into smaller particles which are soluble in water and which can pass through the wall of the gut into the bloodstream.

3   Digestion involves two types of processes:
    ● **physical processes** which divide food into smaller pieces, e.g. chewing.
    ● **chemical processes** which break down food into smaller molecules. These chemical processes are catalysed by digestive enzymes.

4   The main parts of the alimentary canal and their roles are:
    (i)   **salivary glands** – produce mucus which helps us to swallow food and amylase (an enzyme) which catalyses the breakdown of starch.
    (ii)   **gullet** – with muscular walls which push the food along the gut.
    (iii) **stomach** – muscular contractions churn up the food. Gastric juices contain pepsin (an enzyme) which catalyses the breakdown of proteins to peptides.
    (iv)   **duodenum** – the **gall bladder** stores bile which enters the duodenum after a meal. This helps to break up fat and enables it to mix with watery liquids (emulsification).
    (v)   **pancreas** – produces pancreatic juices which contain enzymes. These enter the duodenum and cause the breakdown of starch to sugars, proteins to peptides, and fats to fatty acids and glycerol.
    (vi)   **ileum** – glands in the ileum produce more enzymes to break down our food. Small molecules of digested food pass through the walls of the ileum into the bloodstream.
    (vii) **colon** – water is now absorbed through the walls of the colon into the bloodstream. The remaining undigested material becomes more solid.
    (viii) **rectum** – semisolid waste matter collects in the rectum as **faeces** prior to excretion.

Quick test 4

1   A scientist found that 2 g of starch was changed to maltose in 1 hour when mixed with saliva at 15 °C. The experiment was repeated at a temperature of 30 °C. How much starch was broken down in the second experiment?
   A 0.5 g   B 1 g   C 2 g   D 4 g

Questions 2 and 3

• The graph shows the rate of digestion of protein in the stomach at different temperatures.
   2   Digestion of protein is fastest at
      A 10 °C   B 20 °C   C 30 °C   D 40 °C
   3   If someone has a cold drink, digestion in the stomach will
      A   stop completely.   C   stay at the same rate.
      B   slow down.   D   speed up.

Questions 4 to 9

   4   In which parts of the alimentary canal is starch broken down?
   5   In which part of the alimentary canal are proteins broken down?
   6   In which part of the alimentary canal are fats emulsified?
   7   In which part of the alimentary canal are small molecules absorbed into the blood?
   8   What part does hydrochloric acid play in digestion?
   9   In which two parts of the alimentary canal does most physical digestion occur?

Questions 10 to 13

Pat wants to find out how quickly amylase (an enzyme) breaks down starch at two different temperatures.
   10   Which chemical (reagent) is used to test for starch?
   11   What colour does the reagent change to if starch is present?
   12   State *three* things which must be kept the same in the two experiments if the results are to be fairly compared?
   13   In the experiment, what is produced when starch breaks down?   *(ULEAC)*

Questions 14 to 22

The table below shows the pH in the mouth after eating food with a high sugar content.

Time/min	0	5	10	15	20	25	30	35	40
pH	6.9	4.6	4.4	4.8	5.2	5.6	5.9	6.4	6.9

   14   What does pH measure?
   15   What is the 'normal' pH of the mouth (i.e. before food is eaten)?
   16   When the pH in the mouth falls below 5.5, the enamel on the teeth is likely to be attacked. About how long after eating the food could dental attack start?
   17   About how long does the pH in the mouth remain at a level at which attack may continue?
   18   Dentists advise against eating sweets between meals. Using the evidence above, suggest why it is sensible to follow this advice.
   19   Name the type of organism which may cause the pH to decrease.
   20   What should the pH of toothpaste be?
   21   Explain your answer to question 20.
   22   Dental attack may be prevented by strengthening the enamel of the tooth. This is often done using a chemical in toothpaste or in drinking water. Name one chemical that is often used in this way.   *(ULEAC, modified)*

Chapter 5
The blood system

5.1 What is blood?

Blood looks like an ordinary liquid. Using a microscope, however, it is possible to see **cells** floating in a watery liquid called **plasma**. The four main constituents of blood and their functions are shown in Fig. 5.1.

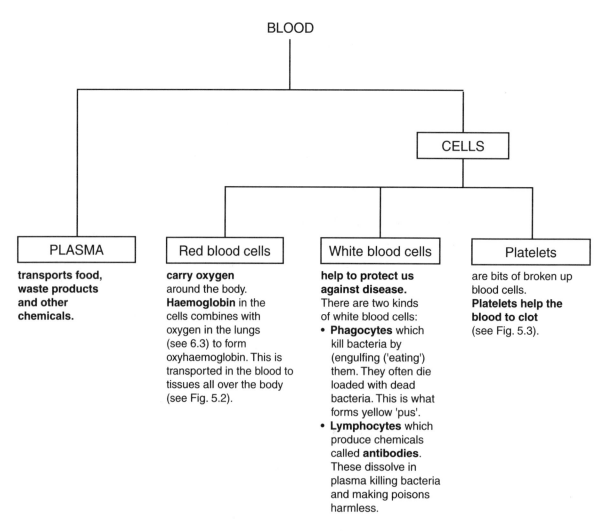

Fig. 5.1 The main constituents of blood and their functions

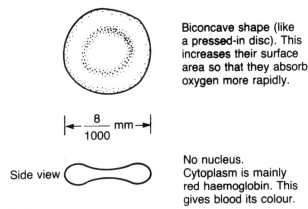

Biconcave shape (like a pressed-in disc). This increases their surface area so that they absorb oxygen more rapidly.

$$\frac{8}{1000}\text{ mm}$$

Side view

No nucleus. Cytoplasm is mainly red haemoglobin. This gives blood its colour.

Fig. 5.2 Red blood cells

Plasma

Plasma is a pale yellow liquid. It is 90% water and 10% dissolved substances. These dissolved substances include:

- *soluble foods* from digestion (see 4.1 and 4.2), e.g. glucose, amino acids and fat droplets
- *salts* (*minerals*) as ions (see 15.3), e.g. Na^+, Cl^-, Ca^{2+}
- *hormones* (see 7.9) in minute traces, e.g. insulin and adrenaline
- *waste products*, e.g. carbon dioxide and urea
- *blood proteins*, e.g. *globulin*, a protein consisting of antibodies, *albumen*, which thickens the blood, and *fibrinogen*, which is needed for clotting (see Fig. 5.3).

1 Platelets form a temporary plug in any blood vessels which are cut.	plug of platelets
2 On exposure to air, platelets produce an enzyme which converts fibrinogen (a blood protein) into a mesh of fibres called **fibrin**.	fibres form in plug
3 The fibrin traps blood cells and then dries to form a **scab**. This scab allows the wound to heal and prevents harmful germs entering the body.	cells trapped in fibrin to form a scab

Fig. 5.3 What happens when blood clots

Fibrinogen can be removed from plasma. This is done by allowing the plasma to clot and then removing the clot. The remaining plasma without fibrinogen is called **serum**. Serum is stored in hospitals for transfusions.

5.2 The functions of blood

Examiner's tip

Learn the key functions of blood.

The functions of the separate constituents of blood were described in 5.1. Blood has three important functions – transport, protection and regulation:

❶ Transport
- Blood carries *oxygen* from the lungs to other tissues. It carries *carbon dioxide* back to the lungs to be expelled (exhaled).
- Blood carries *dissolved foods* from the gut to different parts of the body.
- Blood carries *waste products* to the kidneys to be excreted in urine (see 5.6).
- Blood carries *hormones* and *antibodies* around the body.

2 Protection
- Blood contains *platelets* and *fibrinogen* so that blood will clot preventing severe loss of blood after injury.
- Blood contains *white blood cells* which protect us against germs. Our bodies' natural defences can be enhanced by medicines which kill germs or by immunisation. During immunisation, killed or modified microorganisms are injected. This stimulates the body to produce lots of white blood cells which make antibodies and give lasting protection against the infection caused by the injected microorganisms.

3 Regulation
- Blood helps to keep our body temperature constant by allowing us to retain or lose heat.
- Blood helps us to control the amount of water and other chemicals in different parts of the body.

5.3 Blood vessels

Blood flows around the body continuously and acts as a transport medium. This flow is called **circulation**. The main organ involved in blood circulation is the **heart**. The heart pumps blood round the body through a system of tubes called **blood vessels**. Blood vessels are classified in three groups:

1 Arteries carry blood away from the heart. Arteries have thick muscular walls to withstand the pumping pressure from the heart. If an artery is cut, there is a rapid loss of blood. Bleeding may be stopped by pressing on a wound or by pressure at a point where the artery comes near to the skin surface and runs close to a bone.

2 Veins carry blood back to the heart. They tend to be closer to the surface of the body than arteries. Blood in the veins is at a lower pressure than in the arteries and there are valves to prevent the backward flow of blood. Veins have thinner, less muscular walls than arteries.

3 Capillaries are narrow, thin-walled tubes which divide from the arteries and then rejoin to form veins. There are thousands and thousands of capillaries in every organ and every cell in your body is close to a capillary. If your capillaries were laid end to end, they would form a very fine tube about 80 000 km long!

As the blood flows through capillaries, water, oxygen and dissolved foods diffuse out through the thin walls to the surrounding cells. At the same time, waste materials diffuse out of the cells and into the capillaries. In this way, capillaries provide those materials which cells need for good health and also remove their waste products. The capillaries in our skin play an important role in regulating our body temperature.

5.4 Circulation of blood

Examiner's tip

Read section 5.4 carefully and be sure to understand the circulation of blood.

The main organs in our bodies through which blood circulates are shown in Fig. 5.4. These organs have the following functions:
- The **heart** pumps blood around the system. The pumping effect produces a regular beating of the heart. Every time the heart beats it produces a dull throb in the chest and a wave of pressure through the main arteries. You can feel this as a pulse in the artery in your wrist.
- The **lungs** allow the blood to pick up oxygen and get rid of carbon dioxide.
- The **intestines** supply digested food to the blood.
- The **liver** processes and stores some of the food carried by the blood.
- The **kidneys** remove waste products.

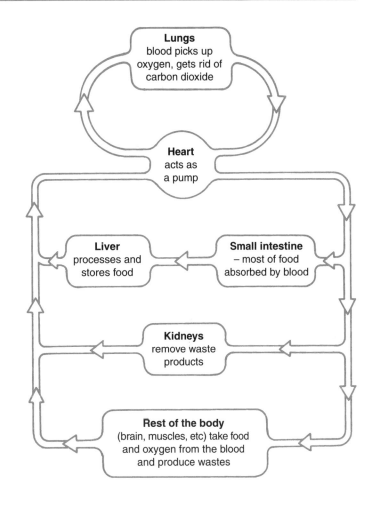

Fig. 5.4 The main organs through which blood circulates in the human body

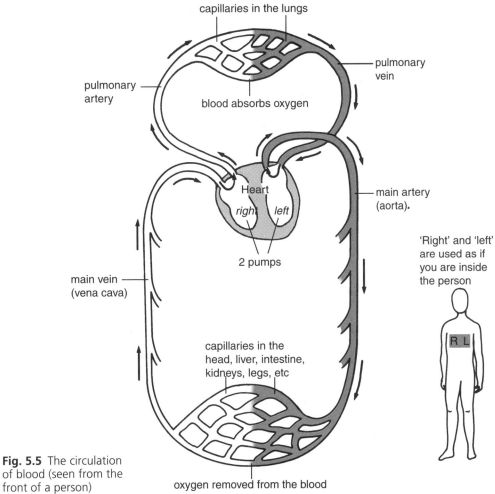

Fig. 5.5 The circulation of blood (seen from the front of a person)

● The **rest of the body** uses the food and oxygen in the blood and produces waste products which are carried away by the blood. Notice in Fig. 5.4 that there are two circuits from the heart. One circuit goes to the lungs and back to the heart. The other circuit goes to the rest of the body and back to the heart. To provide for these two circuits, the heart acts as two pumps side by side (see Fig. 5.5). The pumps work in unison. The pump on our right drives blood to capillaries in the lungs where oxygen is absorbed and dissolved in the blood. The pump on our left takes this oxygenated blood from the lungs and pumps it to other organs in the body. As the oxygenated blood passes through the various organs, the oxygen is used for respiration (see 6.5) and other reactions. The deoxygenated blood then returns to the heart and the cycle is repeated. Notice that the blood passes through the heart twice during one complete cycle.

The heart

Each pump in the heart has two chambers: an entry chamber called an **atrium** (plural: *atria*) and a pumping chamber called a **ventricle** (see Fig. 5.6). A one-way valve between each atrium and ventricle prevents blood being pumped the wrong way. There is also a one-way outlet valve from each ventricle to stop blood flowing back. The ventricles have thick muscular walls. When these contract, the pressure inside increases and blood is forced into the arteries. This causes your pulse. When the muscles relax, the ventricles expand and blood flows into them from the atria.

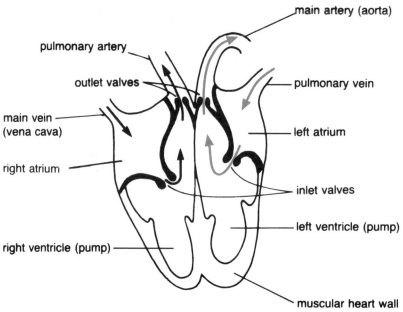

Fig. 5.6 The structure of the heart

Your heart beats about 70 times every minute, day and night. To do this, the heart muscles must have a good supply of oxygen. This is supplied through a system of arteries spread over the heart wall. These are called the **coronary vessels**.

5.5 Diseases of the circulation system

As the heart pumps blood into the arteries, there is an increase in pressure. This pressure on the walls of our arteries is called **blood pressure**. If the blood pressure is too low, blood circulates around the body too slowly. If the blood pressure is too high, there is a greater strain on the heart and on the walls of the arteries. The walls of the arteries may be stretched so much that they burst. If an artery in the brain bursts, the leakage of blood will damage cells in the brain. We call this a **stroke**. This may result in paralysis (loss of use) of parts of the body and speech difficulties. The causes of high blood pressure are not fully understood. However, it is more likely to occur when someone is old, overweight, under stress or a heavy smoker.

As we get older, our arteries become thicker and harder. This is due to a layer of fat forming on the inside of the vessels. The arteries become narrower and the flow of blood slows down. An artery may become blocked by a clot of blood. This is called a **thrombosis**. If a thrombosis occurs in one of the coronary vessels (called a **coronary thrombosis**), the heart muscle is deprived of oxygen and may stop beating. We call this a **heart attack**. Hardening of the arteries is thought to be made worse by eating too much animal fat, by drinking too much alcohol and by smoking.

Tobacco smoke contains several poisonous substances, including nicotine and carbon monoxide. Carbon monoxide affects our blood because it combines with haemoglobin in red blood cells about 300 times more readily than oxygen. This means that the blood can carry less oxygen to our body tissues. In order to improve the supply of oxygen, the heart pumps faster, putting strain on itself and increasing the blood pressure.

People with heart problems in which their heart beats too weakly can be helped by pacemakers. Pacemakers contain very small nuclear batteries with a long life. The battery is placed inside the chest near the heart. It produces tiny regular shocks to keep the heart beating steadily.

5.6 Getting rid of waste

Chemical processes in our bodies produce a variety of waste products. The blood plays an important part in helping us to get rid of these waste products. This process is called **excretion**. The main organs involved in excretion are the **lungs** and the **kidneys**:
- The lungs enable us to excrete *carbon dioxide* (see 6.3).
- The kidneys enable us to excrete *urea* and *salts*. They also control the amount of water in our bodies.

The kidneys
We take in water when we eat and drink. We lose water from our bodies as sweat and urine. When urine contains only a small amount of waste products, it is almost colourless, like water. When the waste products are more concentrated, it looks yellow. One of the important waste products in urine is urea. This is produced when proteins are metabolised (broken down into amino acids). Urea contains a high percentage of nitrogen.

Fig. 5.7 shows how the kidneys are connected to the rest of the excretory system. We have two kidneys at the back of the body just above the waist.

How do the kidneys remove waste products?
As you would expect, the kidneys have an excellent supply of blood (see Fig. 5.8). The **renal arteries** carry blood to the kidneys and the **renal veins** carry it back to the heart. About 1 cubic decimetre (1000 cm^3) of blood flows through the kidneys every minute.

As branches of the renal arteries pass into the kidneys, they divide into a vast network of blood capillaries. These capillaries are wrapped around thousands of tiny **tubules**. As the blood flows over the tubules, excess water and waste products (**urine**) diffuse into them. The tubules join up to form collecting ducts which lead into the **ureter**. At the same time, the blood capillaries join up again to form a single vein leading to the renal veins. The ureters, one from each kidney, carry urine to the **bladder**. The bladder expands as urine collects in it. Urine is passed out of the bladder through the **urethra**. The urethra runs to an opening in front of the vagina in a female and down the middle of the penis in a male.

The ring of muscle near the top of the urethra is usually contracted. This closes the urethra and prevents urine from running out of the bladder (and out of the body). As urine collects in the bladder, pressure on the ring of the muscle increases. In time, we feel the need to urinate. When we urinate, the ring of muscle relaxes.

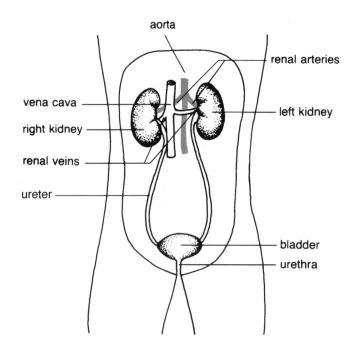

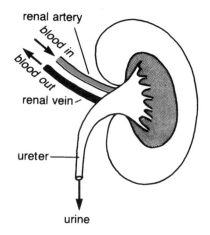

Fig. 5.7 The kidneys and the excretory system

Fig. 5.8 Cross section through a kidney

5.7 Kidney failure

Occasionally, a person's kidneys begin to fail. This may be caused by infection or by faulty diffusion of materials from the blood into the urine.

If only one of the kidneys is affected, the person can survive. If both kidneys are affected, treatment is essential. Without treatment, he/she will be poisoned as urea and other waste products accumulate in the blood. There are three kinds of treatment for kidney failure:

❶ A **controlled diet** with a reduced intake of water, protein and salt. This reduces the volume of urine and the amount of waste products.

❷ A **kidney machine** which acts as an artificial kidney. Blood from an artery in the patient's arm passes through thin tubing surrounded by special solution in the machine. Waste products diffuse out of the patient's blood into the solution. The blood then returns to the patient through a vein. This treatment is called **dialysis**. Someone with severe kidney failure must spend 15 to 20 hours each week connected to a kidney machine.

❸ A **kidney transplant** from a donor who has just died may replace a failing kidney by a healthy one. This treatment will only work if the kidney donor has the same blood group as the patient. If the operation is successful, the person can then lead a normal life.

Summary

1   Blood contains cells in a watery fluid called **plasma**.

2   The cells in blood are of three types:
    - **red blood cells** containing haemoglobin which enables them to carry oxygen around the body.
    - **white blood cells** which protect us from disease by engulfing bacteria and making poisons harmless.
    - **platelets** which help the blood to clot.

3   Blood has three important functions:
    ● the **transport** of oxygen, dissolved foods, waste products and other nutrients.
    ● **protection** after injury and against germs and poisonous substances.
    ● **regulation** of our body temperature and the amounts of water and other chemicals in different parts of the body.

4   The heart pumps blood round the body through a system of tubes called **blood vessels**. **Arteries** carry blood away from the heart. These arteries divide up to form narrower and narrower tubes called **capillaries**. Eventually, the capillaries rejoin to form **veins** which carry blood back to the heart.

5   As the heart pumps blood around the body:
    ● the **lungs** allow the blood to pick up oxygen and get rid of carbon dioxide.
    ● the **intestines** supply digested food to the blood.
    ● the **liver** stores some of the food carried by the blood.
    ● the **kidneys** remove waste products.
    ● the **capillaries** allow water, dissolved foods and oxygen to diffuse into the surrounding cells whilst waste materials diffuse out of the cells and into the capillaries.

6   The pumping of blood by the heart results in **blood pressure**.
    ● If an artery in the brain bursts, the leakage of blood will damage brain cells. We call this a **stroke**.
    ● Arteries become thicker and harder with age. A **thrombosis** occurs if an artery becomes blocked. A coronary thrombosis (**heart attack**) occurs if one of the arteries supplying blood to the heart is blocked.

7   The main organs involved in excretion are the lungs and the kidneys.
    ● The lungs enable us to excrete carbon dioxide.
    ● The kidneys enable us to excrete urea and salts and control the amount of water in our bodies.

Quick test 5

1   Which of the following actions is most sensible if your finger is bleeding badly?
    A Submerge your finger in very cold water.
    B Put your head between your knees.
    C Lie horizontally on the floor.
    D Put a tight bandage around the wound.
2   Which of the following tissues makes up the wall of the heart?
    A cartilage   B muscle
    C fat   D tendon
3   Healthy people have about 500 red blood cells for every white blood cell. After some infections, this changes to about 100 red blood cells for every white blood cell. These changes may have occurred because
    A extra white blood cells are produced to fight the infection.
    B the blood has been diluted.
    C white blood cells are destroyed by the infection.
    D red blood cells destroy white blood cells.

Questions 4 to 6

Blood is composed of several parts, each of which has a particular job. Name the part of the blood whose main job is
4   transport of oxygen.
5   fighting against disease.
6   transport of dissolved foods.

(SEG, part question)

The chart shows the death rates from heart diseases of men and women between the ages of 35 and 74 in different countries.

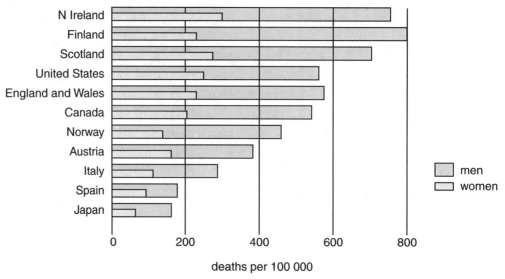

deaths per 100 000

7   Which country has the lowest death rate from heart diseases for men?
8   Which country has the highest death rate from heart diseases for men and women together?
9   Which countries have the same death rate from heart diseases for women?
10 Which one of the following conclusions can be made from the chart?
    A   Smoking causes an increase in the death rate from heart diseases.
    B   People who suffer from heart disease should visit Japan.
    C   More men die of heart disease than women.
    D   Heart diseases are more common in colder countries.   (*ULEAC*, modified)

Jean and Paula go jogging. They measured their heart rates before and after jogging.

| | Heart rate (beats per minute) | |
	Jean	Paula
Before jogging	75	65
Immediately afterwards	150	150
2 mins afterwards	120	100
4 mins afterwards	85	65

11 Which girl is the fitter?
12 Give two reasons for your choice in question 11.

13 Give four factors that can affect the pulse rate.
14 What causes a coronary thrombosis?
15 What causes anaemia?
16 Give two differences between an artery and a vein.
17 What test must be carried out before someone has a blood transfusion?
18 Humans belong to one of four blood groups: A, B, AB and O. In a recent survey, 40% were type A; 10% were type B; 5% were type AB; 45% were type O. Display this information in a pie chart.

Chapter 6
Respiration

6.1 Introduction

The term 'respiration' is used to summarise three processes in organisms: **breathing**, **gaseous exchange** and **cellular respiration**.

RESPIRATION

Breathing	**Gaseous exchange**	**Cellular respiration**
Chest movements which bring air (oxygen) into the lungs.	Diffusion of oxygen into the blood and of carbon dioxide out of the blood. Diffusion occurs through the thin moist tissue in the lungs.	Chemical reactions occurring in cells result in the release of energy from foods.

Breathing and gaseous exchange are physical processes occurring *outside cells*. They are sometimes referred to together as **external respiration**. On the other hand, cellular respiration involves chemical processes *inside cells*. It is sometimes called **internal respiration**.

6.2 Breathing

Our bodies and those of animals cannot work without a supply of oxygen. When we breathe in (inhale), air enters our lungs. Oxygen from the inhaled air can then pass through the thin tissue of the lungs into the blood. At the same time, carbon dioxide passes from the blood into the lungs. This carbon dioxide is then expelled when we breathe out (exhale). In order to help this exchange of gases, the chest and ribs act like a pump, transferring gases into and out of the lungs.

The lungs are situated inside the chest cavity or **thorax** (see Fig. 6.1). The sides of the thorax are bounded by the rib cage and there are muscles linking the ribs. At the bottom of the thorax, there is a flexible sheet of muscular tissue called the **diaphragm**.

Although the lungs have a spongy consistency, they behave like a pair of large, elastic bags. These bags stretch and inflate when the thorax increases in volume. When we breathe in, muscles pull the diaphragm downwards and the ribs upwards and outwards. The thorax increases in size and air is drawn into the lungs. When we breathe out, the diaphragm relaxes and moves upwards and the ribs move inwards. The thorax decreases in size, increasing the pressure on the lungs and air is forced out.

The total volume of an adult's lungs is between 4 and 5 dm^3 (4000–5000 cm^3). Whilst resting we inhale about 0.5 dm^3 of air each breath. After exercise, we breathe more deeply and inhale as much as 2 dm^3 with each breath. Table 6.1 shows the composition by volume of atmospheric air and exhaled air.

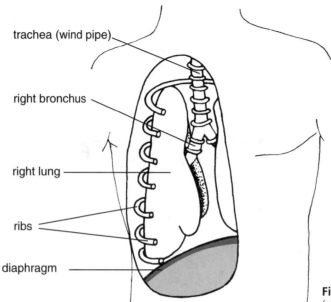

trachea (wind pipe)

right bronchus

right lung

ribs

diaphragm

Fig. 6.1 Part of the human thorax (chest cavity)

Table 6.1 The percentage composition by volume of atmospheric and exhaled air

	Atmospheric air (inhaled air)	Exhaled air
Oxygen	21	17
Carbon dioxide	0.03	4
Nitrogen	78	78

6.3 Gas exchange in the lungs

When we breathe in, air passes through the mouth or nose. At the back of the nose there is a large space called the **nasal cavity** (see Fig. 6.2). This is divided up by bony partitions giving a large surface area. The surfaces are lined with fine hairs called **cilia** and they secrete slimy **mucus**. This mucus plays an important part in trapping dust and germs before they can get into the lungs. Movements of the cilia sweep the mucus towards the throat where it is swallowed, or coughed up as catarrh or phlegm (pronounced 'flem'). Mucus in the nasal passages can also be expelled by blowing your nose.

From the mouth or nose, the air passes through the **larynx** ('voice box') to the **trachea** (windpipe). The trachea branches into two bronchi (singular: *bronchus*), one to each lung. Rings of cartilage strengthen the trachea and bronchi to prevent them collapsing.

In the lungs, the bronchi divide into hundreds of thin tubes called **bronchioles**. The structure of the bronchioles is like the branches and twigs on a tree. The whole network is sometimes called the **bronchial tree** (see Fig. 6.3).

Each bronchiole ends in a bunch of tiny air sacs called **alveoli**. Each alveolus is only about 0.2 mm in diameter, but there are about 300 million alveoli in your lungs. This gives a very large surface area across which gases (oxygen and carbon dioxide) can diffuse.

The alveoli are covered with a network of capillaries like a string bag (see Fig. 6.4). The walls of the alveoli and the capillaries are extremely thin. Their surfaces are also covered in a thin layer of liquid. The thin walls and the layer of moisture make the diffusion of gases easier. Oxygen inside the alveoli dissolves in the layer of moisture and passes through the walls of the alveoli into the capillaries. It can then be carried away by red blood cells to different parts of the body.

For carbon dioxide, the process is reversed. Carbon dioxide is carried by the blood into the capillaries around the alveoli. Here it passes out of the blood and into the alveoli. It is then expelled from the lungs when we breathe out.

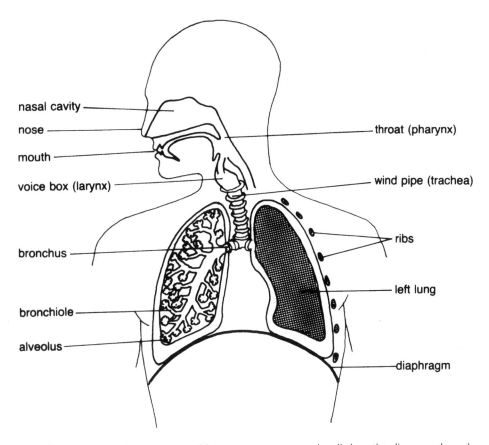

Fig. 6.2 The human respiratory system (there are many more alveoli than the diagram shows)

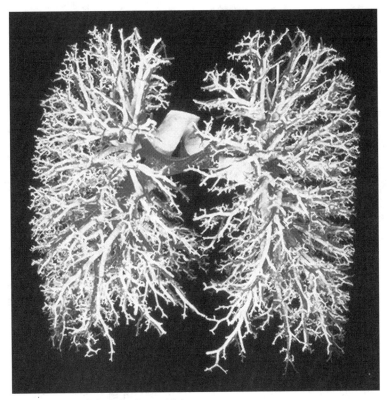

Fig. 6.3 A model of the bronchial tree

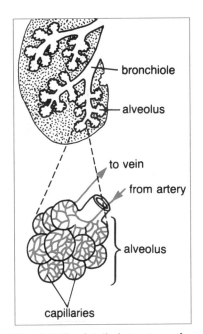

Fig. 6.4 The detailed structure of part of a lung

6.4 Smoking or health

During the last 20 years, doctors and government health departments have collected data on smokers and non-smokers. This data shows that:

● Someone who smokes ten cigarettes a day is eight times more likely to die from lung cancer than a non-smoker.
● A smoker who gives up smoking soon halves his/her risk of death from lung cancer.
● A smoker is twice as likely to suffer a heart attack (coronary thrombosis) as a non-smoker.

The following are diseases associated with smoking.

Lung cancer

Cigarette smoke contains fine droplets of **tar**. This tar stains the filter when a filter cigarette is smoked (but the filter does not remove all the tar). The tar contains chemicals which cause cancer. These are described as **carcinogens**. Carcinogenic chemicals make the cells of various tissues reproduce in an uncontrolled way. Affected tissue grows but cannot function in the normal way. When this happens to lung tissue, people often die of lung cancer.

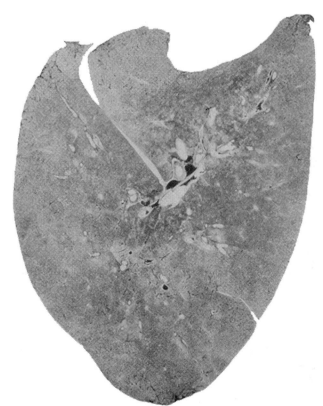 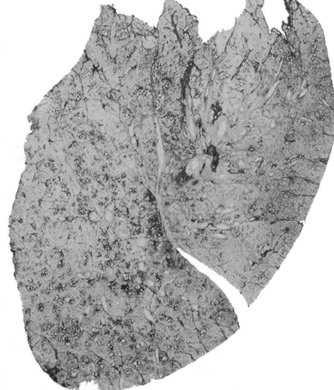

Fig. 6.5 Left: A section of a healthy human lung   Right: A human lung permeated with deposits of tar caused by cigarette smoking

Bronchitis

Substances in cigarette smoke also irritate the walls of the trachea and the bronchial tubes. Extra mucus is produced which clogs up the respiratory passages. This makes breathing difficult and leads to a 'smoker's cough'. Very often, the bronchial tubes become infected and the disease lasts a long time instead of clearing up in a few days. This is called *chronic bronchitis*.

Emphysema

Cigarette smoke contains acidic and irritant substances. These substances attack the sensitive walls of the alveoli. The alveoli break down and this reduces the surface area in the lungs over which gaseous exchange can occur. This disease is called emphysema. Smokers suffering in this way become very short of breath.

Although smoking mainly affects the lungs, it has other harmful or unpleasant effects:
- It increases the risk of coronary thrombosis (heart attack) and other diseases of the blood system (see 5.5).
- It can cause cancer of the mouth or throat.
- It reduces your senses of taste and smell.
- It gives your breath and clothes an unpleasant smell.

6.5 Cellular respiration

Respiration is the overall process of breathing, gas exchange in the lungs and the breaking down of chemicals to provide energy in living things.

Cellular respiration refers to the chemical reactions which occur in cells and which result in the release of energy from foods.

During respiration we use up foods and oxygen and produce carbon dioxide, water and energy. The same thing happens during combustion when fuels burn.

The food (or fuel) reacts with oxygen, so these reactions are called *oxidation* reactions. We say that the food (or fuel) is *oxidised*.

$$\text{Food (or fuel)} + \text{oxygen} \rightarrow \text{carbon dioxide} + \text{water} + \text{energy}$$

Because of these similarities between foods and fuels, foods are sometimes called 'body fuels' or 'biological fuels'.

Although cellular respiration and burning are similar processes, there are important differences. When an energy food such as glucose is oxidised in our body cells, there are no flames and the reaction is very slow compared to burning. In fact, the oxidation of simple foods takes place through a large number of separate chemical reactions.

The cellular respiration of glucose can be summarised by the equation:

$$\underset{\text{glucose}}{C_6H_{12}O_6} + \underset{\text{oxygen}}{6O_2} \rightarrow \underset{\substack{\text{carbon}\\\text{dioxide}}}{6CO_2} + \underset{\text{water}}{6H_2O} + \underset{\text{energy}}{2900 \text{ kilojoules (kJ)}}$$

When this process occurs in our cells, about twenty separate chemical reactions are needed to convert the reactants (glucose and oxygen) into the products (carbon dioxide and water). Notice, in the equation above, the large amount of energy produced. This energy from respiration enables other life processes to occur. It can be used as:
- **heat** to keep us warm,
- **mechanical energy** in our muscles to help us move around and to keep our heart and breathing muscles working.

About half of the energy from cellular respiration is released as heat. This explains why you get hot whilst running or working hard. Your body uses up more food, therefore more heat is produced.

6.6 Respiration in all living things

All living things respire in order to obtain the energy they need. In plants, the intake of oxygen and the release of carbon dioxide takes place through the stomata (see 2.7).

The production of carbon dioxide during respiration

This can be investigated using the apparatus shown in Fig. 6.6. When air is drawn through the apparatus, the lime water in flask C turns cloudy after a minute or two. This shows the presence of carbon dioxide. The lime water in flask A stays clear. This shows that the insects must be producing the carbon dioxide.

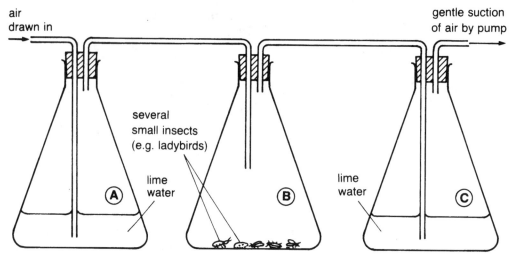

Fig. 6.6 Investigating the production of carbon dioxide when living things respire

The experiment can be carried out using different living things in flask B. If plants are used:
- flask B must be covered so that the plant will not photosynthesise and use up any carbon dioxide which may be produced;
- the apparatus should be set up without the pump working and left for 24 hours. Plants respire more slowly than animals. After 24 hours, the pump is turned on gently. The lime water in flask C turns milky if it has not already done so.

The production of heat during respiration

This can be investigated using the apparatus in Fig. 6.7. When seeds germinate and start to sprout, they respire rapidly. Food reserves (mainly carbohydrates) in the seeds are used to produce energy for the sprouting plant.

The peas in both flasks were allowed to soak in water for 24 hours before the experiment. The temperature rises in flask A but stays the same in flask B. This shows that heat is being produced by the respiring seeds. If small insects are used in place of peas, the temperature in flask A rises even more quickly.

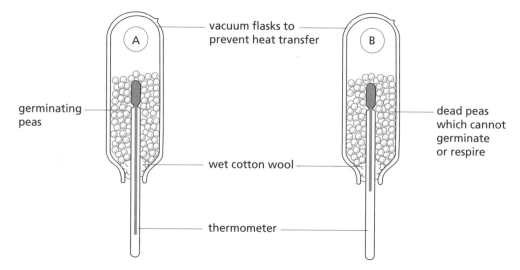

Fig. 6.7 Investigating the production of heat by germinating (respiring) peas

6.7 Living without oxygen

So far, we have only considered respiration in air. This kind of respiration is called **aerobic respiration**. However, respiration is also possible when there is no air and no oxygen. This is called **anaerobic respiration**. Anaerobic respiration can occur in animals and plants.

The most important application of anaerobic respiration is **fermentation**. Fermentation is used to make beer and wines. It involves the use of **yeast**. Yeast contains tiny single-celled organisms which can respire aerobically like animals and plants. When yeast is mixed with a solution of sugar or glucose, it quickly starts to respire. The yeast uses sugar and oxygen dissolved in the solution to produce carbon dioxide, water and energy. This, of course, is *aerobic* respiration.

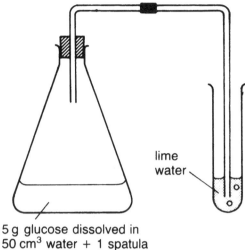

5 g glucose dissolved in 50 cm³ water + 1 spatula measure of yeast

Fig. 6.8 Making alcohol by fermentation

Examiner's tip

Make sure you understand the differences between aerobic and anaerobic respiration.

sugar (glucose)	+	oxygen	→	carbon dioxide	+	water	+	energy
$C_6H_{12}O_6$	+	$6O_2$	→	$6CO_2$	+	$6H_2O$	+	2900 kJ

However, when all the available oxygen has been used, the yeast goes on respiring. Under these *anaerobic* conditions, the yeast uses up more glucose, but instead of producing carbon dioxide and water, the products are *carbon dioxide* and *ethanol*.

sugar (glucose)	→	carbon dioxide	+	ethanol	+	energy
$C_6H_{12}O_6$	→	$2CO_2$	+	$2C_2H_5OH$	+	84 kJ

Although anaerobic respiration allows the yeast to survive without oxygen, it is very inefficient. Notice in the equations above that one formula mass of glucose ($C_6H_{12}O_6$) produces 2900 kJ of energy in aerobic respiration, but only 84 kJ in anaerobic respiration. Under anaerobic conditions, most of the energy that the yeast could get from glucose remains 'locked up' in the ethanol.

The common name for ethanol is *alcohol*, so this example of anaerobic respiration is sometimes called **alcoholic fermentation**, as shown in Fig. 6.8.

6.8 Brewing and breadmaking

Anaerobic respiration is important in brewing and breadmaking.

Brewing and wine-making

Alcoholic drinks are made by fermenting a sugary solution. Wine is usually made from sugars present in grapes. The grapes are crushed to extract the juice. This contains sugar and wild yeast. The yeast ferments the sugar and gradually produces alcohol. Although the alcohol produced is always the same (ethanol), each wine has its own flavour. This

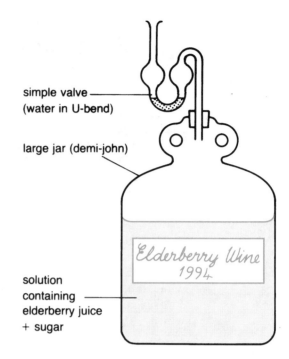

Fig. 6.9 Home-made wine can be made from various flowers and fruits. Fermentation is usually carried out in a large jar put in a warm place to speed up the process. The jar is fitted with a simple valve which allows carbon dioxide to escape, but prevents oxygen and bacteria entering the jar.

simple valve
(water in U-bend)

large jar (demi-john)

solution
containing
elderberry juice
+ sugar

depends mainly on the type of grapes used. Wines can also be made from a wide variety of flowers and fruits.

Yeast cannot live in solutions containing more than 14% alcohol, so fermentation stops when the alcohol reaches this concentration. Strong alcoholic drinks, like whisky and gin, which contain about 40% alcohol, are made by distilling wines and other weaker alcoholic solutions (see 12.3).

Beer is made from barley. Barley grain is mashed with warm water and hops. This produces a dilute sugary liquid to which yeast is added. Fermentation converts the sugar to alcohol.

In small amounts, alcohol helps to make people relaxed and sociable, but in larger amounts it can be dangerous. It can make us aggressive and impairs our mental abilities. These effects can have disastrous results if people drink and drive. It is important to remember that alcohol is a drug which may become addictive. Alcoholism causes damage to the brain and liver cells.

Breadmaking

Brewers are interested in the alcohol produced by fermentation, but bakers are more interested in the carbon dioxide. Bakers add yeast to their bread dough. The yeast respires, producing bubbles of carbon dioxide which make the dough rise. When the dough is baked, heat kills the yeast and any alcohol evaporates. If dough is baked without using yeast, it is said to be *unleavened*. Unleavened bread does not rise, e.g. pitta bread.

6.9 Anaerobic respiration in our muscles

xaminer's tip

Note the difference between anaerobic respiration in muscles and that in yeast.

Animals like whales and mudworms which live where there is very little oxygen can respire anaerobically. In animals, anaerobic respiration produces lactic acid, *not* ethanol and carbon dioxide as with yeast.

sugar $\rightarrow$ lactic acid + energy
(glucose)
$C_6H_{12}O_6$ $\rightarrow$ $2C_3H_6O_3$ + energy

Our own muscle cells also respire anaerobically for short periods. This happens when our muscles have to work very hard for a short period, for example during a sprint race. Under these conditions we cannot breathe fast enough, or pump our blood fast enough, to get sufficient oxygen to our muscles. So, there is an 'oxygen debt' in our muscles during vigorous exercise. Our muscles respire anaerobically and lactic acid is produced. Unfortunately lactic acid is a mild poison. It causes our muscles to ache and cramp. When we rest, the blood brings oxygen to the muscles which can then respire aerobically again. This uses up the lactic acid and relieves the pain.

Summary

1   Respiration involves three processes:
  • **breathing** – chest movements moving gases into and out of the lungs.
  • **gaseous exchange** of oxygen into the blood and carbon dioxide out of the blood.
  • **cellular respiration** – chemical reactions in cells which result in the release of energy from foods.

2   When we breathe in, air passes from the mouth or nose into the **trachea** (wind pipe). The trachea branches into two **bronchi**, one to each lung. In the lungs, the bronchi divide into hundreds of thin tubes called **bronchioles**. Each bronchiole ends in a bunch of tiny air sacs called **alveoli**. The alveoli provide a large surface area across which gases (oxygen and carbon dioxide) can diffuse.

3   Cigarette smoke contains tar which is **carcinogenic**. Chemicals in the tar make cells reproduce in an uncontrolled way causing **lung cancer**. Substances in cigarette smoke also irritate the wall of the trachea and bronchi. Very often the bronchial tubes become infected causing **bronchitis**.

4   Cellular respiration can be summarised as:

   food   +   oxygen $\longrightarrow$ carbon dioxide   +   water   +   energy

   The energy released during respiration can be used as heat to keep us warm or as mechanical energy in our muscles.

5   Respiration may be **aerobic** or **anaerobic** depending on the availability of oxygen. Aerobic respiration occurs when air or oxygen is present. Anaerobic respiration occurs when there is no air or oxygen.

6   The most important application of anaerobic respiration is fermentation involving yeasts. The yeasts respire anaerobically producing carbon dioxide and ethanol. So, the process is used to make beer and wines.

   sugar $\longrightarrow$ carbon dioxide   +   ethanol
   (glucose)

7   Anaerobic respiration can also occur in animals (e.g. in mudworms which live where there is very little oxygen and in our own muscles when we take vigorous exercise and the supply of oxygen is insufficient). In animals the product of anaerobic respiration from starch and glucose is lactic acid.

Quick test 6

Questions 1 to 4

Billy is a runner. For a short time after he has been running, he breathes more deeply and more often.

	Normal breathing	After running
Volume of air taken in each breath/cm³	500	1000
Number of breaths each minute	20	35
Total volume of air taken in each minute/cm³	10 000	

1   Use the information in the table to calculate the volume of air Billy breathes during one minute after running.
2   How much *more* air does Billy take in during one minute after running compared with the volume of air taken in during one minute of normal breathing?
3   What fraction of the air is oxygen?
4   Use your answers to questions 2 and 3 to find the volume of extra *oxygen* Billy takes in during one minute after running compared with normal breathing.

(*ULEAC,* part question)

Questions 5 to 7

The diagram shows how our bodies obtain the energy they need.

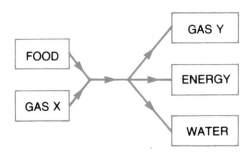

5   What is gas X?
6   What is gas Y?
7   What do we call the whole process shown in the diagram?   (*NEAB*)

Questions 8 to 13

In industrial brewing processes, yeast is added to a sugary solution and left at 25 °C. The sugars are first converted to glucose and then this undergoes fermentation.

The equation for the reaction is

$$C_6H_{12}O_6 \xrightarrow{\text{yeast}} 2C_2H_5OH + 2CO_2 + 84 \text{ kJ}$$
glucose   ethanol

8   What is the source of sugar for breweries?
9   What is (are) the product(s) of fermentation?
10 What will be the effect of raising the temperature to 35 °C?
11 Why does boiling the yeast/sugar mixture stop the reaction?
12 How many carbon atoms are present in one molecule of ethanol?
13 How many hydrogen atoms are present in one molecule of ethanol?

Questions 14 to 19

Jenny set up the apparatus shown below to find whether water is produced by a respiring plant.

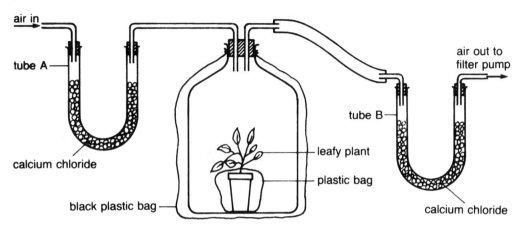

Explain why Jenny took the following precautions.
14   She dried the air before it entered the bell jar, using calcium chloride.
15   She used small lumps, rather than large lumps, of calcium chloride in the U-tubes.
16   She covered the plant pot with a plastic bag.
17   She covered the bell jar with a black plastic bag.
18   What measurements would Jenny take?
19   How would Jenny check that the air going to the filter pump was dry?   (*ULEAC*)

Chapter 7
Senses and responses

7.1 Detecting changes and responding

Crossing the road can be dangerous. In order to cross safely, we rely on various senses:
- *sight* to see the traffic,
- *hearing* to hear the traffic, and
- *touch* to move off the kerb.

Without our senses we would not survive for very long. Our senses detect changes in the environment to which we respond. They warn us about danger and help us to find food.

If someone tapped you on the shoulder, you would probably look round. The tap on your shoulder causes a change in your sense of touch. Changes like this which can be detected by our senses are called **stimuli** (singular: *stimulus*). Our reactions to stimuli are called **responses**.

Fig. 7.1 summarises our six senses and the stimuli for our sense organs.

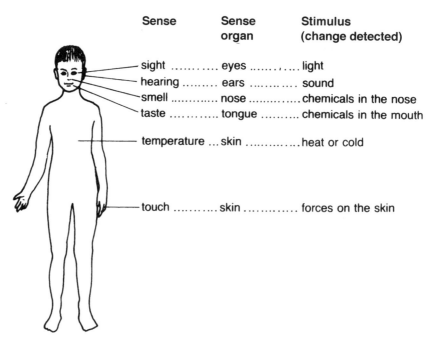

Sense	Sense organ	Stimulus (change detected)
sight	eyes	light
hearing	ears	sound
smell	nose	chemicals in the nose
taste	tongue	chemicals in the mouth
temperature	skin	heat or cold
touch	skin	forces on the skin

Fig. 7.1 Senses, sense organs and stimuli

When one of our sense organs detects a stimulus, impulses (messages) pass along nerves to the **central nervous system (CNS)**. The central nervous system consists of *the brain and the spinal cord*. When the central nervous system receives a message, it must decide whether to respond. If it responds, then impulses pass along nerves and cause our muscles to move. The flow diagram below shows what happens when you touch a hot plate.

Stimulus → **Detection** → **Transmission** → **Transmission** → **Response**
Heat from by skin (sense of messages to of messages to from muscles to
hot plate organ) CNS via nerves muscles from move hand
CNS via nerves away from heat

We will consider the central nervous system further in 7.6.

Our bodies have another system for responding to stimuli as well as nerves. This second system involves the action of chemicals called **hormones**. Most animals have these two methods of responding to stimuli. Plants, however, do *not* have a nervous system. They rely on hormones alone. We will look at hormones in 7.9 and 7.10.

7.2 Detecting light – the eye

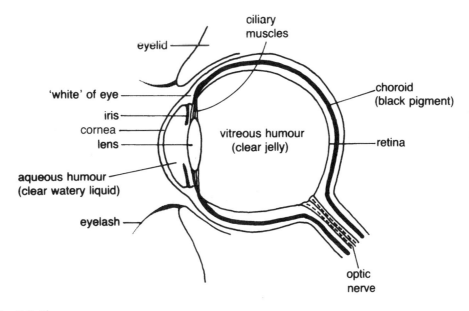

Fig. 7.2 The eye

Our eyes enable us to detect light. They are very sensitive to changes in the intensity of light (light and dark). Although our eyes are very complex organs, they have three essential parts:

1. the **iris**, which controls the amount of light entering the eye. Your iris might be blue, brown or hazel. In bright light, the hole in the centre of your iris (the **pupil**) becomes smaller. In a dark room, the pupil becomes larger to let in more light.
2. the **lens** and **cornea**, which help us to form an image of the outside world on the retina. This is called *focusing*.
3. the **retina** at the back of the eye, which is sensitive to light. The retina contains more than 100 million light-sensitive cells. These cells send messages (nerve impulses) to the brain along the **optic nerve**. Our brains can use these messages to form a picture of the outside world.

How do our eyes focus?

The eye focuses on objects at different distances by changing the shape of its lens. It does this using the **ciliary muscle** which forms a ring around the lens.

Suppose you look at something *close up*, e.g. a book. The ciliary muscle *tightens* and pushes on the lens. This makes the lens fatter and more powerful (Fig. 7.3(a)).

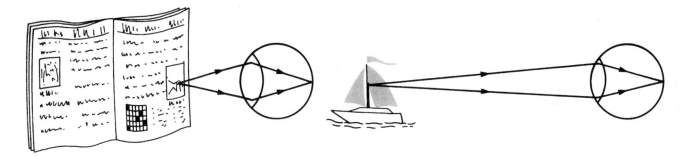

(a) Looking at something close-up.
The ciliary muscle makes the lens fatter and more powerful.

(b) Looking at something far away.
The ciliary muscle makes the lens thinner and less powerful.

Fig. 7.3 Focusing on near and distant objects

Now suppose you look at something *far away*. In this case, the ciliary muscle *relaxes* and the lens becomes thinner and less powerful (Fig. 7.3(b)). This change in shape of the lens to focus on near or distant objects is called **accommodation**.

If you have good eyesight, you will be able to focus on objects as near as 25 cm (the **near point**) or as far away as the stars (the **far point**).

Eye defects

Long sight   Some people cannot see close objects clearly. The lenses of their eyes cannot get fat enough to focus light on the retina. This defect can be overcome by wearing spectacles with *convex* lenses (or convex contact lenses). These help to converge the light to a focus on the retina (see Fig. 7.4).

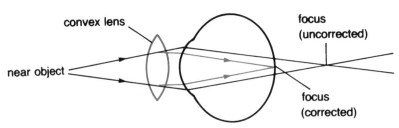

Fig. 7.4 Long sight and its correction

People who cannot focus on objects close up can usually see distant objects clearly. Because of this we say they are *long sighted*. People often become long sighted in middle age as their ciliary muscles get weaker and their eye lenses are less pliable.

Short sight   People who are *short sighted* can see close objects clearly. They cannot focus on objects in the distance. For example, someone who is short sighted can read a book close up, but not a wall poster on the other side of the street. In this case, light from distant objects is focused in front of, rather than on, the retina (see Fig. 7.5).

Short sightedness can be corrected by wearing spectacles with *concave* lenses (or concave contact lenses). These spread out (diverge) the light before it enters the eye. The light is then focused on the retina.

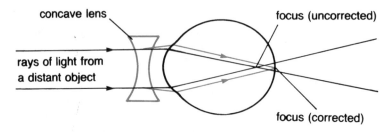

Fig. 7.5 Short sight and its correction

7.3 Detecting sound and balancing – the ear

Our ears are very sensitive to sound. They have three main sections: the outer ear, the middle ear and the inner ear (see Fig. 7.7).

How do our ears hear?

As sound waves reach our ears, they pass down the ear canal. The waves cause the membrane of the **ear drum** to vibrate and this moves the ear bones back and forth. These vibrations pass to the membrane in the **oval window** and this causes the liquid in the **cochlea** to move. Delicate sensitive cells pick up the vibrations in the cochlea. These cells then send messages to the brain via the **auditory nerve**.

Fig. 7.6 The large ears of this North African eagle owl gather in even the faintest sounds. This helps the owl to detect its prey even in the dark.

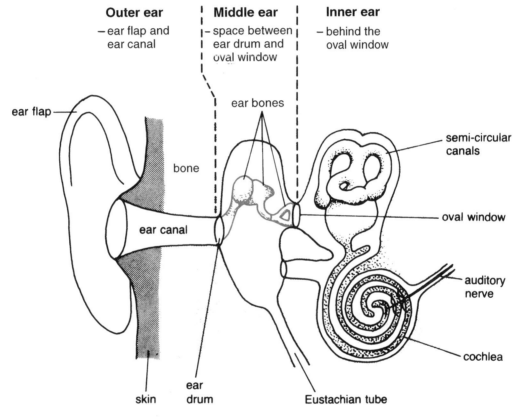

Fig. 7.7 A simplified diagram of the human ear

The inner ear also contains **three semi-circular canals** at right angles to each other. These organs are filled with liquid like the cochlea. But, unlike the cochlea which is concerned with hearing, the semi-circular canals are concerned with our sense of balance. As we move around, the liquid in the canals also moves. This stimulates nerves attached to the canals which pass messages to the brain. These messages help us to keep our balance.

7.4 Detecting smell and taste – the nose and mouth

Have you noticed how food seems to lose its flavour when your nose is blocked? This is because your sense of smell also plays an important part in detecting taste and flavour.

We detect tastes with our tongues. However, our tongues are only sensitive to four different tastes – sweet, sour, bitter and salty. Other food flavours, e.g. fruity and minty, are detected by our noses.

Fig. 7.8 shows the positions of cells which help us to detect tastes and smells. Groups of **sensory cells**, like these, which are sensitive to stimuli are called **receptors**. Notice that the nasal cavity and the mouth are connected. So, it is not surprising that the nose helps to detect the flavour of food.

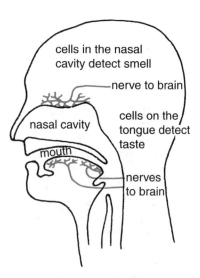

Fig. 7.8 Sense organs of smell and taste

Smell

Smell receptors are situated in the roof of the nasal cavity. They are stimulated by certain chemicals. Other chemicals have no effect on the smell cells. These chemicals have no smell – they are said to be *odourless*. Chemists think that chemicals which have similar smells have similar structures. Although our noses are sensitive to many different smells, our sense of smell is very poor compared with that of other animals.

Taste

Look at your tongue in the mirror. Notice that it is covered with dozens of short hair-like structures at the front and tiny bumps near the back. These are your taste receptors, usually called **taste buds**. There are four types of taste bud. Each type is sensitive to one of the four tastes – sweet, sour, bitter and salty. The different taste buds are concentrated on different areas of the tongue (see Fig. 7.9). This is why wine tasters swill the wine around their mouths. By doing this, they are sure to detect all the flavours in the wine.

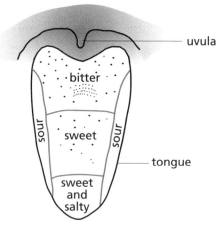

Fig. 7.9 Taste areas of the tongue

7.5 Detecting temperature and touch – the skin

Our skin forms a continuous layer over the whole of our bodies. It has two main layers: a thin outer layer, the **epidermis**, and a thicker layer underneath called the **dermis**. The outer epidermis consists of dead cells. These flake off and are replaced from below.

The functions of skin

The skin has three important jobs:

1 It protects body tissues. The epidermis forms an elastic barrier which stops germs entering the body. The skin is also waterproof. Its waterproof property is increased by oil produced from **oil glands**. Oil glands open into the **follicles** from which hairs grow. The waterproof property of the skin is useful for two reasons. It stops water getting into the body, for instance when we have a bath. It also keeps essential water inside the body and stops it drying out (dehydrating).

2 It is sensitive to touch, pain and temperature. Our skin contains groups of sensory cells (receptors). Some receptors are sensitive to touch, some to pain and others to heat and cold. Each receptor is connected to a nerve which carries impulses to the brain.

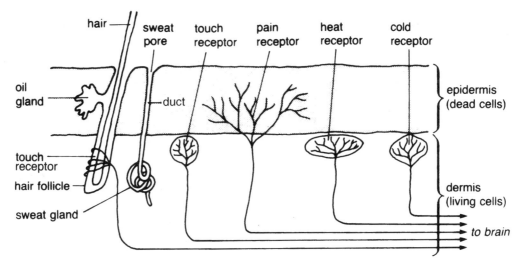

Fig. 7.10 The structure of human skin

Gently stroke the hairs on the back of your hand. **Touch receptors** at the bottom of your hair follicles detect the stimulus and send messages to your brain. Other touch receptors are stimulated if you place the point of a needle in contact with your skin. All of our skin is sensitive to touch, but some parts, for instance our fingertips and lips, are more sensitive than others.

Touch receptors are sensitive to forces and pressure on the skin. If the pressure becomes large, then **pain receptors** start to respond by sending messages to the brain. Pain receptors in the skin consist of free nerve endings which extend into the epidermis.

Our skin also contains **temperature receptors**. Some temperature receptors detect heat, others detect cold. Temperature receptors detect temperature changes and tell us whether our skin is gaining heat or losing it.

❸ **It helps to control our body temperature**. Warm-blooded animals, like humans, have various ways of keeping their bodies at a more or less constant temperature:

- *Hair and feathers*. Some animals which live in cold climates, for example polar bears and husky dogs, have thick hairy coats. The thick hair traps a layer of air close to the skin. Air is a poor conductor of heat, so heat loss is reduced. Feathers and clothing can also trap a layer of air, so they too can reduce heat loss.

- *Changes in blood vessels and capillaries*. During cold weather, the blood vessels and capillaries near the surface of our skin contract. This means that less blood flows through them and so less heat is lost from the blood. With less blood near the skin surface, the skin can look pale, even bluish, when the weather is very cold.

   In warm weather, the reverse happens. Blood vessels and capillaries in the skin expand. More blood flows through them, so excess heat can be lost from the body. This is why we look flushed in hot weather.

- *Sweating*. As soon as our body temperature rises above normal (37 °C for humans), we begin to sweat. Sweat is mainly water. It is secreted from sweat glands just below the surface of the skin (Fig. 7.10). As the sweat evaporates, the heat needed for vaporisation is taken from the skin and this causes cooling.

   If people get extremely cold, their body processes can slow down so much that they become unconscious and may die. This condition is called *hypothermia*. Temperature control in warm-blooded animals is an example of *homeostasis* (see 7.11 for details of how this controls body temperature).

7.6 The nervous system

When one of your sense organs, such as your eyes or skin, detects a stimulus it sends impulses (messages) through the nervous system. The nervous system has two parts:

❶ the **central nervous system (CNS)** consisting of the brain and the spinal cord;

2 a network of **nerves** which link the central nervous system with the various sense organs. Some nerves come out of the brain and go to sense organs in the head such as the eyes and ears. Other nerves come out of the spinal cord and go directly to the arms, legs and body.

The structure of a nerve cell (**neurone**) is shown in Fig. 7.12. The main part of the cell containing the nucleus is called the **cell body**. The cell body is located in the central nervous system. Long **nerve fibres**, called **axons**, run from the cell body to different sense organs and muscles. Usually the nerve fibres are grouped into bundles which are simply called nerves. The messages which pass along nerve fibres are tiny electric currents.

Nerve cells differ from other cells in having protruding branches called **dendrites**. These dendrites link up with other nerve cells to form a complicated network. This network enables messages to be sent in many different directions via the nervous system.

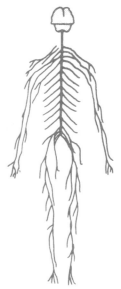

Fig. 7.11 The nervous system

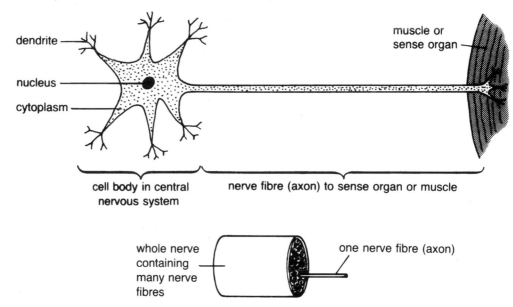

Fig. 7.12 The structure of a nerve cell and bundles of nerve fibres (axons) in a nerve

7.7 Reflex and conscious actions

If your throat tickles, you cough. If dust gets in your eye, you blink. If your hand touches a hot plate, you pull it away immediately. Each of these three actions happens automatically. They are spontaneous and out of your control. You don't think about doing them. Automatic rapid responses like these are called **reflex actions**. Reflex actions are rapid because the nervous impulses travel by the shortest possible route. These shortest routes are called **reflex arcs**. A lot of our behaviour can be explained in terms of reflex arcs. The reflex arc involved in pulling your finger away from a sharp point follows the route shown in the following flow diagram and in Fig. 7.13.

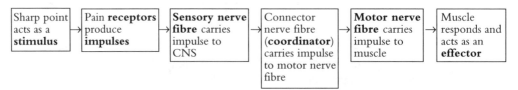

Sharp point acts as a **stimulus**	Pain **receptors** produce **impulses**	**Sensory nerve fibre** carries impulse to CNS	Connector nerve fibre (**coordinator**) carries impulse to motor nerve fibre	**Motor nerve fibre** carries impulse to muscle	Muscle responds and acts as an **effector**

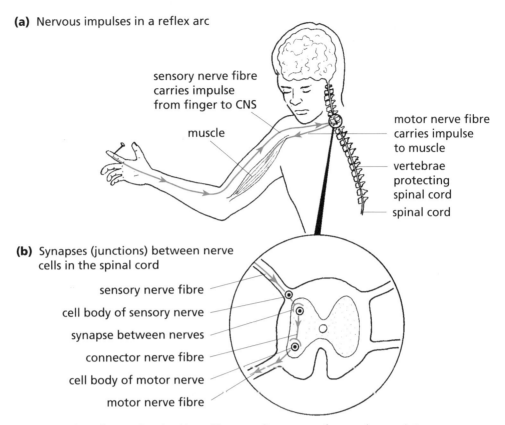

(a) Nervous impulses in a reflex arc

sensory nerve fibre
carries impulse
from finger to CNS

muscle

motor nerve fibre
carries impulse
to muscle

vertebrae
protecting
spinal cord

spinal cord

(b) Synapses (junctions) between nerve
cells in the spinal cord

sensory nerve fibre
cell body of sensory nerve
synapse between nerves
connector nerve fibre
cell body of motor nerve
motor nerve fibre

Fig. 7.13 The reflex arc involved in pulling your finger away from a sharp point

Nerve cells are connected to each other at junctions in the spinal cord. These junctions are called **synapses**. When an impulse travels through a reflex arc, it must cross at least two synapses. These synapses allow the impulse to pass in only one direction, i.e. from sense organs to spinal cord and on to muscles.

Most of our actions are *not* automatic reflexes, but thoughtful, **conscious actions**. Conscious actions involve the brain as well as the spinal cord. In these cases, impulses travel to the spinal cord, then up to the brain. They then travel back from the brain, down the spinal cord and out to the muscles.

The pathways of impulses which result in conscious actions are much longer than reflex arcs. They also cross more synapses. This is why conscious actions are slower than reflex actions.

7.8 The effect of drugs on the CNS

Some substances can seriously affect the central nervous system and damage your health. These include alcohol, solvents, tobacco and other drugs such as cannabis, LSD, ecstasy, cocaine and heroin. The use of these substances is sometimes common in one country but illegal in another. For example, in the UK alcohol is acceptable but cannabis is illegal. The exact opposite applies in some countries in the Middle East.

There are four types of drug which affect the brain and the nervous system:

1. **Sedatives** slow down the brain and make you feel sleepy. They can help people suffering from anxiety. They include Valium, barbiturates and alcohol.
2. **Stimulants** speed up the brain and make you more alert. They include ecstasy and cocaine. Coffee, tea and Coca-Cola contain a mild stimulant called caffeine. Nicotine in tobacco is also a mild stimulant.
3. **Hallucinogens** cause hallucinations (i.e. experiences and sensations which are very different from real life). They include marijuana (cannabis, 'pot', dope) and LSD.
4. **Painkillers** reduce our sense of pain. They include paracetamol, morphine and heroin.

Why are drugs dangerous?

1. **They can damage your health**. For example, alcohol poisons and kills liver cells and brain cells; cannabis damages brain cells; solvents such as those in glue, damage kidney, liver and brain cells.

2. **They impair your senses and affect your behaviour**. For example, alcohol lengthens your reaction time which is very dangerous if you are driving. In larger quantities, alcohol makes some people aggressive and violent.

3. **They may lead to damaging social effects**. For example, excess spending on drugs may lead to financial problems elsewhere.

4. **Their use may lead to addiction**. Most drugs (including tobacco (nicotine) and alcohol) can become habit forming. In some cases, the person has to have regular amounts otherwise he or she may suffer from headaches, depression or even sickness. When people become so dependent on a drug, they are said to be addicted.

7.9 Hormones and hormonal control

The central nervous system allows messages to be sent from one part of our body to another. It can control our actions and responses second by second. The **hormone system** also controls our bodies, but its effect is much slower. For example, hormones control the rate at which we grow and the development of our sexual characteristics.

The hormone system consists of a number of **glands**. These glands release chemicals called **hormones** into the bloodstream. The circulation of the blood then carries the hormones to all parts of the body. Different hormones affect different organs and different parts of the body. They carry messages from one part of the body to another so they are sometimes called **chemical messengers**.

The positions of our hormonal glands are shown in Fig. 7.14. The effects of the different hormones are summarised in Table 7.1. Notice that as well as growth hormone, the pituitary gland produces other hormones which stimulate other glands. Because of this, it is sometimes called the 'master gland'.

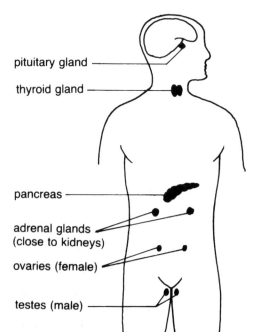

Fig. 7.14 The main hormone-producing glands in the human body

The action of *insulin* in controlling the amount of glucose in the blood is an example of homeostasis (see 7.11 for details of the action of insulin and the result of a lack of it).

Other hormones can be used to control growth, development and fertility. They must, however, be used and monitored very carefully under supervision by a doctor.

Table 7.1 The effects of some important hormones

Hormone	Gland	Effect of the hormone
Growth hormone	pituitary	speeds up growth
Tropic hormones	pituitary	stimulate other glands (e.g. thyroid, ovaries, testes) to produce their hormones
Thyroxine	thyroid	controls the rate of chemical processes in the body
Insulin	pancreas	controls the amount of sugar in the blood (deficiency causes diabetes)
Adrenaline	adrenals	prepares body for action by • increasing heart beat and breathing rate • diverting blood from the gut to limb muscles
Female sex hormones	ovaries	control female sexual development and menstrual cycle (see 8.4)
Male sex hormones	testes	control male sexual development and sperm production (see 8.4)

7.10 Plant hormones

Plants do not have muscles or a complex central nervous system. They do, however, need to respond to stimuli and control their growth. They do this using hormones.

Growth hormones

Plants grow faster near the tip of the main shoot. This growth is controlled by a plant hormone called **auxin**. Auxin is produced in the tip of the plant and it stimulates growth.

Gardeners sometimes pinch off the tips of growing plants. This stops the production of auxin and slows down the growth at the tip. Side shoots begin to grow and the plant becomes more bushy. Auxin and other plant hormones are now produced commercially and used by farmers and gardeners. For example, hormone rooting powders are chemicals which stimulate plant cuttings to grow roots. Hormone weed killers are synthetic chemicals which make weeds grow so fast that they use up all their food supply and then die.

Responding to stimuli

Have you noticed how pot plants on a windowsill grow towards the light? The stems bend towards the window and leaves and flowers turn to the light. By responding in this way, plants can expose a larger area for photosynthesis. Responses such as these which plants make to stimuli are called **tropisms**. Tropisms occur much more slowly than responses in animals and they are less varied. The main tropisms involve *light* and *gravity*.

The response of plants towards light is called **phototropism**. Scientists believe that phototropism occurs because auxin collects on the side of the shoot furthest away from the light. This makes the plant grow faster on the dark side, bending the shoot towards the light (see Fig. 7.15).

The response of plants to gravity is called **geotropism.** As a result of geotropism, trees grow vertically, even on steep hillsides, and seeds produce shoots which grow upwards and roots which grow downwards.

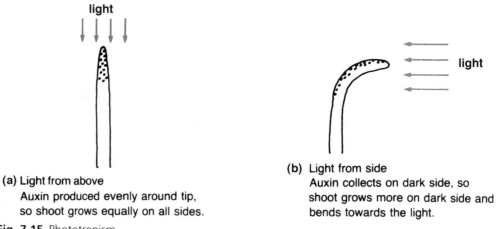

(a) Light from above
Auxin produced evenly around tip, so shoot grows equally on all sides.

(b) Light from side
Auxin collects on dark side, so shoot grows more on dark side and bends towards the light.

Fig. 7.15 Phototropism

7.11 Homeostatic control

It is important that the conditions inside our bodies, such as temperature and pH, are fairly constant and under control. Temperature control in warm-blooded animals is like the temperature control of a room using a thermostat. In a thermostat, there is 'feedback' of information to switch off the heater if the temperature gets too high. Similarly, if our skin senses that the temperature is too high, it 'feeds back' a signal to the brain. The brain then passes messages to our muscles, hairs, arteries and sweat glands to put things right (see 7.5).

Fig. 7.16 compares various parts of these two control systems. Both systems have a **sensor** which detects the **variable** under control. The sensor **feeds back** information to the **comparator** which compares the present state of the variable with its desired value. The comparator then controls the **actuator** which puts things right.

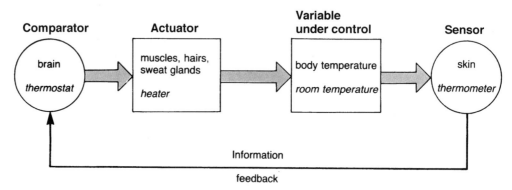

Fig. 7.16 Comparing temperature control in our bodies with temperature control in a room

This control of machines and organisms by feedback of information which keeps conditions more or less the same is called **homeostasis**. This word comes from the Greek word *homeo*, meaning 'the same', and a Latin word *status*, meaning 'state' or 'condition'. There are many other examples of homeostasis. These include the control of traffic, control of the amount of light entering your eyes and the control of glucose in the blood (see Table 7.2).

Table 7.2 A summary of some homeostatic systems

Variable under control	Sensor	Comparator	Actuator
Body temperature	skin	brain	muscles, hairs, sweat glands
Room temperature	thermometer	thermostat	heater
Amount of light entering the eye	retina	brain	iris
Glucose in the blood	pancreas	brain	insulin produced by pancreas
Traffic flow	TV cameras	police HQ	diversions, traffic signals

Control of glucose in the blood

When carbohydrates, like starch, are broken down, glucose is produced. If the concentration of glucose in the blood is too high, we become weak and dizzy. To prevent this happening, certain cells in the pancreas release insulin into the bloodstream. This insulin triggers off the conversion of glucose to glycogen, so the concentration of glucose falls.

Some people cannot produce enough insulin. Without treatment, they would go into a coma and eventually die. These people are called *diabetics* and their illness is known as **diabetes**.

Diabetics can live normal lives provided they control the amount of glucose in their blood. They can do this by:
- following a careful diet with very little carbohydrate,
- taking tablets to control the amount of glucose in the blood, or
- injecting regular doses of insulin into their bodies.

Insulin cannot be taken in tablet form because it is broken down by digestive enzymes in the gut. This is why diabetics have to inject themselves using a hypodermic needle.

Summary

1   We have six important **senses** – sight, hearing, smell, taste, touch and temperature.

2   Changes which can be detected by our senses are called **stimuli**.

3   Our reactions to stimuli are called **responses**.

4   When we detect a stimulus, impulses pass along our nerves to the **central nervous system** (the brain and the spinal cord).

5   Our bodies also have a second system for responding to stimuli – **hormones**.

6   Our eyes enable us to detect light. They have three essential parts:
- the **iris** which controls the amount of light entering the eye,
- the **lens and cornea** which focus the light,
- the **retina**, at the back of the eye, containing light-sensitive cells.

7   The change in shape of the lens and cornea to focus near or distant objects is called **accommodation**.

8   Our ears detect sounds. Sound waves cause, first the **ear drum**, then the **ear bones** and finally the membrane in the **oval window** to vibrate. This causes the liquid in the **cochlea** to move and sensitive cells detect these movements and send messages to the brain.

9   Groups of sensory cells, called **receptors**, in the nasal cavity and on the tongue enable us to detect smells and tastes, respectively.

10   Receptors in the skin are sensitive to touch, pain and temperature.

11   Skin also helps to control body temperature by means of
- hair or feathers
- changes in blood vessels
- sweating

12   After detecting stimuli, sense organs send impulses (messages) through the nervous system. Nervous impulses travel by the shortest possible routes called **reflex arcs**. These make possible the rapid response to a stimulus.

13   Substances in certain drugs, solvents, tobacco and alcohol affect the central nervous system.

14 Drugs are dangerous because
- they can damage your health,
- they impair your senses,
- they can lead to damaging social effects,
- they may lead to addiction.

15 **Hormones**, released by glands into the bloodstream, control our bodies at a much slower rate than the nervous system.

16 The control of machines and organisms by feedback of information which keeps conditions more or less the same is called **homeostasis**. Examples of homeostasis include control of body temperature and control of the amount of glucose in the blood.

Quick test 7

1 Which of the following is *not* a sense organ?
  A eye   B hair   C nose   D tongue
2 A stimulus is
  A a reaction to change.
  B a reflex action involving our nerves.
  C something which causes a reaction.
  D a nerve ending in a sense organ.
3 Plant hormones are not used for
  A killing weeds.
  B controlling fruit ripening.
  C accelerating rooting in cuttings.
  D increasing water movement through a plant.

Questions 4 to 8

We use many different devices to extend our senses. Consider the following senses:
A hearing   B sight   C smell
D taste   E temperature   F touch

Which of these senses are extended by
4   a barometer?
5   binoculars?
6   a thermostat?
7   a stethoscope?
8   a walking stick?

Questions 9 to 12

Name the sense organ in each case which makes it possible for
9   an architect to study a plan.
10 a musician to tune a violin.
11 a blind person to tell the difference between two sorts of yoghurt.
12 a cosmetic scientist to develop a new perfume.   (ULEAC)

Questions 13 to 16

Consider the following structures in the eye.
A ciliary muscle   B iris   C pupil
D optic nerve   E retina   F tear gland

Which of the structures A to F is responsible for
13 protecting the cornea?
14 detecting light?

15 carrying messages to the brain?

16 preventing too much light entering the eye?

17 Write the following in the order in which they are involved a reflex action:
   A central nervous system
   B effector
   C motor neurone
   D receptor
   E sensory neurone
   F stimulus

Questions 18 to 21

Javed and Debra wanted to find out if cuttings grew roots more quickly if a growth hormone was used. They set up three tests, each using a different amount of growth hormone. The diagram shows their results after 10 days.

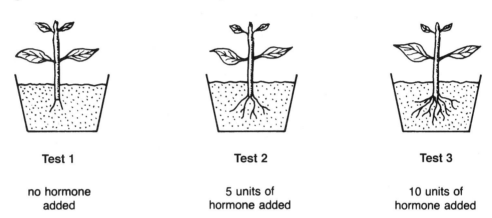

| **Test 1** | **Test 2** | **Test 3** |
| no hormone added | 5 units of hormone added | 10 units of hormone added |

18 State which part of the plant has been used for the cutting.

19 In which test did the roots develop most quickly?

20 What was the purpose of test 1?

21 State three things which must be kept the same if the results are to be fairly compared.

(ULEAC)

Chapter 8
Reproduction

8.1 Sexual and asexual reproduction

Living things cannot live forever. Eventually, they die. But animals and plants do not disappear from the Earth because they produce offspring. This is called **reproduction**. Living things can reproduce in two different ways – by **sexual reproduction** and by **asexual reproduction**. Reproduction in humans is always sexual. This involves the union or mating of a male and a female. Almost all animals and some plants reproduce sexually. But most plants and some animals can also produce offspring by asexual reproduction. Asexual reproduction does not involve the union of male and female. It takes place when part of the parent is detached and allowed to grow separately.

Sexual reproduction
Sexual reproduction is similar for all organisms. It involves special sex cells called **gametes**. Gametes are formed by a process of cell division called **meiosis** (see 9.2). *Female* gametes are called **egg cells**. These are produced in the ovary of the female animal or plant. *Male* gametes are called **sperms** in animals and **pollen** in plants. When a male gamete meets a female gamete, the two join together. This is called **fertilisation** and the fertilised cell is called a **zygote**. The zygote grows by dividing into two cells, then again into four cells and so on. Eventually, the cells form an **embryo**, which grows into an adult.

As both parents contribute part of themselves to the fertilised egg, the offspring has similarities to each. But it is not identical to the mother or father. Sexual reproduction is therefore a source of genetic variation.

Asexual reproduction
In contrast to sexual reproduction, asexual reproduction requires only *one* parent. It involves a different type of cell division called **mitosis** (see 9.2), in which new cells are produced simply by the division of old ones. Each new cell is a copy of the original. So in asexual reproduction all the offspring from one parent are identical. These identical offspring are called **clones**.

The two methods of reproduction are summarised and compared in Fig. 8.1.

8.2 Asexual reproduction – cloning

There are various methods of asexual reproduction forming clones. Three of these are:
1. **Binary fission** This method is used by simple organisms such as amoeba (Fig. 8.2), and by bacteria. The 'parent' cell divides to produce two identical 'daughter' cells.
2. **Budding** In some organisms, such as yeasts, budlike growths start to form on the parent. These eventually separate from the parent and form a new organism.

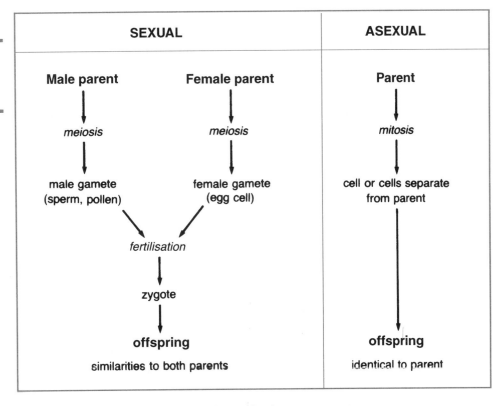

Fig. 8.1 Comparing sexual and asexual reproduction

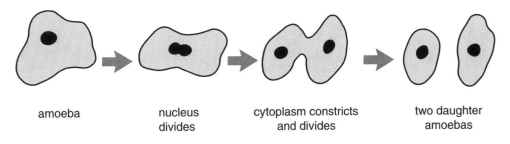

Fig. 8.2 An amoeba reproducing by binary fission

❸ **Vegetative reproduction** This is an important form of asexual reproduction in plants. The most common methods of vegetative reproduction are:

● *Cuttings* – A short stem with a few leaves is cut from the parent plant, such as a geranium. When this is put into damp soil, it produces roots and grows into a new plant.

● *Runners and stolons* – Some plants, for example strawberries, send out side branches (runners) from the main stem. Roots and shoots form at intervals along the runner and these make new plants. Some plants, for example spider houseplants, form drooping branches (stolons) which develop roots and shoots for a new plant.

● *Tubers* – Potatoes are tubers. They are formed as the potato plant grows during the summer. They contain a store of carbohydrate (starch). Each tuber (potato) provides a food supply for a new plant which grows from the potato the following spring.

● *Bulbs* – These are storage organs like tubers. But, unlike tubers, they enable the *same plant* to survive the winter and come back year after year. Onions, daffodils and tulips all form bulbs. Towards the end of the growing season, the bulb may sprout a new bulb from its side. Food from the leaves goes into the developing new bulb and a new plant grows from this the following spring.

8.3 Sexual reproduction in animals

Almost all animals reproduce sexually. This involves the mating of a male and a female. For fertilisation to occur, a sperm cell from the male must fuse (join) with an egg cell from the female (see Fig. 8.3). Notice in Fig. 8.3 that sperm cells are much smaller than egg cells. Sperm cells have a 'tail' which enables them to move around in search of egg cells. Only one sperm cell needs to enter the egg cell for fertilisation to occur.

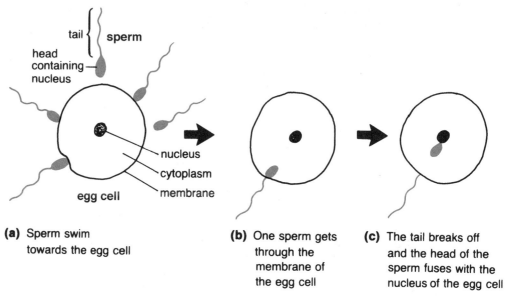

(a) Sperm swim towards the egg cell

(b) One sperm gets through the membrane of the egg cell

(c) The tail breaks off and the head of the sperm fuses with the nucleus of the egg cell

Fig. 8.3 Fertilisation of an egg by a sperm

In some animals, including fish and amphibians, the female lays unfertilised eggs. The male then pours his sperm over them. This is called **external fertilisation** because it takes place *outside* the female's body. External fertilisation can only occur in water because sperm will die if they become dry. This is why frogs, toads and newts must return to water in order to mate.

Most land animals mate by passing sperm from the male into the female's body. Fertilisation takes place *inside* the female, so this is called **internal fertilisation**.

In birds and reptiles, the male passes sperm into the female. The sperm swim up the female's reproductive passage until they meet an egg. After fertilisation, a shell is added to the egg before it is laid. A period of incubation is then necessary before young hatch from the fertilised eggs.

In humans and most other mammals the fertilised egg develops inside the female. The fertilised egg becomes a **fetus** (pronounced 'feetus') which grows into a young animal before it is born.

8.4 Human reproduction

The male reproductive system

The male reproductive system is shown in Fig. 8.4. Sperm are made in the **testes** and then stored in the **epididymis**. The sperm leave a man's body by passing along the **sperm duct**. In the sperm duct they mix with a white liquid produced by the prostate gland and the seminal vesicles. This mixture of white liquid plus sperm is called **semen** (pronounced 'seemen'). During sexual intercourse, semen passes down the urethra very quickly and is ejected from the penis by a muscular reflex action.

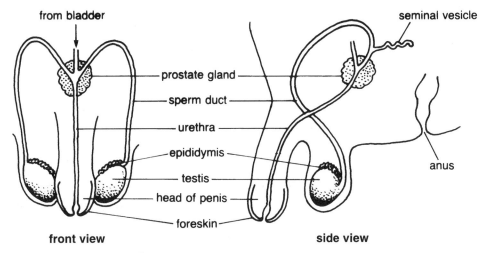

Fig. 8.4 The male reproductive system

Notice in Fig. 8.4 that both urine and semen pass out through the urethra. However, urine and semen cannot pass through the urethra at the same time.

The female reproductive system

Fig. 8.5 shows the female reproductive system. Eggs are released from the **ovaries**. At roughly monthly intervals, an egg moves into one of the **oviducts** (egg tube) and down towards the **uterus** (womb). If the woman has sexual intercourse at this time, the egg may be fertilised by sperm which swim up the egg tube. If fertilisation occurs, the fertilised egg (zygote) passes down the egg tube and into the uterus where it embeds itself in the lining. The lower end of the uterus opens into the **vagina**. Notice that a woman's urethra has a separate exit. Just in front of the urethra is a small lump called the **clitoris**. Like the man's penis, this becomes erect and sensitive when it is stimulated during sexual intercourse.

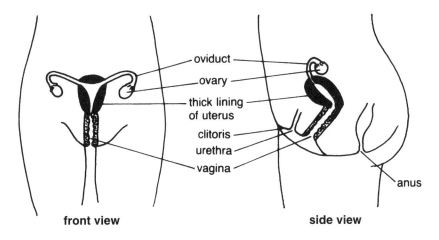

Fig. 8.5 The female reproductive system

Summary

1   Living things can reproduce in two different ways.
   - **Sexual reproduction** involves the union or mating of a male and a female.
   - **Asexual reproduction** does not require the union of male and female. It occurs when part of the parent is detached and allowed to grow.

2   Sexual reproduction involves sex cells called **gametes** formed by a process of cell division known as **meiosis**.
   ● Female gametes are called **egg cells**.
   ● Male gametes are called **sperm** in animals and **pollen** in plants.

3   **Fertilisation** occurs when a male gamete meets a female gamete and the two join together. The fertilised cell is called a **zygote**. The zygote grows by cell division and forms an **embryo**.

4   Asexual reproduction requires only one parent. It involves a type of cell division called **mitosis**. In mitosis, each new cell is a copy of the original. So asexual reproduction from one particular parent produces identical offspring called **clones**.

5   Asexual reproduction can take place by **binary fission** in microorganisms and through budding, cuttings, runners and stolons in plants.

6   Almost all animals reproduce sexually.
   ● In some animals (e.g. fish, amphibians), the female lays unfertilised eggs and the male pours his sperm over them. This is called **external fertilisation**.
   ● Most land animals mate by passing sperm from the male into the female's body. This is called **internal fertilisation**.

Quick test 8

Questions 1 to 4
Diagrams A to E show five different cells as seen through a microscope.

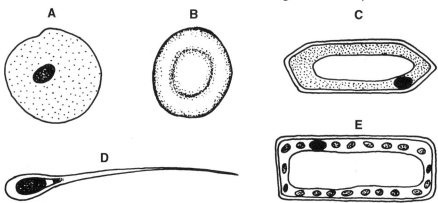

From the letters A to E, choose the one cell which
1   has no visible nucleus.
2   must be a plant cell.
3   is a sperm cell.
4   might be a female gamete.

Questions 5 to 8
The graph shows the relative growth rate of girls and boys from 6 to 18 years of age.
5   At what age are boys growing most rapidly?
6   At what age are boys growing least rapidly?
7   At what age are girls growing most rapidly?
8   At what age are girls growing least rapidly?

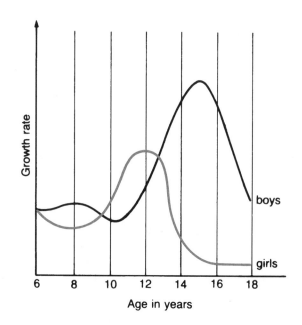

Questions 9 to 11

A   embryo   B   fruit   C   gamete
D   seed   E   zygote

Which *one* of the words A to E above is best used to describe
9   a pollen grain?
10 a fetus?
11 a peanut?

12 Gardeners often use methods based on asexual reproduction to produce beautiful plants. Give *two* reasons why they prefer to use these methods rather than methods based on sexual reproduction (i.e. pollination–seeds–growth).

Chapter 9
Genetics and evolution

9.1 Introduction

Clare has dark brown hair like her mother and blue eyes like her father. Perhaps you have some characteristics from your mother and some from your father. The way in which we inherit characteristics from our parents and grandparents is called **heredity**. The branch of science which studies the inheritance of characteristics is called **genetics**. This is because the information for different characteristics is passed from one generation to the next in the form of **genes**.

Fig. 9.1 Some features persist from generation to generation. Look at the similar features of father and son, Donald and Kiefer Sutherland.

9.2 Chromosomes and cell division

In order to understand how characteristics are passed in genes from parents to offspring, we need to know how information is carried in cells and what happens when cells divide. Every cell in your body contains enough information to make a complete copy of you. Normally, however, one particular cell (e.g. a nerve cell) only uses that part of the information which is needed to make a copy of itself. The information to make a copy is stored in long thin strands called **chromosomes** in the nucleus of the cell (see Fig. 9.2).

When the nucleus of a cell is stained with a dye, the chromosomes look like fine pieces of thread under the microscope. The chromosomes are made of a complex *polymer* (see

the nucleus of a cell contains long thin threads called chromosomes

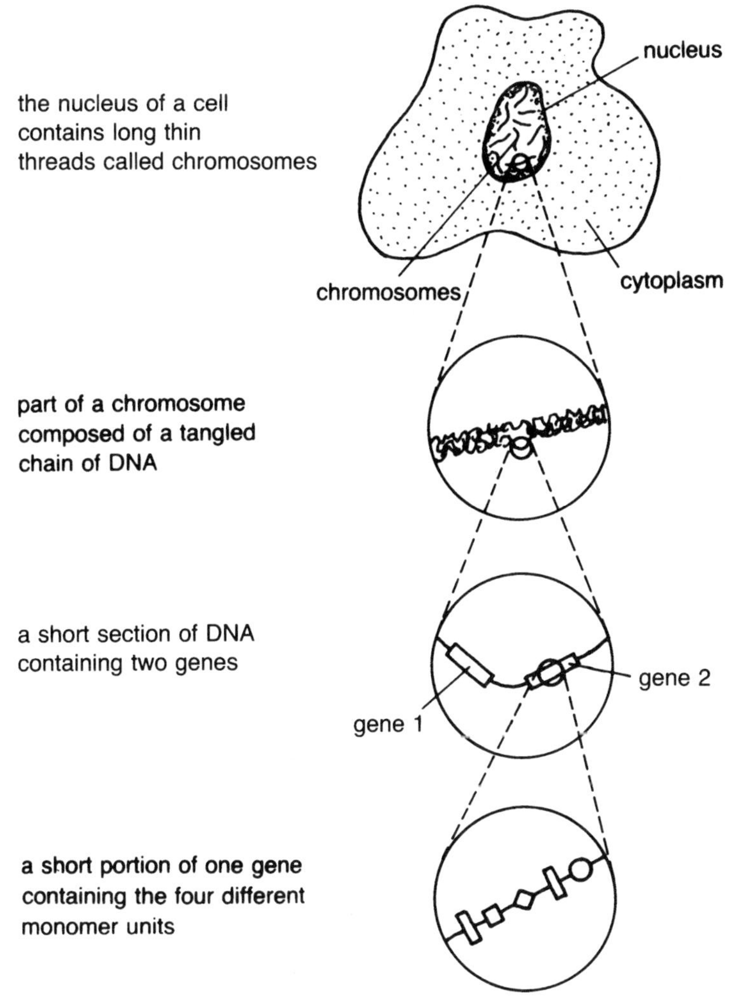

part of a chromosome composed of a tangled chain of DNA

a short section of DNA containing two genes

a short portion of one gene containing the four different monomer units

Fig. 9.2 A cell with its nucleus, chromosomes, DNA, genes and monomers

18.9) called **DNA (deoxyribonucleic acid)**. The DNA polymer is made up from four different monomers.

Each **gene** is a section of the DNA polymer. Genes are responsible for your characteristics. For example, if you have brown hair, you must have a gene which causes brown hair. If you have freckles, you must have a gene which causes freckles.

Different organisms have different numbers of chromosomes. *Humans have 46 chromosomes in each cell*, chickens have 36, peas have 14 and fruit flies have only 8. These chromosomes can be arranged in pairs. The members of each pair look alike and carry genes which control the same characteristics. They are called **homologous pairs**. For example, the homologous pair of chromosomes which control eye colour will contain the eye colour gene at the same position. However, the two genes may not carry the same instructions. One gene might carry information for blue eyes, the other gene might carry information for brown eyes. Later, we shall see how the different information leads to only one eye colour.

In each homologous pair, one chromosome comes from the male parent and the other comes from the female parent. So, 23 of your chromosomes came from your father and the other 23 came from your mother.

Cell division

There are two different kinds of cell division – mitosis and meiosis. **Mitosis** occurs when an organism is growing or when its cells are being replaced. It occurs in the formation of all cells, *except* male sex cells (sperms, pollen) and female sex cells (eggs). **Meiosis** occurs only in the formation of male and female sex cells during reproduction.

Mitosis

Most of the time, the chromosomes in a cell are thin and difficult to see even with a microscope. But, just before cell division, the chromosomes get shorter and fatter and can often be seen with a microscope. At the same time, each chromosome makes a copy of itself. The original chromosome and its copy are joined somewhere near the middle (Fig. 9.3(b)).

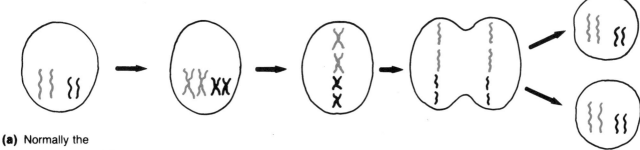

(a) Normally the chromosomes consist of single threads. The nucleus of this cell has four chromosomes – two homologous pairs

(b) Just before cell division, each chromosome makes a copy of itself

(c) Chromosomes joined to their copies move to the centre of the cell

(d) The copies separate and the cells begin to divide

(e) Each of the new cells has exactly the same chromosomes as the parent cell

Fig. 9.3 The stages in mitosis

The chromosomes, joined to their copies, then arrange themselves near the centre of the cell (Fig. 9.3(c)). The copies separate and the cell begins to divide (Fig. 9.3(d)). Each of the new cells has exactly the same chromosomes as the parent cell (Fig. 9.3(e)).

Notice that *mitosis produces exact copies*. This is what happens when an organism grows and when an organism reproduces asexually, forming clones.

Mitosis in human cells occurs by the process shown in Fig. 9.3, except that human cells have 46 chromosomes (i.e. *23 homologous pairs*) not four chromosomes (two homologous pairs).

During mitosis, the process of cell division is very carefully controlled. Scientists think that many cancers start when this control of cell division is lost.

Meiosis

Sex cells (sperm and eggs) called **gametes** contain only half the normal number of chromosomes. Gametes cannot be produced by mitosis because this would produce cells with the normal number of chromosomes.

When gametes are produced, cell division occurs by meiosis (Fig. 9.4). In this case, one chromosome from each homologous pair is taken at random by each of the new cells.

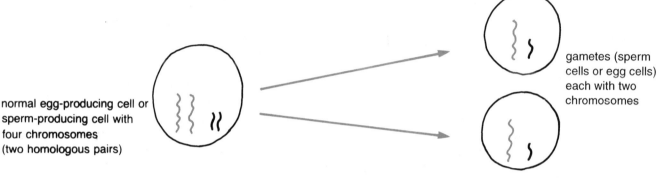

Fig. 9.4 Separation of chromosomes in meiosis

9.3 Sexual reproduction and meiosis

Meiosis occurs during sexual reproduction. When an egg is fertilised by a sperm, the two nuclei join together. The egg and the sperm each contain only half the normal number of chromosomes. But, after fertilisation, the fertilised egg will contain the normal number of chromosomes.

Fig. 9.5 summarises the process in humans. Notice that 23 chromosomes come from the mother and 23 from the father. These form 23 homologous pairs. After fertilisation, the zygote starts to grow by cell division. These cell divisions involve mitosis.

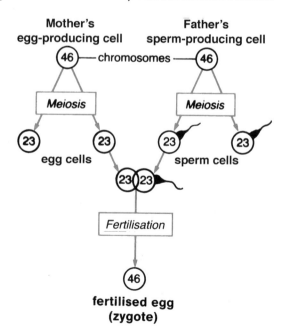

Fig. 9.5 The numbers of chromosomes involved in meiosis and sexual reproduction in humans

Boy or girl?

The sex of a baby is determined by one of its 23 pairs of chromosomes. The chromosomes in this pair are called the **sex chromosomes**. There are two types of sex chromosomes: a long one called the **X chromosome** and a short one called the **Y chromosome**.

In females, every cell has two X chromosomes.

In males, every cell has one X and one Y chromosome.

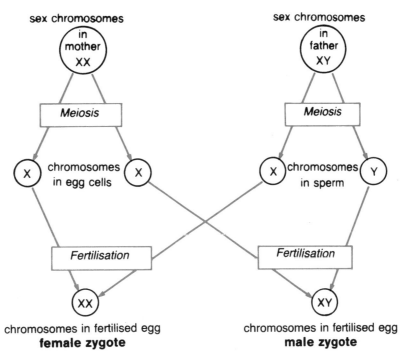

Fig. 9.6 The sex of a fertilised egg depends on the sex chromosomes

Fig. 9.6 shows what happens to the sex chromosomes when:
❶ eggs and sperm are produced by meiosis;
❷ the eggs and sperm fuse to produce a fertilised egg.

All the eggs which the mother produces contain an X chromosome. But half the sperm from the father contain an X chromosome and the other half contain a Y chromosome. So there is an equal chance that an egg will be fertilised by an X sperm or by a Y sperm. If an X sperm fertilises the egg, the zygote will contain two X chromosomes. This zygote will develop into a girl. If a Y sperm fertilises the egg, the zygote will contain an X and a Y chromosome. This will develop into a boy.

9.4 Genes and genetics

During the 19th century, an Austrian monk called **Gregor Mendel** (1822–84) studied the way in which characteristics were passed on from one generation to the next. Mendel carried out experiments with **pea plants**. He studied the inheritance of various characteristics such as height, flower colour and seed shape. The patterns which Mendel deduced from his experiments with pea plants have been found to apply to all plants and animals, including humans.

As a result of his experiments, Mendel made some important statements. These statements are now called the **rules of genetics**.
- An organism gets its characteristics (e.g. eye colour, nose shape) from its **genes**.
- Often a particular characteristic is controlled by a pair of genes. One gene in the pair comes from the father, the other from the mother.
- Genes may be **dominant** or **recessive**.

● If a dominant gene and a recessive gene are both present, the dominant one will decide the characteristic.

These simple rules can be used to explain how characteristics are passed on from one generation to the next. They can also be used to predict characteristics in the next generation.

Explaining eye colour

Suppose a brown-eyed man and a blue-eyed woman have a baby with brown eyes. Why does the baby have brown eyes and not blue eyes?

Scientists use the word **phenotype** to describe the *characteristics of an organism*. So, in this case:

● father's phenotype is brown,
● mother's phenotype is blue,
● baby's phenotype is brown.

Each parent has a pair of genes which control eye colour. These genes can produce brown eyes or blue eyes. We can represent the brown-eye gene with the letter **B** and the blue-eye gene with the letter **b**. Now suppose the father has two brown-eye genes which we represent as **BB**, and the mother has two blue-eye genes which we represent as **bb**. Combinations of genes such as **BB** and **bb** are called **genotypes**. Genotypes describe the *genetic make-up of an individual*.

Fig. 9.7 shows what happens to the genes for eye colour when:

❶ eggs and sperm are formed;
❷ fertilisation takes place.

All sperm contain one **B** gene and all eggs contain one **b** gene. So, after fertilisation, the baby's cells will have one **B** gene and one **b** gene. The baby's *genotype* is **Bb**.

The baby has brown eyes, even though its cells have one blue gene, **b**. This is because the brown gene, **B**, is dominant and the blue gene, **b**, is recessive. The **B** gene somehow suppresses the **b** gene. Mendel's rule stated that if a dominant gene and a recessive gene are both present, the dominant one will decide the characteristic. So the baby with a genotype of **Bb** has brown eyes.

In genetics, a *dominant gene is represented by a capital letter and a recessive gene by a small (lower-case) letter.* Genes such as **B** and **b** which control the same characteristic but which produce different results are known as **alleles**.

Notice that there are three possible genotypes for eye colour: **BB**, **Bb** and **bb**. Two of these genotypes, **BB** and **Bb**, result in brown eyes. One genotype, **bb**, gives blue eyes.

When the genotype for a particular characteristic consists of two identical alleles (e.g. **BB** or **bb**), we say that the organism is **homozygous**. When the genotype consists of two different alleles (e.g. **Bb**), we say the organism is **heterozygous**.

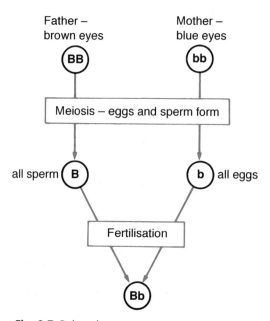

Fig. 9.7 Baby – brown eyes

We can now use the rules of genetics to predict what happens when parents with other eye-colour genotypes have children. Two possible combinations are shown in Fig. 9.8.

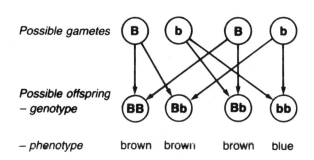
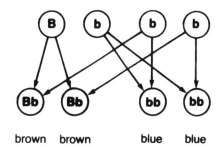

Fig. 9.8 What happens when parents with different eye-colour genotypes have children?

The offspring (children) from the father and mother in Fig. 9.8 belong to the first generation or **F₁ generation**. In plants and animals, members of the F$_1$ generation will often mate and produce a second or **F₂ generation**.

9.5 Why is genetics important?

Understanding hereditary diseases

The study of genetics has helped us to understand and treat several diseases. Most people don't mind whether they have brown eyes or blue eyes. However, the genes which children inherit from their parents are sometimes faulty. In some cases, the faulty genes cause serious diseases or disabilities.

Diseases which offspring inherit from their parents are called **hereditary diseases**. The genes which cause hereditary diseases can be dominant or recessive. For example, the gene which causes **cystic fibrosis** is recessive, just like the gene for blue eyes. So, if both parents carry the faulty recessive gene, their children may suffer from cystic fibrosis.

Two other diseases caused by faulty genes are **colour blindness** and **haemophilia**. These diseases are *more common in males* than females. This is because the disease is caused by a *recessive gene on the X chromosome*. Females have two X chromosomes, but males have only one. It is unlikely that both of the X chromosomes in a female will carry the recessive, disease-causing gene.

The diseases caused by abnormal genes can sometimes be spotted in 'family trees'. Couples with a family history of hereditary diseases often have a higher risk of passing the diseases to their children. A *genetic counsellor* can often give these couples help and advice. The counsellor may also be able to estimate the risk of the disease occurring in their children.

One of the most common methods of detecting abnormal genes is by **amniocentesis** during pregnancy. A small volume of *amniotic fluid* is collected by inserting a needle through the mother's abdomen into the uterus. Laboratory tests can then be carried out on the baby's cells which are present in the fluid.

Selective breeding

Farmers and gardeners have been using genetics for hundreds of years. Year by year, they have taken seeds for their next crop from the most attractive, the highest yielding and the most disease-resistant plants. Farm animals and domestic animals, like cats and dogs, have also been selected and bred in the same way. In some cases, selective breeding has led to new varieties of animals or plants.

Decades of **selective breeding** have resulted in cows which yield high quantities of milk, cereal crops which are resistant to plant diseases and fruits with distinctive flavours. Nowadays, geneticists can breed varieties more systematically and advise farmers and gardeners on ways in which they can improve their animals and plants. Using these techniques, selective breeding has resulted in enormous economic benefits.

Fig. 9.9 Pigs (left) have been produced from wild boars (right) by centuries of selective breeding

Genetic engineering

During the last 15 years, scientists have found ways in which they can change the genes in a chromosome. It has even become possible to remove one gene and replace it with another. These techniques are called **genetic engineering**. Genetic engineering has already been used to:

● produce antibiotics by adding a particular gene to bacteria;
● produce insulin and growth hormones by adding genes to bacteria.

At the present time, scientists are looking for ways in which they can replace the 'faulty' genes which cause hereditary diseases such as haemophilia. The possibilities for genetic engineering are endless, but some of them raise difficult moral questions. For example, suppose it were possible to make people more intelligent by genetic engineering. Do you think we should use the process for this sort of purpose?

9.6 Evolution

Have you ever wondered how living things first began? Where did all the different plants and animals come from?

These questions can be explained by the **theory of evolution**. This is the idea that the first living things on Earth were very simple. Slowly, over millions of years, these simple creatures developed (evolved) into the thousands of organisms in the world today. The theory of evolution also suggests that the very first single-celled creatures appeared on the Earth over 3000 million years ago. These simple creatures had themselves 'evolved' from chemicals which were being formed all the time in warm seas.

Evidence for evolution

The main evidence for evolution comes from **fossils**. Fossils are the remains of animals and plants that lived long ago. When an animal or plant dies, its soft tissue decays. Sometimes, however, the animal or plant is buried in mud which eventually becomes sedimentary rock. The skeleton of the animal or the cell wall of the plant may then be preserved in the rock for millions of years.

Fig. 9.10 Fossil ammonites in a sample of rock from the lower Jurassic period (195 to 172 million years ago). The sample was found at Robin Hood's Bay, Yorkshire.

By studying these fossils, scientists can work out what the animal or plant was like when it was living. Using a technique called radioactive dating (see 26.6), they can also work out when the animal or plant lived. From the fossil record, a detailed picture can be built up of the time at which different plants and animals appeared on the Earth. The fossil record also shows that plants and animals have evolved very slowly over millions of years.

The first human fossils come from rocks which are between one and two million years old. Fig. 9.11 compares the skull of one of these fossils (*Homo erectus*) with that of modern man (*Homo sapiens*).

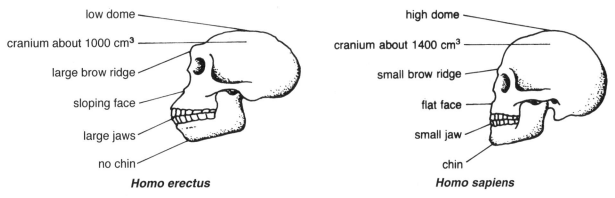

Fig. 9.11 Comparing the skulls of prehistoric man, *Homo erectus*, and modern man, *Homo sapiens*

9.7 How has evolution occurred?

In 1831, a young scientist called **Charles Darwin** (1809–82) was appointed naturalist on *HMS Beagle*. During the next five years, Darwin sailed around the world in this ship taking part in important scientific and geographical expeditions. Darwin visited many different countries where he studied the animals and plants. He gradually became convinced that various species which he observed had come into being by a slow process of evolution.

In 1859, Darwin published his observations and ideas in a book called *The Origin of Species*. In this book, Darwin put forward his theory of evolution which he called a theory of natural selection.

Darwin's theory of natural selection

Darwin's theory of natural selection involved three key ideas:

1 variations within a species,

2 survival of the fittest, and

3 adaptation of organisms.

Variations within a species

Even within the same species, there are many differences between the individuals. Look at all the boys or all the girls in your class. Features such as height, weight, hair colour and texture, skin colour, speed at running and intelligence vary greatly from one person to another. These differences between individuals are called **variations**. Variations within a species can occur through both genetic (inherited) and environmental causes. There are, in fact, four ways in which variation occurs:

1 **Meiosis**: This 'shuffles' the chromosomes. When gametes (eggs and sperms) are formed by meiosis, the pairs of chromosomes divide in a completely random way (see 9.2).

2 **Fertilisation**: This brings together new sets of chromosomes from the father and mother.

3 **Environmental influences**: For example, poor soil will result in stunted plants and a poor diet will affect a person's weight and health.

4 **Mutation**: A mutation is a sudden change in the genetic make-up of an organism. Mutations can be caused in a number of ways. For example, the structure of a gene may be changed by harmful chemicals or by radiation. Alternatively, bits of chromosomes may be lost or extra bits added during abnormal meiosis or fertilisation. For example, children born with Down's syndrome have an extra chromosome.

Mutations are occurring all the time. Very often the mutations go unnoticed. Sometimes they are harmful, causing mental and physical handicap in humans. Occasionally, mutations produce useful new characteristics. In this case, the animal or plant affected has advantages over other members of its species.

A good example of *beneficial mutation* is provided by the peppered moth (Fig. 9.12). The peppered moth inhabits woodland areas. For most of the time, it rests on tree trunks. In unpolluted areas, the lighter-form is well camouflaged by lichen-covered trunks. The darker form is easily seen and is taken by predatory birds such as thrushes. In polluted areas where the trunks of trees are blackened by soot, the darker, mutant moth is better camouflaged and is more likely to survive.

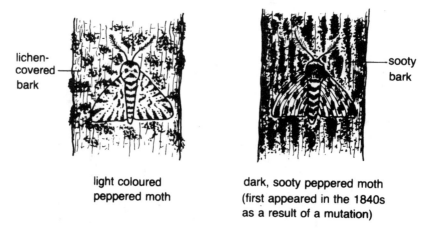

lichen-covered bark

sooty bark

light coloured peppered moth

dark, sooty peppered moth (first appeared in the 1840s as a result of a mutation)

Fig. 9.12 The two forms of the peppered moth

Survival of the fittest

In the course of his travels, Darwin noticed the wide variations within a species. Some were taller, others were fatter or could run faster. Darwin also noticed that both animals and plants had a continual struggle to survive:

- They had to avoid **predators**.
- They had to avoid **disease**.
- They were in **competition** for food, space and shelter.
- They had to survive the **climate**.

The animals and plants that survive are usually the fittest. They are less likely to suffer from disease and are more able to find food and escape from predators. They have favourable variations in their characteristics which give them a better chance of survival. For example, tall plants will receive more light and faster deer will escape from lions. Darwin summed up these ideas using the term '**survival of the fittest**' (Fig. 9.13).

In turn, the survivors would be more likely to pass on the favourable characteristics to their offspring. The whole process is called **natural selection** and leads to the evolution of the species.

In some cases, however, the variations of an organism may lead to animals or plants which have difficulty in surviving. This may lead to the extinction of the species.

The legs of these birds are too short. The birds cannot wade in the water without drowning

These birds have the best leg length for wading and obtaining food

The legs of these birds are too long. They cannot wade in the water and reach the water with their beaks

Fig. 9.13 Survival of the fittest: waders with the right leg length for the depth of water in their area are more likely to survive

Adaptation of organisms

The variations which help a species to survive are most likely to be passed on to the next generation. This is because those organisms with the most favourable characteristics are most likely to reproduce. For example, if thicker winter coats help rabbits to survive, thick-coated animals are most likely to live long enough to produce young. So later generations will tend to inherit thicker winter coats. By this process of natural selection, a species evolves so that individual animals and plants are better suited to their environment. The *changes which take place and allow an organism to survive more easily* are called **adaptations**.

The key ideas in Darwin's theory of natural selection are summarised in Fig. 9.14.

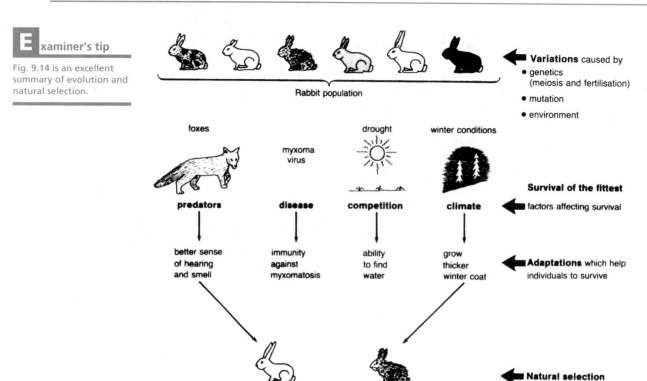

Fig. 9.14 A summary of Darwin's theory of natural selection

Summary

1   The way in which offspring inherit characteristics from their parents is called **heredity**. The study of inherited characteristics is called **genetics**.

2   Information for different characteristics is passed from one generation to the next in **genes**.

3   Each gene is a section of **DNA polymer** which makes up the **chromosomes** in the nucleus of a cell. Chromosomes occur in **homologous pairs**. Each pair look alike and carry genes which control the same characteristics.

4   There are two kinds of cell division:
   ● **mitosis** occurs when an organism is growing or when an organism reproduces asexually. Mitosis produces exact copies called **clones**.
   ● **meiosis** occurs only in the formation of male and female sex cells (gametes) during sexual reproduction. Gametes contain only half the normal number of chromosomes.

5   The sex of a baby is controlled by a pair of sex chromosomes. There are two types of sex chromosomes – long X chromosomes and short Y chromosomes. In females, every cell has two X chromosomes. In males, every cell has one X and one Y chromosome.

6   Often, a particular characteristic is controlled by a pair of genes. One gene in the pair comes from the father, the other from the mother. Genes may be **dominant** (e.g. **B** for brown eyes) or **recessive** (e.g. **b** for blue eyes). If a dominant gene and a recessive gene are both present, the dominant one will decide the characteristic.

7   Genes such as **B** and **b** which control the same characteristic but which produce different results are known as **alleles**.

8   The study of genetics has helped us to understand and treat several **hereditary diseases** such as cystic fibrosis, colour blindness and haemophilia.

9   **Selective breeding** can be carried out systematically to improve animals and plants.

10 Using **genetic engineering**, it is now possible to replace one gene by another in a chromosome or to add a gene to a chromosome. This technique has been used to produce antibiotics and hormones.

11 **Darwin's theory of evolution** says that, over millions of years, simple creatures developed (evolved) into the thousands of organisms in the world today. Evolution occurred through **natural selection**.

12 The main evidence for evolution comes from fossils.

13 Variations in a species can arise from both genetic and environmental causes.

14 Sexual reproduction involving meiosis and fertilisation is a source of genetic variation. Mutation is also a source of genetic variation and can be caused in a number of ways.

15 Variation may lead to the evolution or extinction of a species.

16 The distribution and relative numbers of organisms in a habitat will depend on adaptation, competition and predation.

Quick test 9

1 Cells contain information which controls how they develop. This information is contained in
  A the cell wall.
  B the chloroplasts.
  C the cytoplasm.
  D the nucleus.

2 Kangaroos have 12 chromosomes in each body cell. This means that each sperm cell of the kangaroo will have
  A 6 chromosomes.
  B 12 chromosomes.
  C 18 chromosomes.
  D 24 chromosomes.

3 Which one of the following statements is correct?
  A Chromosomes are made of DNA and contain genes.
  B Genes are made of DNA and contain chromosomes.
  C Genes are made of chromosomes and contain DNA.
  D DNA is made of genes and contains chromosomes.

4 Which *one* of the following is *least* likely to bring about evolution?
  A artificial selection
  B mutation of genes
  C temporary changes in the environment
  D naturally occurring radiation

5 In a breed of cattle, the gene for horns, **n**, is recessive to the genes for no horns **N**. Hornless cows (genotype **NN**) are mated with horned bulls (genotype **nn**). What proportion of the calves will be hornless?
  A none
  B half
  C three quarters
  D all

6   The fusion of two sex cells in a plant is called
    A   pollination
    B   fertilisation
    C   meiosis
    D   germination

Questions 7 to 9

Human sex chromosomes may be represented as X and Y. The sex chromosomes of parents may be represented as XX or as XY.
7   Which parent's sex chromosomes are represented as XX?
8   What are the possible sex chromosomes of female egg cells?
9   What are the possible sex chromosomes of male sperm?

Questions 10 to 12

The table below shows some external characteristics of two organisms which look very similar.

	Honey bee	Hoverfly
Body	3 segments	3 segments
Legs	3 pairs	3 pairs
Wings	2 pairs	1 pair
Colour	yellow and black stripes	yellow and black stripes
Length	1.5 cm	2 cm
Sting	present	absent

A predator of insects will not eat either of these organisms even though the hoverfly is harmless.
10 Explain the reason for the predator's behaviour.
11 What is the meaning of the term 'genetic mutation'?
12 Explain how genetic mutations in the ancestors of the hoverfly account for the similarities between it and the bee.

13 Mutations in disease-causing bacteria are a serious medical problem. Suggest a reason for this. *(ULEAC)*

Questions 14 to 17

A boy has two rabbits. The male is grey and the female is white. He has allowed them to mate so that he can make some money from selling baby rabbits. *All* the baby rabbits were grey. When the grey baby rabbits had grown, he let two of them mate several times. One quarter of their babies turned out to be white.
14 Which coat colour was dominant?
15 Explain why the first two rabbits (shown in Fig. A) did not have any white babies.
16 Explain why the grey offspring were able to have white babies (see Fig. B).
17 White rabbits are more popular and fetch a higher price than grey rabbits. Suggest how the boy could arrange mating so that only white babies were produced.

(ULEAC, part question)

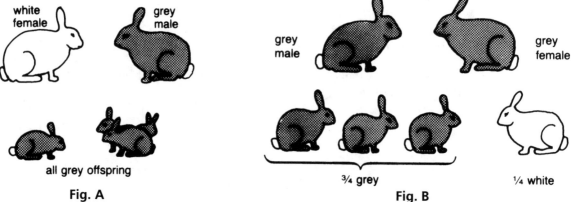

white female   grey male

all grey offspring

Fig. A

grey male   grey female

¾ grey   ¼ white

Fig. B

Questions 18 to 20

Rabbit populations which live in different environments have evolved in different ways. The table below contains some information about four different rabbit populations.

Population	**A**	**B**	**C**	**D**
ear size				
habitat	hot desert	open grassland	evergreen forest	cold desert
main feeding time	night	early morning and late evening	day	day

18 State two reasons why the rabbits in population A have evolved with very large ears.
19 Rabbit populations B and C both live in a temperate climate. The temperature never gets very hot or very cold. Explain why they have evolved with different sized ears.
20 State *one* feature of the rabbits in population D not shown in the table which you would expect to see on animals which live in a cold environment.   *(ULEAC)*

Chapter 10
Our effect on the environment

10.1 Waste and its disposal

Examiner's tip

As you read this chapter, make sure you identify key issues related to the environment and conservation.

Rubbish and waste can be a problem. The biggest problem is getting rid of it so that it does not spoil the environment. Every year we throw away about 30 million tonnes of refuse in the UK.

The most common ways in which we deal with waste are:

- landfill,
- incineration, and
- recycling.

Some waste, such as paper, wool and food, will rot away (decay) if it is left for a time. These materials break down due to the action of bacteria. Because of this, they are described as **biodegradable**.

Other kinds of waste, such as glass and plastics, will not rot away. They remain unchanged because bacteria cannot use them as food. Because of this, they are described as **non–biodegradable**. If we throw these materials away carelessly, they litter our streets and the countryside for years.

The effects of humans can produce local changes in the environment. These changes may have disastrous effects on plants and animals. Many of our disruptive influences on the environment can be related to one or more of the following four factors.

➊ **Agricultural practices**: Throughout the world, vast areas of woodland, marshland and heathland have been cleared in order to grow crops. This has destroyed entire ecosystems. In addition to this, deforestation (clearing of forests) has sometimes resulted in soil erosion and pesticides have been used to kill unwanted plants and animals. Modern mechanised farming has resulted in artificial ecosystems (see 10.2).

➋ **Industrial practices**: Throughout history, men and women have strived for more comfortable lifestyles with more possessions, more tools and more appliances. In order to meet these demands, the number of industries has rapidly increased. These industries have taken over land, turned countryside into concrete and increased our problems with pollution. There is more about the impact of industry on the environment in 14.8 and 17.1.

➌ **Pollution**: Various forms of pollution have damaged communities, habitats and food webs. Smoke from factories has killed lichens and, in the worst-affected areas, whole forests have been stunted by acid rain. Industrial chemicals have been discharged indiscriminately into the air and into rivers and this has damaged animals, plants and habitats (see 10.3).

➍ **The population explosion**: During the last hundred years, improved hygiene, better diets and increased medical care have enabled people to live longer. At the same time, the birth rate has increased because there are more healthy men and women able to reproduce. These factors have resulted in a rapid increase in the world population since 1850 (see 1.9).

In some respects, all of our impact on the Earth is due to the increasing human population. More and more people need more food, more water, more space and more goods. This means that we require more land for agriculture and for industries. At the same time, we take more of the Earth's resources and we create more pollution.

Our effects on ecosystems and on the environment have been appreciated more fully during the last few years. Fortunately, steps are now being taken to conserve ecosystems and protect the environment.

10.2 Agricultural practices

Modern agricultural methods have allowed farmers to produce increasing amounts of food. This has involved:
- ploughing which aerates the soil, improves the drainage and turns organic matter, such as stubble, into the soil to decay;
- breeding better plant and animal species (see 9.5);
- using fertilisers to increase soil fertility (see below and see 17.6);
- using pesticides to remove the pests which attack animals and crops.

Fertilisers and pesticides have been responsible for significant changes in ecosystems. We must now consider these in more detail.

Fertilisers

When plants are grown year after year on the same land, the soil becomes depleted of vital elements. This results in weak and stunted plants. Most farmers get round the problem of soil depletion by using fertilisers. Fertilisers add to the soil those elements removed by crops. Three of the most important elements which are needed to keep the soil fertile are **nitrogen**, **potassium** and **phosphorus**.

There are two types of fertiliser – organic and inorganic.

Organic fertilisers

Organic fertilisers are obtained from plants and animals. They include bone meal, manure and compost. Leguminous crops, such as clover and peas, are sometimes ploughed into the soil as organic fertilisers because they are rich in nitrogen. Farming methods which use only organic fertilisers are described as **organic farming**.

Inorganic fertilisers

Inorganic fertilisers are obtained from non-living (inorganic) materials such as rocks, minerals and nitrogen in the air. Millions of tonnes of inorganic fertilisers are used every year. They include compounds such as ammonium nitrate, ammonium sulphate and potassium nitrate.

The over-use of fertilisers

Look closely at Table 10.1 which compares organic and inorganic fertilisers. Notice the disadvantages of inorganic fertilisers. However, they are widely used because they are easy to spread and their action is rapid.

Inorganic fertilisers disrupt an ecosystem far more than organic fertilisers. They can harm small insects and decomposers in the soil.

The over-use of fertilisers has also caused problems in our rivers and lakes. Fertilisers dissolve in rain water and get washed into streams and rivers. This enrichment of waterways with minerals is called **eutrophication**. Once in the waterways, the fertilisers encourage the growth of bacteria, algae and water plants. These organisms increase rapidly (see 1.8) and deplete oxygen dissolved in the water. Eventually, all the oxygen is

Table 10.1 A comparison of organic and inorganic fertilisers

	Organic fertilisers	Inorganic fertilisers
Examples	manure, compost	ammonium sulphate, potassium nitrate
Cost	cheap	expensive
Ease of use	awkward, bulky and sticky	easy to spread as powder or granules
Speed of action	slow	rapid
Effect on ecosystem	• provide food for decomposers such as fungi, earthworms, ants and bacteria	• may change the soil pH • can harm decomposers and other small insects • allow elements not required by plants to accumulate • may be washed out of the soil into waterways causing eutrophication (see following)

used up. Without oxygen, the bacteria, algae and plants die and decay and the river becomes a stinking sewer.

Despite these problems, we could not manage at present without inorganic fertilisers. Without them we could not grow enough food to feed the ever-increasing world population. The manufacture of fertilisers is considered further in 17.6 and 17.7.

Pesticides

Pests are organisms which compete with humans for food or spread disease. They include weeds, rats, mice and, worst of all, insects like locusts, mosquitoes, aphids and caterpillars. There are three main methods of controlling pests:

❶ **Chemical control**: This involves using a chemical which poisons and kills the pest. The chemical poison is called a **pesticide**. Pesticides include herbicides which control weeds, insecticides such as DDT for locusts and mosquitoes, and poison for rats and mice.

❷ **Biological control**: This involves using a natural enemy (a predator) to control the pest. For example, cats are used to control rats and mice, whilst ladybirds are welcomed by gardeners because they eat aphids.

❸ **Mechanical control**: This involves using machines and labour to remove the pest or to prevent the population of the pest increasing. So, weeds are controlled mechanically by hoeing or ploughing and traps are used to control mice.

10.3 Pollution

Some of the worst damage to our environment is caused by pollution. Most pollution is caused by waste materials and waste energy from our homes, vehicles, industries, farms and other activities. The word pollution normally brings to mind waste materials such as sewage, sulphur dioxide and CFCs (chloroflurocarbons). But, pollution also includes excessive noise (e.g. from aircraft) and waste heat (e.g. from power stations).

One of the most serious effects from waste gases and waste heat is the warming of the Earth (**global warming**). Different experts have estimated that global warming will have increased the temperature of the Earth by between 1 °C and 3 °C by the year 2050.

The worst contributor to the global warming effect is carbon dioxide produced by the burning of fossil fuels. Molecules of carbon dioxide are larger and heavier than the gases in clean air, such as oxygen and nitrogen. Because of this, heat radiation cannot pass through carbon dioxide as easily as it passes through clean air. So, as the concentration of carbon dioxide in the atmosphere slowly rises, less heat escapes from the Earth and the temperature slowly rises. Carbon dioxide traps heat in the Earth like a greenhouse. This has led to the term **greenhouse effect**.

The greenhouse effect and global warming are already having adverse effects:

- **Changes in the climate** have occurred in some areas with higher average temperatures and changes in rainfall.
- **Patterns and areas of food production have changed.** In some parts of East Africa, rainfall has decreased and food crops have failed more frequently than before.
- Global warming has caused an overall melting of the polar ice caps and this has resulted in **rising sea levels with more frequent coastal floods**.

10.4 Air pollution

Air pollution is caused by the release of poisonous or damaging gases into the air. These gases may harm both living things and non-living things (e.g. stonework).

Most air pollution is caused by burning fuels, so the problems are worse in industrial areas. However, pollutant gases may be carried by prevailing winds to affect areas many miles away. For example, scientists now believe that sulphur dioxide from industrial areas in Britain is partly responsible for the acid rain in Sweden.

In the last few years, many people have become increasingly concerned about the use of CFCs (chloroflurocarbons) as refrigerants and aerosol propellants. One of the most widely used CFCs is dichlorodifluromethane, CCl_2F_2. CFCs have even larger and heavier molecules than carbon dioxide. So, they act as 'greenhouse gases' like carbon dioxide and add to global warming.

CFCs also react with and remove ozone in the upper atmosphere. The ozone normally absorbs ultraviolet radiation in sunlight. The removal of ozone allows more ultraviolet radiation to reach the Earth. The extra ultraviolet radiation causes

- damage to plants and
- increased risks of skin cancer.

10.5 The finite Earth – depleting the Earth's resources

Human beings have always wanted easier living and more possessions. In order to create our present lifestyles, we have spoilt large areas of the Earth with mines, quarries, motorways and pylons. Large buildings have turned our cities into concrete jungles and a lot of countryside has been destroyed, some of it forever.

At the same time, we are using up scarce resources such as copper, oil and natural gas. During the last 200 years, society has benefited greatly from improvements in living standards. These improvements have resulted from the use of raw materials from the Earth. But the Earth's resources will not last for ever. Some raw materials, like coal, will last for centuries but others, like oil and natural gas, will only last a few more decades unless we use them more sparingly (Fig. 10.1).

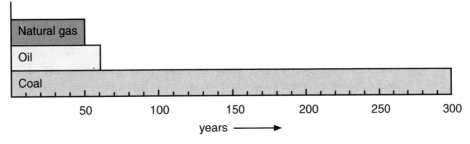

Fig. 10.1 Estimates of how long the Earth's reserves of fossil fuels will last if we continue to use them at present rates. How long will coal last? How long will natural gas last?

Our supplies of metal ores and other minerals are also being depleted. Fig. 10.2 shows the predicted lifetimes of reserves of some metal ores. The estimates refer to the lifetimes of **known reserves**. As these reserves are used up, it is likely that new reserves will be discovered. But this cannot go on forever. *The reserves of the Earth are finite, not limitless.*

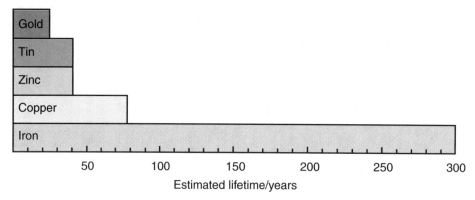

Fig. 10.2 The estimated lifetimes of reserves of some metal ores. Which metal will last longest? Which metal will run out first?

The following steps are already being taken to overcome the problems caused by depletion of resources:

- **Materials are being conserved and used more sparingly**. For example, cars are being designed to use fuel more efficiently. Our homes are better insulated to conserve energy.
- **Chemists are developing new materials** to replace those made from scarce resources. For example, plastic pipes are replacing those made from lead and copper.
- **Materials are being recycled**. These include steel, aluminium, glass and paper.
- **New (renewable) sources of energy are being developed**. These include solar power, wind power, tidal power and hydroelectric power (see Table 18.1).

10.6 Conservation of wildlife and the countryside

In some parts of the world, our effect on the environment has been disastrous. Agricultural practices, industrial pollution and the hunting of animals for 'sport' or fashionable items, like furs and ivory, have destroyed natural habitats and caused the extinction of whole species. The dodo is probably the best known example of an extinct species, but there are thousands of others. These include the Cape lion, the great auk and the passenger pigeon. In addition to these species which have disappeared forever, there are thousands of **endangered species**. These animals and plants are in real danger of extinction. They include pandas, whales and even African elephants.

In some cases, it is already too late to prevent the extinction of certain species and the destruction of large habitats. In other areas, however, important and successful conservation projects and regulations are in operation. They include:

- **Regulations to reduce pollution**: For example, the Clean Air Acts to reduce soot in the atmosphere; laws to reduce the lead in petrol from 0.4 to 0.15 g/dm^3.
- **Restoration of areas damaged by mining and quarrying**: In the Thames Valley, gravel pits have been reclaimed and converted into water sports areas. In parts of South Yorkshire, mining tips have been landscaped and turned into parks and gardens.
- **Careful management of habitats and strict guardianship of nature reserves and national parks**: In some countries, such as Britain and the USA, national parks are well managed. There is little danger to the animals and plants within their boundaries. However, this is not always the case. Rare animals in game parks in Central Africa are still in danger from hunters.
- **Restriction on the number of animals slaughtered for food**: This applies particularly to fish and whales in areas which have been overfished in the past.

Summary

1   Materials which break down due to the action of bacteria are described as **biodegradable**. Waste which cannot rot under the action of bacteria is described as **non-biodegradable**.

2   Many of the disruptive influences on the environment can be related to one or more of four factors:
   ● agricultural practices (particularly the overuse of fertilisers and pesticides),
   ● industrial practices,
   ● pollution, and
   ● the population explosion.

3   Most pollution is caused by waste materials from our homes and industries. One of the most serious pollutants is carbon dioxide produced by the burning of fossil fuels. Carbon dioxide is the major cause of the **greenhouse effect** leading to **global warming**.

4   **Air pollution** is caused mainly by soot, carbon dioxide, carbon monoxide, sulphur dioxide, nitrogen oxides and lead compounds.

5   **Water pollution** is caused mainly by sewage, oil, fertilisers and detergents.

6   **Land pollution** is caused mainly by pesticides, radioactive waste and plastics. Plastics are non-biodegradable.

7   The **reserves** (natural resources) of the Earth are finite. They are *not* limitless. The following steps are being taken to overcome the problems caused by depletion of resources:
   ● Materials are being conserved and used sparingly.
   ● Materials are being recycled.
   ● Chemists are developing alternative materials.
   ● New (renewable) sources of energy are being developed.

Quick test 10

1   Detergents should be biodegradable in order to
   A   reduce the pollution of rivers.
   B   increase their cleaning power.
   C   cause less damage to clothes.
   D   remove fat and oil more quickly.
2   The additives in petrol have changed since 1980. As a result of these changes, our environment will contain less
   A   acid rain.
   B   carbon monoxide.
   C   lead.
   D   radioactivity.
3   Which of the following involves the biological control of ants?
   A   Destroy the ants' nests
   B   Spray the area with insecticide
   C   Introduce birds which eat ants
   D   Keep all food away from the ants

4   A habitat is
    A   a collection of plants and animals.
    B   a place with a given environment.
    C   a study of a particular environment.
    D   a web of animals which depend on each other.
5   Which of the following is a pollutant from fertilisers?
    A   mercury
    B   DDT
    C   lead
    D   nitrate

Questions 6 to 10

Consider the following agricultural practices:
A   crop rotation
B   spreading manure
C   spreading lime
D   scattering artificial fertilisers
E   using pesticides

Which practice
6   quickly increases the nutrient level in the soil?
7   provides food for decomposers?
8   raises the pH level in the soil?
9   acts as a mechanical control of infectious plant diseases?
10 causes the greatest disruption to food webs?

Questions 11 to 15

The graph shows how the numbers of carnivorous birds and field mice, and the mass of growing wheat, varies throughout the year in a particular field.

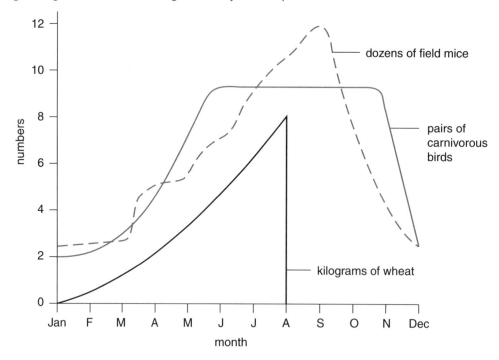

11 Describe how the mass of wheat varies throughout the year.
12 Carefully explain *why* these changes take place.
13 Give *two* possible reasons for the increase in the number of birds from January to May.
14 Explain carefully why the graph line for the number of field mice follows the shape of the wheat line.
15 Suggest a reason why the line for field mice numbers does not rise as smoothly as the line for wheat.
                                                                                    (ULEAC)

Questions 16 to 18

Scrap aluminium can often be used again (recycled). The bar chart shows how much of the aluminium in each 100 tonnes of scrap could be recycled and how much is actually recycled.

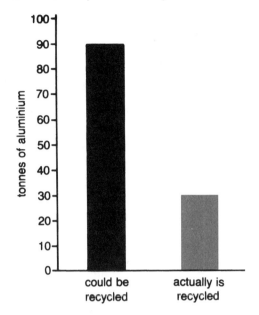

16 How much scrap aluminium is actually recycled?
17 How does the amount of scrap aluminium that *is* recycled compare with the amount that *could* be recycled?
18 Recycled aluminium costs the same as aluminium made from ore. Why then should people bother to recycle the aluminium?

(*NEAB*)

Chapter 11
Earth science

11.1 Origins of the Earth and atmosphere

4600 million years ago the Earth was a mass of molten rock which slowly cooled down over millions of years. During this period, heavier metals sank to the centre of the Earth forming a **core** of dense, partly solid/partly molten iron at about 4000 °C (Fig. 11.1). This core is surrounded by less dense, rocky material in the **mantle** at temperatures between 1500 and 4000 °C. Lighter materials remained on the surface forming a thin **crust** about 50 km thick. The rocks in the Earth's crust consist mainly of silicates and carbonates.

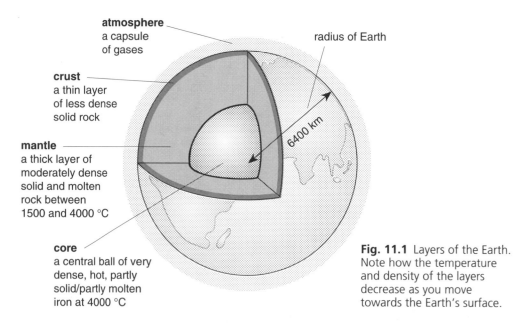

atmosphere a capsule of gases

radius of Earth

crust a thin layer of less dense solid rock

mantle a thick layer of moderately dense solid and molten rock between 1500 and 4000 °C

6400 km

core a central ball of very dense, hot, partly solid/partly molten iron at 4000 °C

Fig. 11.1 Layers of the Earth. Note how the temperature and density of the layers decrease as you move towards the Earth's surface.

Whilst the Earth was still forming, the **atmosphere** above its surface was mainly hydrogen and helium. These gases could escape from the Earth into outer space. As the molten, volcanic surface cooled, other gases were added. These included water vapour, carbon dioxide, methane and nitrogen.

As the temperature dropped still further, water vapour condensed to form rivers, lakes and oceans. When plants appeared, 3500 million years ago, oxygen was formed from water and carbon dioxide by photosynthesis and was also used up during respiration. Flammable gases such as hydrogen and methane burnt in this oxygen, forming more water and carbon dioxide.

In time, animals evolved and used the oxygen for respiration. This further helped to keep a balance between the production and removal of oxygen and carbon dioxide in the atmosphere.

The composition of the atmosphere has remained more or less constant for the last 500 million years. The main constituents are **nitrogen** and **oxygen** (Table 11.1) with smaller amounts of **noble gases** (principally argon), **carbon dioxide** and **water vapour**.

Table 11.1 Gases present in dry air

Nitrogen	78.07%
Oxygen	20.97%
Argon	0.93%
Carbon dioxide	0.03%
Noble gases (helium, neon, krypton and xenon)	Traces

The Earth is the only planet in our solar system with oxygen in its atmosphere and surface water in rivers, lakes and oceans. Other planets, such as Mars, do, however, have some water vapour and polar ice caps.

11.2 Weathering

Look at the photograph in Fig. 11.2. This shows a statue from a church that was built in the 16th century. The statue is about 400 years old. Notice how the stone has been worn away.

The statue in Fig. 11.2 was chiselled from limestone. Limestone reacts very slowly with rain water. Over hundreds of years rain has worn away parts of the statue. This is an example of the **chemical weathering** of rocks.

Fig. 11.2   A mediaeval church statue

Other rocks, like sandstone, granite and quartz, do not react chemically with rain water, but they still get worn away with time. These rocks are broken down and worn away by processes involving expansion and contraction, the freezing of water and moving water. These are examples of the **physical weathering** of rocks. As the temperature changes, rocks expand and contract. This can result in forces which crack and break even the hardest rocks.

When the temperature falls below 0 °C, ice forms. If the ice forms in cracks or crevices, it can break rocks apart because water expands as it freezes.

In mountainous areas, rocks and soil fall down steep slopes into valleys. Fast-moving streams pick up some of this material and carry it along, causing it to break up even further.

The breaking down and wearing away of rocks by temperature changes and by air and water in the environment is called **weathering** or **erosion**.

When the atmosphere is clean, the weathering of rocks takes place very, very slowly. But in polluted air, acid rain causes weathering to occur much more quickly (see 16.1).

Billions of years ago, the Earth's surface was nothing but bare solid rock. Slowly these rocks were broken up (weathered) by rain, wind, waves and frost into smaller particles. Flowing water, wind and ice then carried (**transported**) these smaller fragments of rock away as sediment. Sometimes, dissolved material is also removed by water.

11.3 Rocks in the Earth's crust

When the Earth first cooled, its molten crust solidified to form **igneous rocks**. Over millions of years, two other types of rock were created – **sedimentary rocks** and **metamorphic rocks**. Fig. 11.3 shows how these three types of rock are being formed today.

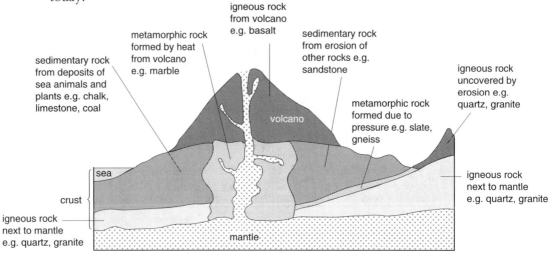

Fig. 11.3 Rocks in the Earth's crust

Igneous rocks

Igneous rocks have been formed by the cooling of molten rock or **magma** in the Earth's mantle. Some igneous rocks are produced when volcanoes erupt and the lava cools quickly in a matter of weeks or years. This produces rocks, such as basalt, with small crystals. Other igneous rocks, such as granite and quartz, are formed deep in the Earth's crust next to the mantle. Here the magma rises, cools very slowly over thousands of years and the rock has much larger crystals.

Sedimentary rocks

When rocks are weathered, they form sediments such as sand and gravel. These sediments may be carried by rivers or ocean currents and deposited elsewhere in layers. This is called **deposition**. As the layers of sediment build up over millions of years, particles get cemented together and the material below is compressed, forming soft rocks such as coal, sandstone and chalk. This compacting and hardening of sediment to form sedimentary rocks is called **consolidation**. If the layers are buried deeper, they get converted to harder rocks like limestone. All these rocks are known as **sedimentary rocks** because they are formed by the buildup of sediment. Some sedimentary rocks, like sandstone, result from the weathering of other rocks by wind and water. Other sedimentary rocks, such as chalk, limestone and coal, have formed from the remains of dead animals and plants.

Metamorphic rocks

Various rocks can be changed into harder rocks by enormous pressures or very high temperatures. The new rock has a different crystal structure from the original rock. It is therefore called 'metamorphic rock' from a Greek word meaning 'change of structure'. Slate and marble are good examples of metamorphic rocks. Slate is formed when clay and mud are subjected to very high pressures. Marble is formed when limestone comes into contact with hot igneous rock.

In some cases, the temperature gets so high that the metamorphic rocks melt to form magma. This may eventually solidify as igneous rock, beginning the **rock cycle** once again (Fig. 11.4).

xaminer's tip

Ensure that you understand the general structure and processes of formation of igneous, sedimentary and metamorphic rocks.

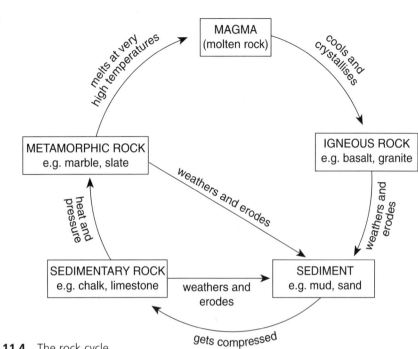

Fig. 11.4 The rock cycle

In the Earth's history, different processes occur on very different **timescales**. Landslides, volcanoes and flash floods operate on *short* timescales of minutes, hours or possibly days. Other processes, such as the cooling of lava and the transport of materials by rivers and glaciers, have *moderate* timescales measured in weeks, years or even decades. Some processes, such as the burial and consolidation of sediment to form sedimentary rocks, the cooling of magma deep below the Earth's surface and the effects of heat and pressure to form metamorphic rocks, are measured in *long* timescales of thousands if not millions of years. These processes operating to different timescales are all part of the rock cycle which has acted continuously since the Earth was formed 4600 million years ago.

11.4 Plate tectonics

The Earth is shaped like an orange and its structure is like a badly cracked egg. The Earth's core can be compared to the 'yolk', the mantle is like the 'egg white' and the crust is the 'cracked shell'. The Earth's crust has cracked into huge sections called **plates** (Fig. 11.5). These vast rigid plates, 100 to 150 km thick in some places, move very slowly due to convection currents in the liquid mantle below the crust.

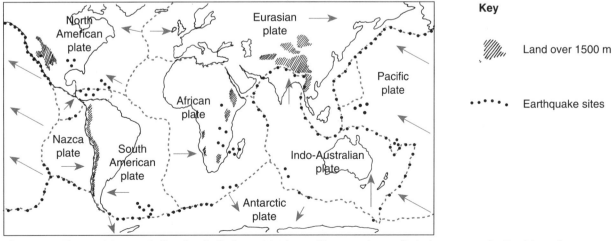

Fig. 11.5 The Earth's crust is like the shell of a cracked egg. Huge sections called plates cover the Earth's surface. Most earthquakes and volcanoes occur near the edges of the plates. Why? Look at the distribution of mountain ranges on the map. Where do the major mountain ranges occur and why are they found in these areas?

When the plates slide past each other, move apart or push towards each other, various things can happen.

- **When two plates slide past each other**, stresses and strains build up in the Earth's crust. This may cause the plates to bend. In some cases, the stresses and strains are released suddenly. The Earth moves and the ground shakes violently in an **earthquake** (Fig. 11.6(a)). During an earthquake, the ground breaks as the Earth moves. These breaks in the ground are called **faults** (Fig. 11.6(b)).

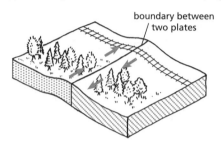 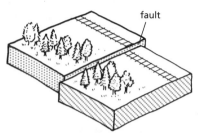

(a) Plates in the Earth's crust are bent as they slide past each other in opposite directions. The earth and rocks are displaced sideways.

(b) Stresses in the bent planes are suddenly released as a break appears in the earth. The ground shakes (an earthquake) and a fault has formed.

Fig. 11.6 How an earthquake occurs

- **When plates move apart**, cracks appear in the Earth's crust. Hot molten rock escapes through the cracks and erupts as a **volcano** in a shower of dust, smoke and burning liquid. As the plates move further apart, surface rocks sink forming vertical **faults**. When two vertical faults occur alongside each other, rift valleys are formed.

  Most of the volcanoes in the world have never been seen. They lie deep under the oceans where plates are moving apart. An important example of this is the submerged ocean ridge along the boundary between the North and South American plates and the Eurasian and African plates (Fig. 11.5). This ridge extends down the centre of the Atlantic Ocean from the Arctic to the Antarctic. It has formed as vast amounts of lava pour out from volcanoes onto the ocean floor.

- **When plates push towards each and collide**, rocks are squeezed together. Along the western edge of South America, the Nazca plate is being pushed against the South American plate (Fig. 11.5). Here the ocean crust in the Nazca plate is being forced beneath the advancing South American plate. This is pushing up the land mass and creating the Andes Mountains.

  The last phase in the tectonic cycle occurs when two land masses collide and the ocean between them disappears. When this happens, layers of the Earth's crust are squeezed into **folds**. Over millions of years, mountains and valleys are formed. This happened when the Indo-Australian plate moved north and collided with the Eurasian plate. The ancient Tethys Ocean disappeared and the Himalayas formed.

  Notice how plate tectonics contributes to the recycling of rocks. As plates move apart, lava pours out onto the Earth's surface forming igneous rock. This igneous rock begins to weather, producing sediment for the formation of sedimentary rocks. When plates collide, the land is pushed upwards forming mountains. These mountains are eroded by wind and water and in a hundred million years they will have gone. Mountain ranges have come and gone several times in the 4600 million years since the Earth began.

11.5 The theory of plate tectonics

The theory of plate tectonics was developed in the 1960s.

- In 1912, the German scientist Alfred Wegener noticed that the east coast of South America could fit neatly into the west coast of Africa.
- He also knew of evidence to suggest that a major ice sheet had once covered most of southern Africa, southern Australia and India.

Wegener suggested that all the continents once formed part of a supercontinent which he called **Pangaea**, from a Greek word meaning 'all the earth' (Fig. 11.7). About 200 million years ago, part of Pangaea lay near the South Pole. Since then, the continents have been drifting apart. Wegener used the term 'Continental Drift' for this and suggested that the continents were giant blocks or plates floating and moving on the liquid mantle below the Earth's crust. This led to the theory of plate tectonics.

The occurrence and explanation of volcanoes, earthquakes, faults and folds supports the theory. The latest evidence to support the theory has been obtained from lasers mounted on satellites. These lasers have been able to measure changes of as little as 2 or 3 cm per year in the movement of continents, the width of oceans and the height of mountains.

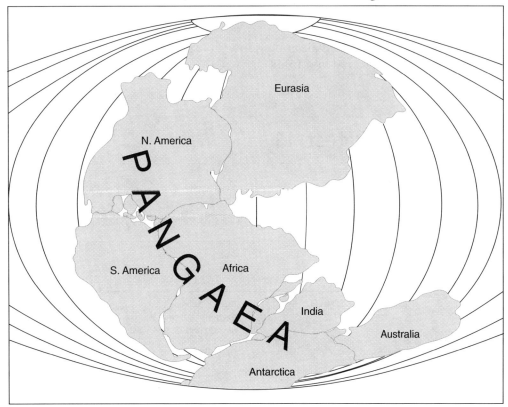

Fig. 11.7   Pangaea – the Earth 200 million years ago

Summary

1 The Earth has a dense **core** of molten iron at 4000 °C. This is surrounded by less dense, rocky material in the **mantle** at temperatures between 1500 and 4000 °C. Lighter materials form a thin surface **crust** about 50 km thick.

2 The main constituents of the Earth's atmosphere are nitrogen and oxygen, 78% and 21% of dry air, respectively.

3 The cycle of water from the Earth's surface into the clouds and back to the Earth as rain or snow is called the **water cycle**.

4 The breaking down and wearing away of rocks by air and water in the environment is called **weathering** or **erosion**.

5 The movement of sediment from one location to another by flowing water, wind and ice is called **transport**.

6 **Igneous rocks** have formed from the solidification of molten rock or magma in the Earth's mantle.

7 **Sedimentary rocks** have formed from sediments as a result of the pressure of overlying materials.

8 **Metamorphic rocks** have formed from sedimentary rocks by the action of enormous pressure or very high temperatures.

9 The Earth's crust has cracked into huge sections called **plates**.

10 **Earthquakes** occur when two plates slide past each other, bend and then suddenly move into new positions. This produces breaks in the ground called **faults**.

11 **Volcanoes** occur when the plates move apart and cracks appear in the Earth's crust. Hot molten rocks can then escape through the cracks.

12 When two plates push towards each other, layers in the Earth's crust are squeezed into **folds**.

Quick test 11

Questions 1 to 9

Some facts about four planets in a different solar system are given in the table below.

Planet	Temperature range/°C	Atmosphere	Surface conditions	Mass compared with Earth (Earth = 1)
Helios	0 to 50	Nitrogen, oxygen, carbon dioxide and cloud	Water and sandy soil	1.4
Rheagos	−25 to −10	Hydrogen and carbon dioxide, no cloud	Very hard rock with some powdered material	4.6
Solos	−10 to 12	Carbon dioxide and a lot of cloud	Swampland and water	3.2
Carmel	−45 to 40	None	Very hard rock	0.9

1 Which planet is most likely to support plant and animal life as we know it?
2 Give *three* reasons for your answer in question 1.
3 Which planet has the greatest temperature variations?
4 Why do you think Solos has a lot of cloud in its atmosphere?
5 Which of the planets is nearest the Sun?
6 Give a reason for your answer to question 5.
7 On which planet would a whistle be useless?
8 Give *one* reason for your answer to question 7.
9 Explain why the atmosphere on Solos would be particularly useful in a greenhouse.
(*WJEC*)

Questions 10 to 16

Consider the following rocks
A   Granite
B   Limestone
C   Slate
D   Coal
E   Sandstone

Which of these rocks
10   can easily be split into thin sheets?
11   is probably the oldest rock?

12 fizzes with acid?
13 is most likely to contain the fossil of a plant?
14 is a metamorphic rock?
15 reacts slowly with rain water?
16 forms a high proportion of the rocks in the Pennines?

Questions 17 to 20

The diagram shows a volcano. In which of the regions J, K, L or M would you find

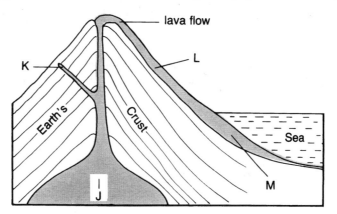

17 the largest rock crystals?
18 medium-sized rock crystals?
19 very small rock crystals?
20 glass-like material?

Chapter 12
Materials, elements and compounds

12.1 Raw materials

Look around you. Consider the variety of different materials such as wood, glass, water, air, rocks, sand, paper and steel.

These different and distinct materials are called **substances**. Some substances, such as air, sand, water, rocks and wood, occur naturally in the world around us. These *naturally occurring* substances are the **raw materials** which we use to make more useful substances, like paper, glass and steel. In fact, most of the materials that we use have been manufactured from raw materials. Manufacture involves turning raw materials into valuable and useful products by chemical reactions. Table 12.1 shows some important sources of raw materials and the substances we obtain from them.

Table 12.1 Important sources of raw materials and the substances we obtain from them

Source of raw material	Substances obtained from the raw material
Plants	foods (eg. sugar, flour, cooking oil), timber, dyes, rubber, cotton
The air	oxygen, nitrogen, argon
Coal	coke, plastics, detergents, paints, explosives, perfumes
Crude oil	petrol, diesel oil, waxes, polishes, lubricants, road tar, plastics
The sea	salt (sodium chloride), magnesium, bromine
Rocks	sand, bricks, glass, metals (eg. iron, aluminium, copper), lime

Rocks, minerals, the sea and the atmosphere provide a vast source of raw materials for the chemical and manufacturing industries.

12.2 Classifying materials by their properties

Materials can be classified in various ways. One way is to classify them as **naturally occurring materials** and **man-made materials**.

Naturally occurring (raw) materials are the materials available in the natural world such as rocks, clays, limestone and wood. Man-made materials are the materials we have made or manufactured. These include metals, plastics, fertilisers and glass.

Another way to classify materials is by their properties. When we classify materials in this way most of them fall into five major groups – metals, plastics, ceramics (pottery), glasses and fibres. Table 12.2 shows the typical properties of these five classes of materials.

Table 12.2 Classifying materials as metals, plastics, ceramics, glasses and fibres

Class of material	Examples	Typical properties	Raw materials from which they are made
Metals	Iron, aluminium, copper, steel	• Hard • Strong • High density (> 5 g/cm³) • Good conductors • Malleable (can be hammered and bent into different shapes) • Burn on heating	Rocks and ores in the Earth's crust
Plastics	Polythene, PVC, polystyrene	• Flexible • Low density (1 g/cm³) • Easily moulded and coloured • Poor conductors • Can be transparent • Melt and may burn on heating	Crude oil
Ceramics (pottery)	China, concrete, bricks, tiles	• Hard • Brittle • Medium density • Very high melting point • Very unreactive – do not burn	Clay, sand and other minerals
Glasses	Bottle glass, crystal glass	• The same as ceramics • Also transparent	Sand, limestone and other minerals
Fibres	Cotton, wool, paper, wood	• Flexible • Low density (1 g/cm³) • May burn on heating • Have long, stringy strands	Natural fibres from plants and animals Man-made fibres from crude oil

Choosing materials

In choosing materials for different jobs, we have to make sure they have suitable properties.

- **Physical properties** include hardness, strength, melting point, conductivity and density.
- **Chemical properties** relate to such questions as 'Does it burn?', 'Does it corrode?' and 'Does it react with water?'.
- The **cost** of raw materials and the cost of manufacture are also important in choosing materials for different jobs.

Sometimes we need to use materials that combine the properties of two different materials. For example, during the 1980s extra strong golf clubs and tennis rackets were made using carbon fibre-reinforced plastic. This material contains plastic reinforced by carbon (graphite) fibres. The shafts of these golf clubs have the flexibility of plastic and the strength of carbon fibres. Fibre-reinforced plastic is an example of a **composite material**. Composites are made of two or more different materials which produce a more suitable material for the job than either of the materials separately (Fig. 12.1).

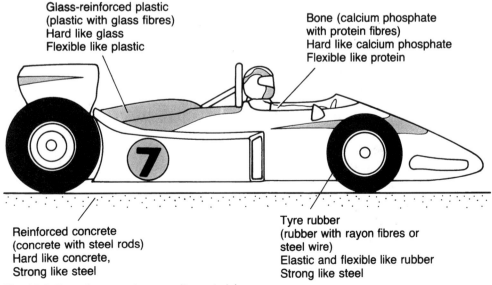

Glass-reinforced plastic
(plastic with glass fibres)
Hard like glass
Flexible like plastic

Bone (calcium phosphate
with protein fibres)
Hard like calcium phosphate
Flexible like protein

Reinforced concrete
(concrete with steel rods)
Hard like concrete,
Strong like steel

Tyre rubber
(rubber with rayon fibres or
steel wire)
Elastic and flexible like rubber
Strong like steel

Fig. 12.1 Some important composite materials

12.3 Separating mixtures

Most materials which occur naturally are mixtures. Very often these mixtures have to be separated before we can use the materials in them. Just think what might happen if we used gritting salt for cooking or crude oil in place of petrol in a car.

(i) Separating insoluble solids from liquids

It is usually easy to separate an insoluble solid from a liquid. There are three possible methods:

1 Decanting (pouring off the liquid) This method is often used when the solid is in large pieces – for example, separating peas, potatoes or other vegetables from the water in which they have been cooked.

2 Filtering This method is used when the particles of solid are small. It is used in making filter coffee (Fig. 12.2) and in separating fine particles from drinking water.

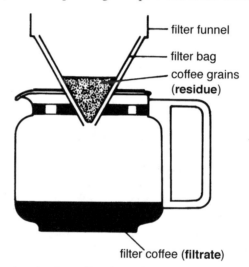

filter funnel

filter bag

coffee grains
(**residue**)

filter coffee (**filtrate**)

Fig. 12.2 How does the filter bag let the coffee through?

3 Centrifuging This method is used when the particles are so small that they float in the liquid and form a cloudy **suspension**. The suspension is spun around very quickly in a machine called a centrifuge. This forces the denser, solid particles to the end of the container. The liquid can then be poured off (decanted) easily. Centrifuging is used to separate blood cells from blood plasma and cream from milk.

(ii) Separating solutions

Tap water is clean but *not* pure. It contains dissolved gases such as oxygen and probably dissolved solids which make the water 'hard'. Tap water is, of course, a **solution**. Sea water is another example of a solution. It contains salt (the **solute**) dissolved in water (the **solvent**). You cannot see the salt in sea water, but it is there – you can taste it.

More salt will dissolve in warm water than in cold water. For most solids, the amount which dissolves increases with temperature. The amount of a solute which dissolves in 100 g of a solvent at a given temperature is known as the **solubility** of the solute. The solubility of salt in water at 15 °C is 36 g per 100 g of water, whereas its solubility at 100 °C is 40 g per 100 g of water.

Solutes also have different solubilities in different solvents. For example, salt is very soluble in water, but is almost insoluble in white spirit (paint thinner). On the other hand, oil is almost insoluble in water, but is very soluble in white spirit.

Evaporation When sea water is left to dry in the sun, the water turns into a vapour (*evaporates*). Salt is left behind as a white solid. The *change of a liquid into a gas or a vapour* is called **evaporation**.

Evaporation can be used to separate a dissolved solid from its solvent. If the solvent evaporates slowly, the dissolved solid is often left behind as evenly shaped *crystals*. This process of forming crystals by evaporation of the solvent from a solution is called **crystallisation** (see Fig. 12.3).

Evaporation is an essential process in
- obtaining salt from sea water in hot countries;
- drying wet clothes;
- producing concentrated evaporated milk;
- obtaining sugar from sugar cane and sugar beets.

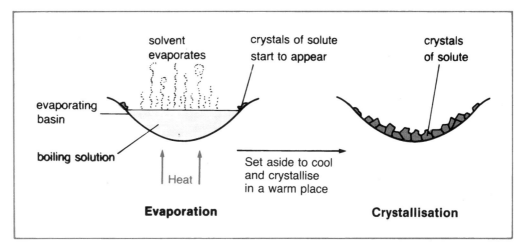

Fig. 12.3 Evaporation and crystallisation

Distillation When sea water is heated, water vapour escapes into the air. If the water vapour is passed into a second container and cooled, it will turn back to water. This process in which a *vapour changes to a liquid* is called **condensation**.

Fig. 12.4 shows how pure water can be obtained from sea water by evaporating the water and then condensing the water vapour. This process of *evaporating a liquid and condensing the vapour* is called **distillation**.

distillation = evaporation + condensation

When sea water is heated in apparatus like that shown in Fig. 12.4, water vapour passes into the inner tube of the condenser. This is cooled by cold water in the outer jacket. The water vapour condenses and drips from the lower end of the condenser into the conical flask. The liquid which collects after distillation is called a **distillate**.

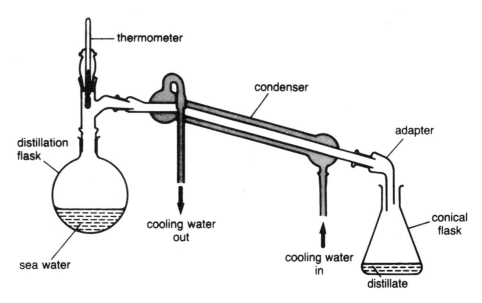

Fig. 12.4 Obtaining pure water from sea water by distillation

Distillation is an essential process in
- making 'spirits', such as whisky, gin and vodka, from weaker alcoholic liquids;
- obtaining pure water from sea water in parts of the Middle East where fuel is cheap.

(iii) Separating liquids

If oil is added to water, the two liquids do not mix. Liquids, such as oil and water, which do not mix are described as **immiscible**. These liquids can be separated by decantation or by using a separating funnel.

If oil is added to petrol, the two liquids mix easily. These liquids are described as **miscible**. Miscible liquids cannot be separated using a separating funnel, but they can be separated by **fractional distillation**. When the mixture is heated, different liquids boil off at different temperatures as each one reaches its boiling point. As the different liquids boil off, they can be condensed separately.

Fractional distillation is an essential process in:
- separating the different constituents in crude oil (see 18.6);
- separating oxygen and nitrogen from liquid air (see 12.9).

12.4 Chromatography

Chromatography is another important technique which can be used to separate mixtures. It is used to separate substances which are very similar, for example dyes in ink, natural colours in foods and drugs in blood and urine.

Fig. 12.5 shows how the dyes in inks can be separated by chromatography. As the solvent soaks up the paper, the dyes separate. Some dyes stick to the paper, while other dyes tend to dissolve in the solvent. The dyes which dissolve in the solvent travel further up the paper.

This method was first used to separate coloured substances. The process was therefore called **chromatography** from the Greek word *khroma* meaning colour. The paper with the substances separated out is called a **chromatogram**. Nowadays, chromatography is also used with colourless substances. When colourless substances are used, the paper is sprayed with chemicals which make the colourless substances show up. These chemicals, called locating agents, react with the colourless substances to form coloured substances.

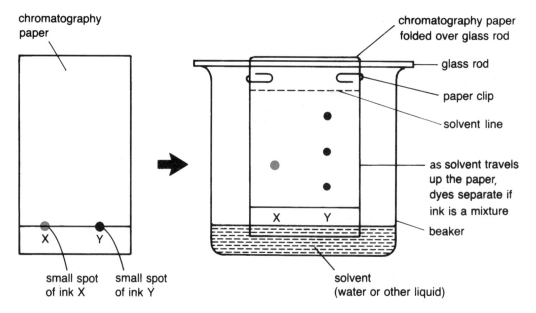

Fig. 12.5 Separating the dyes in inks by chromatography.
How many dyes are there in each of inks X and Y?

12.5 Testing for pure substances

Supermarkets often sell cartons of 'Pure Orange Juice'. This means that the carton contains only the juice of oranges. No colouring or flavouring has been added. However, a scientist would *not* describe the orange juice as pure. To a scientist, **something is pure if it contains only one substance**. Orange juice contains water, sugar, citric acid and other substances. So, it is a mixture.

If a substance is pure, it is all the same. All of it behaves in the same way. When a pure solid is heated, it all melts at the same temperature. When a pure liquid is heated, it all boils at the same temperature. The melting points and boiling points of most pure substances have been measured accurately. If a substance contains an impurity, its melting point and boiling point will be different from those of the pure substance. So, the most useful method of testing whether a substance is pure is to check its melting point or its boiling point.

12.6 Elements – building blocks for all substances

Although there are millions of different substances, they can be sorted into just three groups – *elements*, *mixtures* and *compounds*.

> An element is a substance which cannot be broken down into a simpler substance.

Elements are the building blocks for other substances. They are the simplest possible materials. So far we know of 106 elements. These include iron, aluminium, copper, gold, oxygen, nitrogen and carbon. Every substance in the universe is made of one or more of these 106 elements. For example, glass is made of calcium, silicon and oxygen; wood is made of carbon, hydrogen and oxygen.

Classifying elements as metals and non–metals

Elements can be sorted into groups with similar properties. The simplest way of sorting elements is into two groups – metals and non–metals. The main differences between the properties of metals such as iron and copper and those of non–metals such as oxygen and chlorine are summarised in Table 12.3.

Table 12.3 Comparison of the properties of metals and non-metals

Property	Metals e.g. aluminium, iron, copper, gold	Non-metals e.g. oxygen, nitrogen, chlorine, sulphur
State	usually shiny solids at room temperature	mostly gases at room temperature
Melting point and boiling point	usually high	usually low
Density	usually high	usually low
Effect of hammering	malleable – can be hammered into shapes	solids are brittle or soft
Conduction of heat and electricity	good	poor (except graphite which conducts well)

12.7 Elements and compounds

When aluminium window frames are new they are shiny. Gradually, the frames go dull as a layer of white aluminium oxide forms on the surface. The aluminium has **reacted** or **combined** with oxygen in the air to form aluminium oxide. The aluminium oxide is a completely new substance. Changes such as this, which result in new substances, are called **chemical reactions**. The new substance is called the **product** of the reaction. Virtually all substances, including those in living systems, are made through chemical reactions.

We can summarise the reaction which takes place when aluminium goes dull by writing a **word equation**:

aluminium + oxygen → aluminium oxide

Aluminium and oxygen are elements. They have combined to form a **compound** called aluminium oxide.

A compound is a substance which contains two or more elements combined.

The product of the reaction, aluminium oxide, has very different properties from the starting elements (Table 12.4).

Table 12.4 Comparison of the properties of aluminium, oxygen and aluminium oxide

Elements		Compound
aluminium + oxygen ⟶		aluminium oxide
shiny metal	colourless gas	white solid
fairly reactive	very reactive	very unreactive

When two elements react together to form a compound, the name of the compound ends in **-ide**. For example,

aluminium + oxygen → aluminium ox**ide**

hydrogen + chlorine → hydrogen chlor**ide**

When a metal reacts with a non-metal, the non-metal forms the –ide part of the name of the compound. When two non-metals react, the more reactive non-metal forms the –ide part of the name.

When elements combine to form compounds the reaction is an example of **synthesis**. Photosynthesis is another example of synthesis.

Unlike elements, compounds can be split into simpler substances. For example, aluminium oxide can be split into aluminium and oxygen. This occurs when electricity is passed through molten aluminium oxide. When compounds are split into simpler substances, the reaction is an example of **decomposition**.

Synthesis is the building up of more complex substances by joining together simpler substances.

Decomposition is the breaking down of more complex substances into simpler substances.

Notice that decomposition is the *reverse* of synthesis.

$$\text{aluminium + oxygen} \underset{\textit{decomposition}}{\overset{\textit{synthesis}}{\longrightarrow}} \text{aluminium oxide}$$

When chemical reactions occur and when physical changes take place, it is important to remember that mass is conserved. This point is summarised in the **Law of the Conservation of Mass**. This says:

In any physical or chemical change, the total mass of the products equals the total mass of the reactants.

12.8 Mixtures

Most materials are mixtures. They may be *mixtures of elements*, like air which is mainly nitrogen and oxygen, or *mixtures of compounds*, like sea water which contains water and salt (sodium chloride). The important point about mixtures is that the different substances in them are not combined. This is different from compounds in which elements are combined. The differences between compounds and mixtures are summarised in Table 12.5.

Table 12.5 The differences between compounds and mixtures

Compounds	Mixtures
1 A new substance is produced when the compound forms	1 No new substance is produced when the mixture forms
2 Contain one substance	2 Contain two or more substances
3 Properties are different from the elements in them	3 Properties are similar to the substances in them
4 The elements in them can only be separated by a chemical reaction	4 The substances can often be separated easily
5 The percentages of elements in the compound are constant, i.e. a compound has a definite composition represented by a formula	5 The percentages of substances in the mixture can vary, i.e. a mixture can have a variable composition

Examiner's tip

Note the differences between
• metals and non-metals (Table 12.3)
• elements and compounds (12.7)
• compounds and mixtures (Table 12.5)

12.9 Air – an important mixture

Air is an important raw material. It is used to manufacture oxygen, nitrogen and noble gases for industrial processes. These gases are separated by liquefying air, then fractionally distilling the liquid air. As the liquid air warms, the different constituents boil off at different temperatures (see Fig. 12.6).

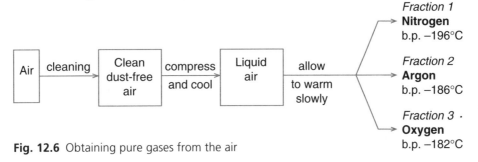

Fig. 12.6 Obtaining pure gases from the air

The main products from air are nitrogen, argon and oxygen. The important uses of these gases are summarised in Table 12.6.

Table 12.6 The important uses of nitrogen, argon and oxygen

Nitrogen	• Manufacture of ammonia, nitric acid and fertilisers (see 17.5 and 17.6) • Used as a cheap unreactive gas 'blanket' to stop materials reacting with oxygen (e.g. in petrol storage tanks)
Oxygen	• Manufacture of steel (see 14.5 and 14.8) • Welding and cutting – oxyacetylene flames are hot enough to melt metals • Breathing apparatus, e.g. for fire fighting, deep-sea diving, mountaineering and in hospitals
Argon	• Used as an unreactive gas to stop materials reacting with air, e.g. in electric light bulbs where the very hot filaments would react with the nitrogen in air

12.10 Reactions with oxygen

Oxygen is the most reactive gas in the air. When substances burn in air they react with oxygen forming oxides, e.g.

magnesium + oxygen → magnesium oxide

When a substance combines with oxygen, we say it is **oxidised**. The process is described as **oxidation**. Burning (see 18.1), breathing (see 6.2 and 6.5) and rusting (see 14.6) are important oxidation processes.

The test for oxygen relies on the fact that oxygen is so reactive.

When a glowing splint is inserted into oxygen, it bursts into flame. Why do you think this happens?

Most elements combine with oxygen. Some elements even react slowly with oxygen at room temperature. For example, things made of iron are slowly covered with rust (iron oxide) when exposed to moist air. Similarly, shiny aluminium articles become covered with a layer of white aluminium oxide as the aluminium reacts with oxygen in air. Table 12.7 compares the properties of metal oxides and non-metal oxides.

Table 12.7 Comparison of metal oxides and non-metal oxides

	Type of oxide	Properties
Metal oxides e.g. sodium oxide, zinc oxide	**Solids** **Basic oxides**	Oxides of reactive metals (K, Na, Ca, Mg) react with water to form alkaline solutions (pH > 7). These are called **alkaline oxides**. Oxides of less reactive metals are insoluble in water
Non-metal oxides e.g. sulphur dioxide, carbon dioxide	**Gases** **Acidic oxides**	React with water to produce acid solutions (pH < 7) e.g. sulphur dioxide + water → sulphurous acid; carbon dioxide + water → carbonic acid (Water is an unusual non-metal oxide being neutral and liquid)

Summary

1   Different and distinct materials are called **substances**.

2   Materials can be classified as **naturally occurring materials** and **man–made materials**.

3   Materials can also be classified by their properties into five major groups – metals, plastics, ceramics (pottery), glasses and fibres.

4   **Composite materials** are made of two or more different materials.

5   A **solution** is a mixture of a dissolved substance and a liquid. The dissolved substance is the **solute**. The liquid in which the solute is dissolved is the **solvent**.

6   Insoluble solids can be separated from liquids by three possible methods – decanting, filtering or centrifuging.

7   Solutions of solids in liquids can be separated by processes involving evaporation, distillation and crystallisation. Distillation involves evaporating a liquid and then condensing the vapour.

8   Miscible (mixable) liquids can be separated by fractional distillation.

9   The most useful way to test whether a substance is pure is to check its melting point or its boiling point.

10   An **element** is a substance which cannot be broken down into a simpler substance. There are two major groups of elements – metals and non-metals.

11   A **compound** is a substance which contains two or more elements combined.

12   Chemical reactions can be summarised using **word equations**.

13   Air is a mixture of substances. Fresh air contains (by volume) about 80% nitrogen and 20% oxygen with small amounts of argon, water vapour and carbon dioxide.

14   When a substance combines with oxygen, we say it is **oxidised**. The product is an **oxide** and the process is described as **oxidation**.

Quick test 12

Questions 1 to 4

The dyes in two food colourings, X and Y, were analysed using chromatography. Five pure dyes (labelled A to E) were tested at the same time. The final chromatogram is shown below

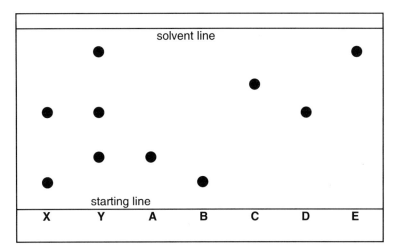

1   Which pure dye is present in both X and Y?
2   How many different dyes are present in X?
3   Which pure dye is not present in X or Y?
4   Which dyes could be mixed to make X?

Questions 5 to 9

A   a pure element
B   a pure compound
C   a mixture of elements
D   a mixture of compounds
E   a mixture of elements and compounds

Choose from A to E, the best description for
5   water
6   steel
7   copper
8   air
9   petrol

Questions 10 to 14

A   chromatography
B   condensation
C   crystallisation
D   distillation
E   filtration

Choose from A to E, the process that occurs when
10   solid sugar is obtained from its solution.
11   tea leaves are separated from tea.
12   sugar is detected in urine.
13   petrol is obtained from crude oil.
14   water vapour turns to water.

Questions 15 to 19

A   calcium   B   copper   C   sulphur   D   iron   E   hydrogen

Choose from the elements labelled A to E, the element or elements that
15   produce acidic oxides.
16   produce alkaline oxides.
17   produce neutral oxides.
18   form solid oxides at room temperature.
19   form oxides which are insoluble in water.

Questions 20 to 21

A word equation for respiration is

food + oxygen → carbon dioxide + water + energy

20   What are the reactants in this process?
21   What are the products in this process?

Chapter 13
Particles

13.1 Introduction

Think about the following questions:
- How does the coffee get through the filter paper when filter coffee is made? Why do the coffee grains stay in the filter paper?
- Why does it require only a tiny amount of curry powder to flavour a large meal?

In order to answer these questions you need to use the idea that **all substances are made up of tiny particles**.

13.2 Evidence for moving particles

The best evidence that particles of matter are constantly moving comes from studies of **diffusion** and **Brownian motion**.

Diffusion

Most people like the smell of fish and chips. How does the smell get from the fish and chips to your nose?

Particles of gas are released from the fish and chips. These particles mix with air particles and move away from the fish and chips. This *movement and mixing of particles* is called **diffusion**. Gases diffuse to fill all the space available to them – even heavy gases like bromine will behave in this way (Fig. 13.1).

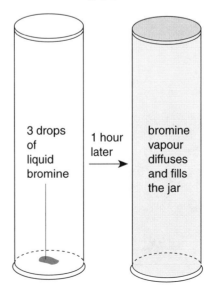

3 drops of liquid bromine

1 hour later

bromine vapour diffuses and fills the jar

Fig. 13.1 Diffusion of bromine vapour in air. How does the bromine vapour get to the top of the jar?

Gases consist of tiny particles, moving around haphazardly. These particles collide with each other and with the walls of their container. The gas particles don't care where they go. Sooner or later, they will spread into all the space available.

Diffusion also occurs in liquids, although it takes place more slowly than in gases. This indicates that liquid particles move around more slowly than gas particles.

Solids do *not* diffuse through other solids, but gases and liquids can diffuse through some solids. For example, dyes can diffuse into fabrics and nutrients (in solution) can diffuse through membranes in living organisms (see 2.3).

Diffusion is very important in living things. It helps to explain how the food you eat gets to different parts of your body.

Brownian motion

In 1827 a biologist called Robert Brown was using a microscope to look at pollen grains in water. To his annoyance, the pollen grains kept moving about randomly. Similar random movements can be seen when you look at smoke particles through a microscope (Fig. 13.2). This *movement of tiny particles in a gas or liquid*, first noticed by Brown, is now called **Brownian motion**.

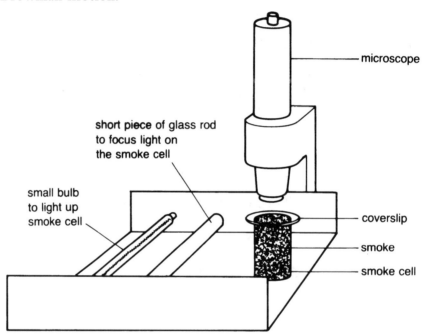

Fig. 13.2 Observing the movement of smoke particles. Smoke from smouldering string is injected into the smoke cell. Through the microscope, the smoke particles look like tiny pinpoints of light which jitter about.

The movement of the smoke particles in Fig. 13.2 is caused by the random motion of air particles around them. The particles of smoke are small, but they are much larger than air particles. We can see individual smoke particles through the microscope. The air particles are much too small to be seen. The air particles move very rapidly and hit the smoke particles at random. The smoke particles are therefore knocked first this way, then that way, so they appear to jitter about.

13.3 Particles in motion – the kinetic theory

The idea that *everything is made of moving particles* is called the **kinetic theory of matter**. The word *kinetic* comes from a Greek word which means 'moving'.

The main points of the kinetic theory are:

1. All matter is made of particles. There are particles in all materials – glass, wood, paper, water, concrete, petrol, grass, air, etc.
2. The individual particles are very, very small. We cannot see them.

❸ The particles of different substances have different sizes. Particles of elements, such as aluminium, iron and oxygen, are very small. Particles of compounds like sugar are larger. Particles of some complex compounds, such as rubber and proteins, are thousands of times larger.

❹ The particles in all substances are continually moving. Small particles move faster than heavier particles at the same temperature.

❺ As the temperature rises, the particles get hotter. They have more energy and move around faster.

❻ **In a solid**, the particles are very close with strong forces between them. This explains why solids are more dense than liquids and gases and why they cannot be compressed. Solid particles can only vibrate about fixed positions (Fig. 13.3(a)). This explains why solids cannot flow and why they have a fixed shape and a fixed volume.

❼ **In a liquid**, the particles are a little further apart. The forces between the particles are not as strong. This explains why liquids are not usually as dense as solids and why they can be compressed slightly. Liquid particles can move around each other (Fig. 13.3(b)). Liquids can flow and can change their shape, but they keep a fixed volume.

❽ **In a gas**, the particles are much further apart. This explains why the densities of gases are so low and why they can be compressed so much. There are no forces to hold the particles together. The particles rush around in all directions in all the space that they can find (Fig. 13.3(c)). Gases flow easily and change their shape and their volume depending on their container.

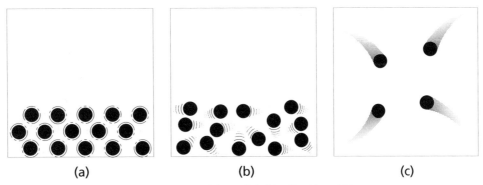

Fig. 13.3 The movement of particles in (a) a solid, (b) a liquid and (c) a gas

13.4 Changes of state

All materials can be classified as either **solid** or **liquid** or **gas** – concrete and ice are solids, petrol and water are liquids, air and steam are gases. *Solid*, *liquid* and *gas* are called the **states of matter**.

Different materials change state at different temperatures. The kinetic theory can be used to explain what happens when a substance changes from one state to another, for example, when ice (solid) melts to become water (liquid). A summary of the different changes of state is shown in Fig. 13.4. These changes are usually caused by heating or cooling. Notice that when a solid changes directly to a gas it is **subliming**. Ice sublimes when it disappears into the air without forming water first.

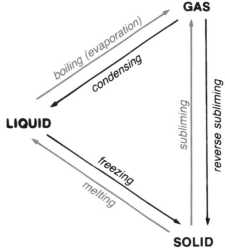

Fig. 13.4 The different changes of state

Melting and freezing

When a solid is heated, the particles gain energy and they vibrate more and more rapidly. Eventually they break free from their fixed positions and begin to move around each other. When this happens the solid melts to form a liquid. The liquid particles have more energy than they had as a solid. The temperature at which the solid melts is called the **melting point**.

The melting point of a solid tells us how strongly its particles are held together. Substances with high melting points have strong forces between their particles. Substances with low melting points have weak forces between their particles. Metals and alloys, such as iron and steel, have very high melting points. This suggests that there are strong forces between their particles. This is why metals can be used for girders, supports and cables.

When a liquid is cooled, the particles move around each other more and more slowly. Eventually, the particles are moving so slowly that they only vibrate about a point. When this happens the liquid has **frozen** to form a solid.

Evaporating, boiling and condensing

When a liquid is heated, the particles move around each other more and more quickly. Some particles near the surface of the liquid gain enough energy to escape from the liquid into the air. When this happens, the liquid **evaporates** to form a gas. The gas particles have much more energy than they had as a liquid.

As the temperature rises, more and more particles escape from the liquid and evaporate. Eventually, particles are moving so rapidly that bubbles of gas start to form inside the liquid. The temperature at which this evaporation *occurs in the middle of the liquid* is the **boiling point**. Liquids which evaporate and boil at low temperatures are described as **volatile**.

Boiling points tell us how strongly the particles are held together in liquids. Liquids with high boiling points have stronger forces between their particles than liquids with low boiling points.

When a gas is cooled, the particles move around more slowly. As the temperature falls, the particles move more and more slowly. Eventually the particles do not have enough energy to bounce off each other as they collide. The particles cling together as a liquid. **Condensation** has occurred.

13.5 Gas pressure

Gas pressure helps us to inflate balloons and tyres (Fig. 13.5). Gas pressure from the air dictates our weather. When atmospheric pressure is high, clouds are driven away and the weather is fine and dry. When atmospheric pressure is low, the weather is often cloudy and rainy.

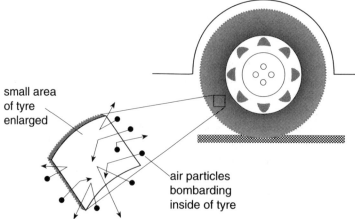

small area
of tyre
enlarged

air particles
bombarding
inside of tyre

Fig. 13.5 Millions of air particles bombard the inside of the tyre every second. This causes the pressure inside. The tyre is also bombarded by air particles on the outside, but the pressure inside is greater than the pressure outside. The extra pressure inside the tyre keeps it inflated.

Pressure and volume

Fig. 13.6 shows what happens to the particles in a gas if you hold your finger over the end of a bicycle pump and push in the handle. The air has been pushed into half the volume. This means that the particles bombard the sides of the pump and your finger twice as often. So the pressure doubles and you feel the increased pressure on your finger.

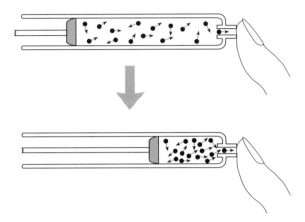

Fig. 13.6

This simple experiment shows that when the volume decreases, the pressure increases by the same proportion. This is an inverse (upside-down) relationship. We can say that:
The pressure of a fixed mass of gas is inversely proportional to its volume if the temperature stays constant.

i.e. $p \propto \dfrac{1}{V}$ or $p = \dfrac{\text{constant}}{V}$

$\therefore \ pV = \text{constant}$

This relationship between p and V was first discovered by Robert Boyle in 1662. It is usually called **Boyle's law**.

Consider the following example: 20 m³ of butane at atmospheric pressure (100 kPa) are forced into a metal container of volume 2.5 m³. What is the final pressure of the butane inside the container?

Using Boyle's law:

$$pV = \text{constant}$$

Initial pressure, p_1 = 100 kPa
Initial volume, V_1 = 20 m³
Final pressure = p_2
Final volume, V_2 = 2.5 m³

Now if pV is constant, $p_1V_1 = p_2V_2$
$\therefore \ 100 \times 20 = p_2 \times 2.5$

$\Rightarrow p_2$, final pressure = 800 kPa

13.6 Temperature scales

Scientists have discovered that the lowest possible temperature that we could ever get to is −273 °C. This temperature is usually called **absolute zero**.

Sometimes, it is helpful to have a temperature scale whose zero is absolute zero. This is called the **absolute temperature scale** or the **Kelvin scale**. On this scale, the units are kelvin (K). So, −273 °C is 0 K and 0 °C is 273 K. To convert from degrees Celsius, °C, to kelvin, K, you just add 273 (Fig. 13.7).

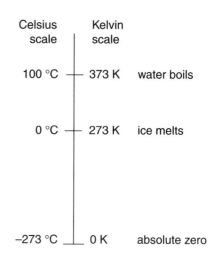

Fig. 13.7 Comparing the Celsius temperature scale with the kelvin temperature scale

Celsius scale	Kelvin scale	
100 °C	373 K	water boils
0 °C	273 K	ice melts
–273 °C	0 K	absolute zero

13.7 Atoms and molecules

All matter and materials can be classified in two ways:
- as **solids, liquids and gases**, or
- as **elements, compounds and mixtures**.

Remember:
- **Elements** are substances that cannot be broken down any further.
- **Compounds** are formed from elements and can be broken down into elements.
- **Mixtures** contain two or more different substances.

In 13.3 we saw how the particle picture of matter could explain the differences between solids, liquids and gases. But how does the particle model explain the difference between elements, compounds and mixtures? The answer to this question was first suggested by **John Dalton** (1766–1844) in 1807.

Dalton's theory of atoms and molecules

In 1807, Dalton put forward his *atomic theory of matter*. In this theory, Dalton was the first scientist to use the word **atom** for the smallest particle of an element.

The main points in Dalton's theory are:

1 All matter is made up of tiny particles called *atoms*.

2 Atoms are the smallest particles of matter. They cannot be split into anything smaller.

3 An *element* is a substance made of only one kind of atom. All atoms of one element are alike.

4 Atoms of one element are different from those of another element. They have different masses, different colours, etc.

5 Atoms of one element can combine with atoms of other elements to form new substances called *compounds*. The larger particles in compounds are called *molecules*.

6 A mixture contains two or more kinds of atoms or molecules, but the different particles are not combined chemically as in a compound.

Fig. 13.8 shows how Dalton pictured the elements iron and sulphur, the compound iron sulphide and a mixture of iron and sulphur. Although Dalton put forward his ideas nearly two hundred years ago, they are still used today.

Atoms in the *element* iron

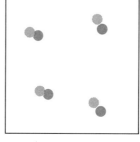

Atoms in the *element* sulphur

Molecules in the *compound* iron sulphide

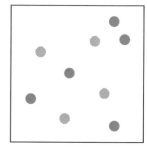

Atoms in a *mixture* of iron and sulphur

Fig. 13.8

Besides atoms and molecules, we now know that some compounds contain particles called **ions**. These are discussed more fully in 15.3.

13.8 Symbols and formulas

Symbols are used to represent the atoms of different elements. Table 13.1 gives a list of the symbols for some common elements. Notice that most elements have two letters in their symbol. The first is a capital letter and the second is always small (lower case).

Table 13.1 The symbols for some elements

Element	Symbol	Element	Symbol	Element	Symbol
Aluminium	Al	Helium	He	Oxygen	O
Argon	Ar	Hydrogen	H	Phosphorus	P
Bromine	Br	Iodine	I	Potassium	K
Calcium	Ca	Iron	Fe	Silicon	Si
Carbon	C	Lead	Pb	Silver	Ag
Chlorine	Cl	Magnesium	Mg	Sodium	Na
Chromium	Cr	Mercury	Hg	Sulphur	S
Cobalt	Co	Neon	Ne	Tin	Sn
Copper	Cu	Nickel	Ni	Uranium	U
Gold	Au	Nitrogen	N	Zinc	Zn

We can also use symbols to represent compounds as well as elements. For example, water is represented as H_2O. The smallest particle of water is a molecule. This contains two hydrogen atoms (H) and one oxygen atom (O). Carbon dioxide is written as CO_2 – one carbon atom and two oxygen atoms. 'H_2O' and 'CO_2' are called **formulas**. Formulas show the relative numbers of atoms of the different elements in a compound. Some of these symbols and formulas are shown in Fig. 13.9.

Like aluminium in Fig. 13.9, most elements can be represented by their symbols because they contain single atoms. But this is not the case for oxygen, hydrogen, nitrogen and chlorine. Experiments show that these elements contain *particles with two atoms joined together* (Fig. 13.10). So the best way to represent oxygen gas is by O_2, not O, and the best way to represent hydrogen gas is by H_2, not H. These molecules containing two atoms are described as **diatomic molecules.**

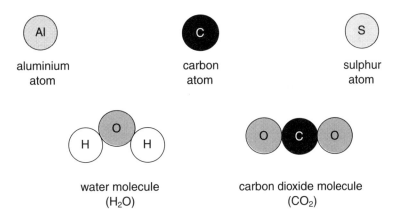

Fig. 13.9 Using symbols and formulas to represent the particles in substances

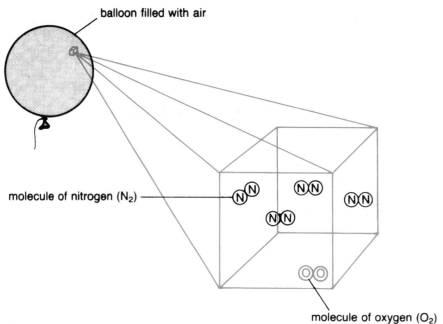

Fig. 13.10 Molecules of oxygen and nitrogen in air

13.9 Chemical equations: word equations and symbolic equations

A chemical equation is a summary of the starting substances and the products in a chemical reaction.

Word equations can be used to summarise what happens when substances react. For example, when zinc and oxygen react, the product is zinc oxide. The word equation for this is:

zinc + oxygen → zinc oxide

Symbolic equations go further than word equations. They show:
- the *symbols and formulas* of the reactants and products, and
- the *relative number of atoms and molecules* of the reactants and products.

Steps in writing symbolic equations

Using the reaction of zinc with oxygen, we can explain the three steps involved in writing a symbolic equation:

Step 1 Write a word equation

i.e. zinc + oxygen → zinc oxide

Step 2 Write symbols and formulas for reactants and products

e.g. $Zn + O_2 → ZnO$

Remember that oxygen, nitrogen, hydrogen and chlorine are written as O_2, N_2, H_2 and Cl_2. All other elements are shown as single atoms, e.g. Zn for zinc, S for sulphur.

Step 3 Balance the equation by making the number of atoms of each element the same on both sides.

e.g. $2Zn + O_2 → 2ZnO$

Remember that you must never change a formula to make an equation balance. The formula of zinc oxide is always ZnO. Zn_2O and ZnO_2 do not exist. You can only balance an equation by putting numbers in front of symbols or in front of the whole formula, e.g. $2Zn$, $2ZnO$, $3ZnO$.

State symbols

Sometimes it is helpful to show the state of a substance in an equation. This can be done using state symbols: (s) for solid, (l) for liquid, (g) for gas and (aq) for an aqueous solution.

These symbols are written immediately after the symbol or the formula of a substance in the equation. For example:

$$2Zn(s) + O_2(g) \rightarrow 2ZnO(s)$$

13.10 Measuring atoms

Atoms are about one hundred millionth (1/100 000 000) of a centimetre across. This means that if you put 100 million of them side by side, they would measure about one centimetre. It is difficult to imagine anything as small as this, but Fig. 13.11 might help you.

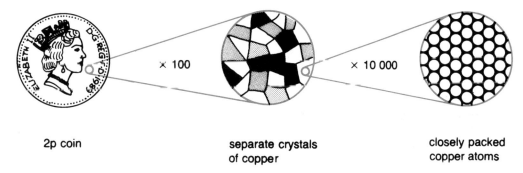

2p coin   separate crystals   closely packed
                           of copper   copper atoms

Fig. 13.11 If the surface of a 2p coin is magnified one hundred times using an ordinary microscope, it is possible to see separate crystals of copper. If these crystals were then magnified 10 000 times, it would be possible to see individual copper atoms. The coin would have been magnified first 100 times, then 10 000 times, i.e. one million times in total (100 × 10 000).

How heavy are atoms? – relative atomic masses

A single atom is far too small to be weighed on a balance. However, the mass of one atom can be compared with that of another atom using a **mass spectrometer** (Fig. 13.12).

By comparing the deflections of different atoms in a mass spectrometer, it is possible to compare their masses and make a list of their **relative masses**. The relative masses

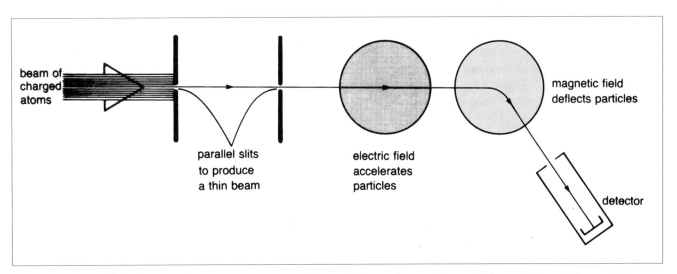

Fig. 13.12 A simplified diagram of a mass spectrometer. A beam of charged atoms is passed along a tube and focused into a thin beam. This beam of particles passes first through an electric field which speeds them up, then through a magnetic field which deflects them. The extent to which an atom is deflected depends on its mass. The greater the mass, the smaller the deflection.

which scientists use for different atoms are called **relative atomic masses** (RAMs). The element **carbon** has been chosen as the *standard* for relative atomic masses. Carbon atoms are given a *relative mass of 12* and the relative masses of other atoms are obtained by comparison with the mass of a carbon atom. A few relative atomic masses are listed in Table 13.2. From the table, you will see that carbon atoms are 12 times as heavy as hydrogen atoms. Oxygen atoms are 16 times as heavy as hydrogen atoms.

The symbol A_r is sometimes used for relative atomic mass. So we write $A_r(C) = 12.0$, $A_r(Cu) = 63.5$, etc. or simply $C = 12$, $Cu = 63.5$, etc.

The relative atomic mass of an element is sometimes referred to as one **mole** of the element. So 12 g of carbon is 1 mole of carbon and 1 mole of copper would be 63.5 g.

Table 13.2 Some relative atomic masses

Element	Symbol	Relative atomic mass
Carbon	C	12.0
Hydrogen	H	1.0
Oxygen	O	16.0
Copper	Cu	63.5
Iron	Fe	55.8

13.11 How much?

Scientists often ask the question 'How much?'. They want to know *how much* of one substance is used up or formed in a chemical reaction. We can answer these questions using relative atomic masses.

So far we have used relative atomic masses to compare the masses of atoms in elements. We can also use relative atomic masses to compare the masses of molecules in compounds. These relative masses of compounds are called **relative formula masses** (RFMs). For example:

● the relative atomic mass of hydrogen (H) = 1, and
● the relative atomic mass of oxygen (O) = 16.

From these relative atomic masses we can calculate:

● the relative formula mass of hydrogen gas $(H_2) = 1 + 1 = 2$,
● the relative formula mass of oxygen $(O_2) = 16 + 16 = 32$, and
● the relative formula mass of water $(H_2O) = 1 + 1 + 16 = 18$.

Notice that *the relative formula mass of a compound is obtained by simply adding up the relative atomic masses of all the atoms* in the formula.

Using the information in Fig. 13.13, the relative formula mass of carbon dioxide, CO_2, is $12 + 16 + 16 = 44$ and of calcium carbonate, $CaCO_3$, is $40 + 12 + 16 + 16 + 16 = 100$.

The relative formula mass of a compound is sometimes referred to as one mole of the compound. So 1 mole of water is 18 g and one mole of carbon dioxide is $12 + 16 + 16 = 44$ g.

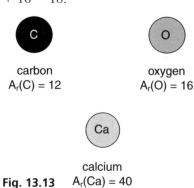

Fig. 13.13

Finding formulas

We have used some formulas already. But how are they obtained? How do we know, for example, that the formula of water is H_2O?

Formulas are obtained by experiments. First, we must find the masses of the different elements in a sample of the compound. These masses can then be used to work out the relative number of atoms of each element present and hence the formula.

Example: A sample of iron pyrites was purified. 12 g of the purified ore contained 5.6 g of iron and 6.4 g of sulphur. What is its formula?

$A_r(Fe) = 56$; $A_r(S) = 32$.

Ratio of masses of iron and sulphur in the ore = 5.6 : 6.4

Ratio of atoms of iron and sulphur in the ore = $\dfrac{5.6}{56} : \dfrac{6.4}{32} = 0.1 : 0.2$

∴ whole number ratio of atoms of iron and sulphur = 1 : 2

So, the iron pyrites sample contained 1 atom of iron for every 2 atoms of sulphur. So, the formula of iron pyrites is FeS_2.

The calculations we have just made are summarised in Table 13.3.

Table 13.3 Calculating the formula of iron pyrites

	Fe	S
Masses present =	5.6 g	6.4 g
Relative atomic masses =	56	32
Ratio of atoms =	0.1	0.2
Whole number ratio =	1	2
∴ formula for the compound is FeS_2		

Reacting amounts

In industry it is often important to know the amounts of reactants and products in a chemical process. Industrial chemists need to calculate how much product they can get from a given amount of starting material. In order to do this they use formulas, equations and relative atomic masses.

For example, suppose we want to know how much aluminium we can get from 1 kg of pure bauxite (aluminium oxide, Al_2O_3).

$$\begin{array}{lcl} \text{aluminium oxide} & \rightarrow & \text{aluminium} + \text{oxygen} \\ Al_2O_3 & \rightarrow & 2Al + \tfrac{3}{2}O_2 \\ 1 \text{ RFM of } Al_2O_3 & \rightarrow & 2 \text{ RAMs of Al} \\ 27 + 27 + 16 + 16 + 16 \text{ g } Al_2O_3 & \rightarrow & 27 + 27 \text{ g Al} \\ \text{i.e. } 102 \text{ g } Al_2O_3 & \rightarrow & 54 \text{ g Al} \\ \therefore 1 \text{ g } Al_2O_3 & \rightarrow & \tfrac{54}{102} \text{ g Al} = 0.53 \text{ g Al} \end{array}$$

So, 1 kg of pure bauxite will produce 0.53 kg of aluminium.

Reacting volumes of gases

Using symbolic equations, it is also possible to calculate the volumes of gases which react. Chemists have found that the relative formula mass of any gas occupies 22.4 litres at standard temperature and pressure (s.t.p., 0 °C and 1 atmosphere).

For example, when limestone (calcium carbonate) is heated, lime (calcium oxide) and carbon dioxide are produced.

$$\begin{array}{lclcl} \text{calcium carbonate} & \rightarrow & \text{calcium oxide} & + & \text{carbon dioxide} \\ CaCO_3 & \rightarrow & CaO & + & CO_2 \\ 40 + 12 + 16 + 16 + 16 \text{ g} & & 40 + 16 \text{ g} & & 2 + 16 + 16 \text{ g} \\ & & & & (22.4 \text{ litres at s.t.p.}) \\ \text{So, } 100 \text{ g } CaCO_3 & \rightarrow & 56 \text{ g CaO} & + & 44 \text{ g } CO_2 \\ & & & & (22.4 \text{ litres at s.t.p.}) \\ \Rightarrow 1 \text{ kg } CaCO_3 & \rightarrow & 0.56 \text{ kg CaO} & + & 224 \text{ litres } CO_2 \\ & & & & \text{at s.t.p.} \end{array}$$

Summary

1   The best evidence that particles of matter are constantly moving comes from studies of **diffusion** and **Brownian motion**.

2   **Diffusion** is the moving and mixing of particles as a result of their kinetic energy.

3   **Brownian motion** is the observed movement of tiny particles of matter (e.g. smoke or pollen grains) as a result of their bombardment by molecules of gas or liquid.

4   The **kinetic theory of matter** says that:
   - all matter is made up of tiny, invisible moving particles,
   - in solids, the particles only vibrate about fixed positions,
   - in liquids, the particles can move around each other,
   - in gases, the particles move rapidly and randomly in all the space available.

5   Solid, liquid and gas are called the **states of matter**.

6   In a gas, pressure is caused by the bombardment from tiny gas particles.

7   The pressure of a fixed mass of gas is inversely proportional to its volume, if the temperature stays constant.

$$p \propto \frac{1}{V} \quad \text{Boyle's law}$$

8   $x \,°C = (x + 273)\, K$

9   Atoms are the smallest particles in elements. Atoms can join together to form **molecules**.

10   **Symbols** are used to represent the atoms of different elements. Symbols can be used in formulas to represent compounds. **Formulas** show the relative numbers of atoms of the different elements in a compound.

11   **Symbolic equations** use symbols and formulas to show the relative numbers of atoms and molecules in a chemical reaction.

12   **State symbols** can be used to show the state of a substance in an equation.

13   Scientists use **relative atomic masses** for the relative mass of different atoms. Carbon is the standard for relative atomic masses. Carbon atoms are given a relative mass of 12 and the relative masses of all other atoms are obtained by comparison with carbon.

14   The relative masses of compounds are called **relative formula masses**. The relative formula mass of a compound is obtained by adding up the relative atomic masses of all the atoms in the formula.

15   The relative formula mass of any gas (e.g. 32 g of oxygen, O_2) occupies 22.4 litres at s.t.p. (0 °C and 1 atm pressure).

Quick test 13

1   If you look at smoke particles through a microscope, you will see them moving about randomly. This movement is due to
   A   air currents blowing on the smoke particles.
   B   air molecules bumping into smoke particles.
   C   forces of attraction between the smoke particles.
   D   smoke particles reacting with oxygen in the air.

2   Gases diffuse faster than liquids because gas molecules are
   A   freer to move than liquid molecules.
   B   more compressible than liquid molecules.
   C   lighter than liquid molecules.
   D   more elastic than liquid molecules.

3   Solids do *not* diffuse like liquids because the particles of a solid
    A   are stationary.
    B   are too close to move.
    C   are too heavy to move.
    D   cannot move around each other.

4   As a liquid freezes, its particles
    A   slow down, but continue to move around each other.
    B   stop moving and form a regular arrangement.
    C   slow down, until they only move around fixed points.
    D   stop moving as they get closer to each other.

5   Which one of the following will change the temperature at which a liquid boils?
    A   The amount of liquid.
    B   Solid dissolved in the liquid.
    C   The air temperature.
    D   The temperature of the Bunsen flame.

6   The pressure in the gas grid pipelines is 800 kPa. Suppose 10 litres of gas in the pipelines escapes into the air where the pressure is 100 kPa. What volume will the gas occupy after it escapes?

7   Five litres of nitrogen at 1 atmosphere pressure and 27 °C were allowed to expand to 10 litres at 327 °C. What was the final pressure?

Questions 8 to 12

In the boxes below, ⬤ and ◉ represent different atoms.

Which box contains
8   a close packed metal?
9   a solid compound?
10 a liquid?
11 a mixture?
12 diatomic molecules?

Questions 13 to 14

How many atoms are there in one molecule of
13 methane, CH_4?
14 sulphuric acid, H_2SO_4?

Questions 15 to 18

Write balanced equations for the reactions of
15 charcoal (carbon) burning in oxygen to give carbon dioxide.
16 natural gas (methane, CH_4) burning in oxygen to give carbon dioxide and water.
17 copper oxide with sulphuric acid (H_2SO_4) to give copper sulphate ($CuSO_4$) and water.
18 nitrogen with hydrogen to give ammonia (NH_3).

Chapter 14
Metals and alloys

14.1 Introduction

Metals and alloys are some of the most useful and important materials. We use them in large quantities to build homes, bridges and vehicles. Most of our work and leisure activities also require the use of metals, whether we use a hammer, a computer, a tractor, a saucepan or a pen.

Most metallic materials used today are alloys and most alloys are mixtures of metals.

14.2 Reactions of metals

How do metals react with air (oxygen)?

As soon as sodium is exposed to the air, it begins to go dull. This is because the sodium reacts with oxygen in the air to form sodium oxide.

$$\text{sodium} + \text{oxygen} \rightarrow \text{sodium oxide}$$
$$4Na + O_2 \rightarrow 2Na_2O$$

Other metals, like aluminium and iron, react more slowly. A shiny aluminium surface can take several weeks to go dull as it forms aluminium oxide.

$$\text{aluminium} + \text{oxygen} \rightarrow \text{aluminium oxide}$$
$$4Al + 3O_2 \rightarrow 2Al_2O_3$$

Have you noticed how new aluminium articles (e.g. pencil sharpeners) lose their shine after a period of time?

Unreactive metals, such as copper, take months or even years before we notice any oxide.

We can summarise these reactions with oxygen as

$$\text{metal} + \text{oxygen} \rightarrow \text{metal oxide}$$

Very unreactive metals, like gold, don't react with oxygen at all. They keep their shine for centuries (see Fig. 14.1).

We can use reactions like these with oxygen to place metals in a **reactivity series** (Table 14.1). Metals at the top of the series, such as sodium and calcium, are the most reactive. Metals at the bottom of the series, such as copper and silver, are the least reactive.

Fig. 14.1 Gold is so unreactive that it stays shiny for centuries, like Tutankhamun's gold burial mask which dates from about 1350 BC

How do metals react with water?

Water (H_2O) is a compound of hydrogen with oxygen. Because of this, reactive metals will take the oxygen from water, leaving hydrogen. For example,

sodium + water → sodium oxide + hydrogen
2Na + H_2O → Na_2O + H_2

Only the most reactive metals, from potassium down to magnesium in Table 14.1, react with cold water in this way. However, metals below magnesium, such as aluminium and zinc, will react with hot water or steam to form hydrogen, e.g.

zinc + water → zinc oxide + hydrogen
Zn + H_2O → ZnO + H_2

These reactions with water can be summarised as

metal + water → metal oxide + hydrogen

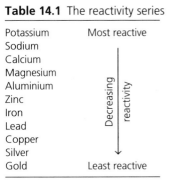

Table 14.1 The reactivity series

Potassium	Most reactive
Sodium	
Calcium	
Magnesium	
Aluminium	
Zinc	
Iron	Decreasing reactivity
Lead	
Copper	
Silver	
Gold	Least reactive

How do metals react with acids?

Fig. 14.2 shows what happened when six common metals were added to dilute hydrochloric acid at room temperature (21°C).

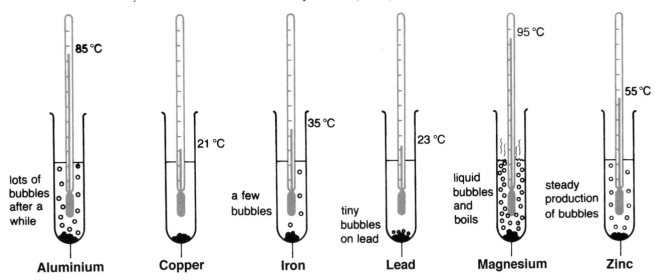

Fig. 14.2 The reactions of six common metals with dilute hydrochloric acid

All the metals in Fig. 14.2, except copper, react with dilute hydrochloric acid. When the metals are written in order of decreasing reactivity, this tallies neatly with that in Table 14.1. The bubbles which form are hydrogen. The other product of the reaction is the chloride of the metal, i.e.

metal + hydrochloric acid → metal chloride + hydrogen
e.g. zinc + hydrochloric acid → zinc chloride + hydrogen
Zn + 2HCl → $ZnCl_2$ + H_2

In these reactions, the metals have taken chlorine from hydrochloric acid (HCl) leaving hydrogen. This is similar to the reaction of metals with water. With hydrochloric acid, the metals are taking chlorine. With water, the metals are taking oxygen. A similar reaction occurs between metals and dilute sulphuric acid. This time the products are hydrogen and a metal sulphate. We can summarise these reactions with metals as

metal + acid → metal compound + hydrogen

When metals react with acids, heat is given out and the temperature of the mixture rises (Fig. 14.2). Reactions like these which *give out heat* are called **exothermic reactions**.

153

Almost all reactions which occur fairly readily are in fact exothermic. A few common reactions, such as the decomposition of calcium carbonate (limestone) to calcium oxide (lime) take in heat. These reactions which *take in heat* are called **endothermic reactions**.

$$\text{calcium carbonate} \xrightarrow{\text{heat}} \text{calcium oxide} + \text{carbon dioxide}$$
$$\text{(limestone)} \qquad\qquad \text{(lime)}$$

$$CaCO_3 \text{ (s)} \xrightarrow{\text{heat}} CaO \text{ (s)} + CO_2 \text{ (g)}$$

14.3 Summarising the reactions of metals

Table 14.2 summarises the reactions of metals with air, water and acids. Notice that the order of reactivity is the same in all three columns in Table 14.2. In fact, the reactivity series applies to all reactions with air, water and acids.

Reactive metals tend to react and form their compounds.

Unreactive metals tend not to react, but to stay as the metal.

Examiner's tip

Table 14.2 is a very helpful summary of the reactions of metals.

Table 14.2 The reactions of metals with air, water and dilute acids

Reactivity series		Reaction with oxygen when heated in air	Reaction with water	Reaction with dilute acids
Potassium	K	Burn with decreasing vigour down the series to form their oxide	React with water less and less vigorously down the series producing hydrogen	React with dilute HCl and dilute H_2SO_4 less and less vigorously down the series producing hydrogen
Sodium	Na			
Calcium	Ca			
Magnesium	Mg			
Aluminium	Al		React with steam producing hydrogen	
Zinc	Zn			
Iron	Fe			
Lead	Pb	Only form a layer of oxide	Do not react with water or steam	
Copper	Cu			Do not react with dilute acids
Silver	Ag	Do not react		
Gold	Au			
General equation		$2M + O_2 \rightarrow 2MO$	$M + H_2O \rightarrow MO + H_2$	$M + 2HCl \rightarrow MCl_2 + H_2$ $M + H_2SO_4 \rightarrow MSO_4 + H_2$

Using the reactivity series, we can predict how a metal will react.

The reactivity series and results such as those in Table 14.2 also explain some of the uses of metals:

- **Magnesium** and **calcium** are very reactive metals. Therefore, they are useless for construction purposes but they are excellent for fireworks.
- **Aluminium** is fairly high in the reactivity series but it forms a thin protective layer of aluminium oxide. This oxide is tough and non-porous so the aluminium underneath does not react with air or water. Because of this, aluminium can be used for everyday articles such as window frames, ladders and foil.
- **Copper** is the least reactive metal which can be produced at a reasonable cost. Because of this it is used for hot water tanks and hot water pipes. However, copper is much more expensive than iron (steel) which can be used for cold water tanks.
- **Silver** and **gold** are rare and too expensive for use in large quantities. They are, however, very unreactive and make excellent jewellery.

Notice from Table 14.2 that metals above copper in the reactivity series will react with acids to form a metal compound and hydrogen. For example:

$$\text{magnesium} + \text{sulphuric acid} \rightarrow \text{magnesium sulphate} + \text{hydrogen}$$
$$Mg + H_2SO_4 \rightarrow MgSO_4 + H_2$$

In this case, magnesium has *displaced* hydrogen (H_2) from H_2SO_4. Now, if magnesium can displace H_2 from H_2SO_4, then it may be able to displace Cu from $CuSO_4$ and other metals from solutions of their compounds.

Experiments show that one particular metal will *only* displace metals below it in the reactivity series from solutions of their compounds.

So, zinc will displace copper from copper sulphate solution, but *not* magnesium from magnesium sulphate solution.

14.4 Alloys and their uses

As soon as our ancestors had built furnaces which could melt metals, they began to make alloys.

Most alloys are mixtures of metals. However, steel (probably the most important alloy) is a mixture of iron and carbon.

The first alloy to be used was probably **bronze**. This is a mixture of *copper and tin*. Bronze swords, ornaments and coins were being made as early as 1500 BC.

Alloys are more useful than pure metals because they can be made with specific properties to suit particular uses. Some alloys are made for hardness, some for resistance to corrosion. Other alloys have unusually low melting points and densities. Yet others have special magnetic or electrical properties.

Making alloys

Alloys are made by mixing appropriate amounts of the constituent metals as liquids. For example, solder is made by adding a small amount of molten tin to molten lead (see Fig. 14.3).

The most important alloys are those based on steel. The constituents, properties and uses of some of the most useful and common alloys are shown in Table 14.3.

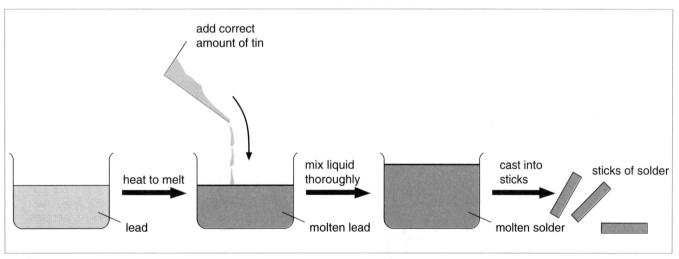

Fig. 14.3 Making solder

Table 14.3 The constituents, properties and uses of some common alloys

Alloy	Constituent elements	Properties	Uses
Solder	lead and tin	very low melting point	joining electrical components
Mild steel	iron with 0.12 to 0.25% carbon	cheap, easily manufactured, harder and stronger than pure iron can be pressed into sheets and cast into different shapes	used as girders in buildings, bridges and towers sheets used as bodywork for vehicles
Stainless steel	iron with about 15% chromium and 0.12 to 0.25% carbon	similar to mild steel, does not rust	cutlery, surgical instruments
Aluminium alloys including duralumin	aluminium with about 4% copper	low density, does not corrode, stronger than pure aluminium	aircraft bodywork, window frames, lightweight tubing
Brass	copper with up to 20% zinc	easily worked, hard, does not corrode, golden appearance	ornaments, picture frames

14.5 Extracting iron

Iron is the most important metal. The world production of iron is about 700 million tonnes per year. Most of it is made into steel. This is used for large machines, vehicles and girders in buildings.

The main ore used to obtain iron is iron ore (*haematite*). This contains iron oxide. Iron ore is converted to iron in special tall furnaces called **blast furnaces**. Fig. 14.4 shows a diagram of a blast furnace with a summary of the reactions to produce iron.

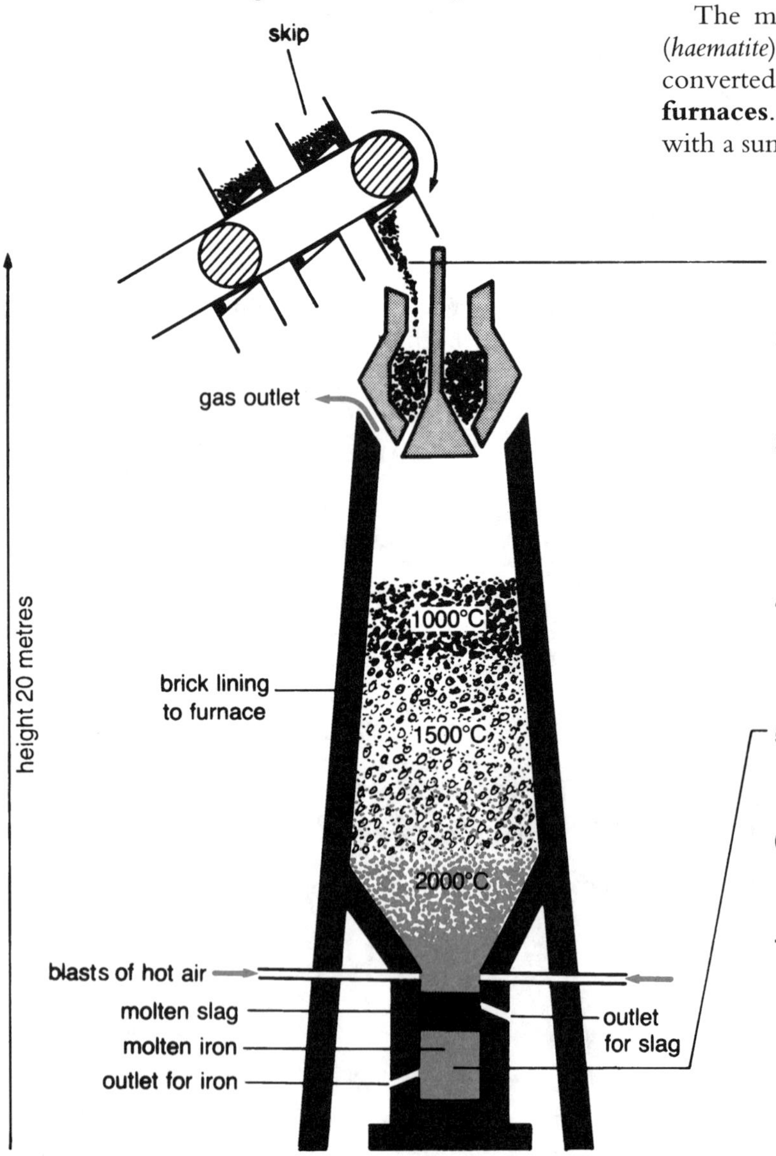

skip
gas outlet
height 20 metres
brick lining to furnace
1000°C
1500°C
2000°C
blasts of hot air
molten slag
molten iron
outlet for iron
outlet for slag
1 A mixture of iron ore, coke (carbon) and limestone is added to the furnace
2 Blasts of hot air are blown through small holes into the bottom of the furnace (this is why it is called a 'blast furnace')
3 The coke burns in oxygen in the hot air producing carbon monoxide and great heat
carbon + oxygen → carbon monoxide
$2C + O_2 \rightarrow 2CO$
(coke)
4 The carbon monoxide takes oxygen from iron ore (iron oxide) to form iron and carbon dioxide
iron oxide + carbon monoxide → iron + carbon dioxide
$Fe_2O_3 + 3CO \rightarrow 2Fe + 3CO_2$
5 Molten iron runs to the bottom of the furnace where it is tapped off periodically. Most of this iron is used to make steel
6 Limestone is added to the furnace to remove impurities. The impurities in the ore react with limestone to form a molten slag
7 The molten slag floats on top of the molten iron and is tapped off periodically. It is used for road making

Fig. 14.4 Extracting iron from iron ore in a blast furnace

14.6 Rusting

Although iron (steel) is the most widely used metal, it rusts more easily than most other metals. Experiments show that iron (steel) will only rust if both **oxygen** (air) and **water** are present.

During rusting, iron reacts with oxygen to form iron(III) oxide. At the same time, the iron combines with water to form hydrated iron(III) oxide, which is rust.

iron   +   oxygen   +   water   →   hydrated iron(III) oxide
(rust)

Preventing rust

Rusting costs millions of pounds every year because of the need to protect iron and steel and the need to replace rusted articles. We can protect iron and steel from rusting by:

- painting
- oiling
- plastic coating
- tin plating
- chromium plating

These methods keep air and water away from the iron or steel.

- alloying – This method changes the properties of the metal. Stainless steel contains chromium, nickel and/or manganese, as well as iron and carbon.
- galvanising (zinc plating) – This method allows a coating of a more reactive metal (zinc) to react rather than the iron or steel.

14.7 Redox

Many common reactions, including burning and rusting, are examples of *oxidation* (see 14.3). For example, during rusting iron reacts with oxygen and water to form hydrated iron(III) oxide.

iron + **oxygen** + water → hydrated iron(III) **oxide**

Reactions in which substances combine with oxygen are called **oxidations**. But if one substance gains oxygen, another substance (possibly oxygen itself) must *lose* oxygen. We say that *substances which lose oxygen* in chemical reactions are **reduced**. The process is called **reduction**. Fig. 14.5 shows the reduction and oxidation processes when iron rusts and when iron is extracted from iron ore (iron(III) oxide).

(a) **Rusting of iron**

(b) **Extraction of iron**

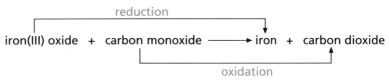

Fig. 14.5 Reduction and oxidation processes when (a) iron rusts, (b) iron is extracted from iron ore

Reduction and oxidation always occur together. If one substance loses oxygen and is reduced, another substance must gain oxygen and be oxidised. The combined process of **RED**uction and **OX**idation is called **REDOX**.

14.8 Extracting metals

Metals are found in the Earth as impure substances called *metal ores*. The extraction of metals from their ores involves three stages:

❶ Mining and concentrating the ore

Very often the ore must be separated from soil and other impurities before it can be processed. There are both advantages and disadvantages in mining for metal ores. Some of these are listed in Table 14.4.

Table 14.4 Advantages and disadvantages of mining for metal ores

Advantages	Disadvantages
Metals are produced and used to manufacture thousands of different articles	Mining destroys the habitats of wildlife
Mining ores and the manufacture of metal articles creates jobs	Mining damages the environment with spoil heaps, quarries and open-cast mines.
The sale of ores, metals and metal products creates wealth for a community	Mining can result in subsidence

If we want metals, then mining is unavoidable. Although it creates problems, the problems can often be reduced. For example, open–cast mines and spoil heaps can be reclaimed and landscaped for wildlife or for leisure activities.

❷ Converting the ore to the metal

Table 14.5 shows the ores from which some important metals are obtained.

Table 14.5 The ores from which some important metals are obtained

Metal	Common ore of metal	Chemical name of ore	Formula of ore
Sodium	rock salt	sodium chloride	$NaCl$
Aluminium	bauxite	aluminium oxide	Al_2O_3
Zinc	zinc blende	zinc sulphide	ZnS
Iron	iron ore (haematite)	iron oxide	Fe_2O_3
Copper	copper pyrites (chalcopyrites)	copper sulphide and iron sulphide	$CuS + FeS$ ($CuFeS_2$)

❸ Purifying the metal

The iron produced from a blast furnace still contains 8% impurity. It is called *pig iron*, which is very hard and brittle compared to pure iron or steel. The impurities must be removed if iron or steel are required.

We must now consider stage 2 in the extraction process in more detail and the methods used to convert ores to metals. The method used to extract a particular metal depends on two key factors:

- the position of the metal in the reactivity series;
- the cost of the process.

(i) Heating the ore

This is the *cheapest method* of conversion. But it only works for *metals at the bottom of the reactivity series*. When the ores of these metals are heated, they decompose to the metal.

For example, mercury is extracted from cinnabar (HgS) by heating in air:

mercury sulphide (cinnabar) + oxygen → mercury + sulphur dioxide

$$HgS \quad + \quad O_2 \quad → \quad Hg \quad + \quad SO_2$$

(ii) Reducing the ore with carbon

This method is commonly used for *metals in the middle of the reactivity series*, such as zinc, iron, lead and copper. The metals are usually obtained by heating their *oxides* with *carbon (coke)*. The carbon reduces the metal oxide to metal, e.g.

zinc oxide + carbon → zinc + carbon monoxide

$$ZnO \quad + \quad C \quad → \quad Zn \quad + \quad CO$$

In some cases, air is blown into the furnace so that coke will react with oxygen to form carbon monoxide. The carbon monoxide then reduces the metal oxide to metal. This is what happens in a blast furnace to manufacture iron (14.5).

Sometimes the metal ores are *sulphides*, not oxides. These ores *must be converted to oxides* before reaction with carbon or carbon monoxide. This is done by heating the sulphide in air, e.g.

zinc sulphide + oxygen → zinc oxide + sulphur dioxide

(iii) Electrolysis of molten compounds

Metals at the top of the reactivity series, such as sodium and aluminium, *cannot* be obtained from their ores by heating with coke (carbon) or carbon monoxide. The carbon and carbon monoxide are not reactive enough to pull oxygen or chlorine away from the ore and leave the metal.

The only way to extract these reactive metals is by *electrolysis of their liquid (molten) compounds*. For example, sodium is obtained by electrolysis of molten sodium chloride (see 15.3) and aluminium is obtained by electrolysis of aluminium oxide dissolved in molten cryolite (Na_3AlF_6) (see 15.5).

14.9 The structure of metals

Look closely at the surface of some galvanised iron on a bucket or a dustbin. You will see irregularly shaped areas separated by clear boundaries. The irregular areas are called **grains** and the boundaries between grains are **grain boundaries**. The grains of zinc on galvanised iron are usually easy to see. The grains in most other metals are too small to see without a microscope. The oxide coating on many metals can also obscure the grains. But if a metal surface is clean and smooth, the grains can be seen under a microscope.

X-ray analysis shows that the atoms in metal grains are packed in a regular pattern, but the grains are irregular-shaped crystals which have grown into each other. In most metals, the atoms are packed as close as possible. This arrangement is called **close-packing**. Fig. 14.6 shows a few close-packed atoms in one layer of a metal crystal. Notice that atoms in the middle of the crystal, such as that labelled X in Fig. 14.6, touch six other atoms in the same layer.

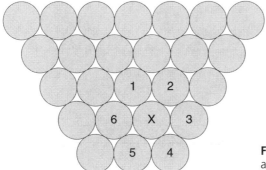

Fig. 14.6 A bird's eye view of close-packed atoms in one layer of a metal crystal

When another layer is placed on top of the first layer, atoms in the second layer sink into the dips between atoms in the first layer (Fig. 14.7). Millions and millions of atoms pack regularly in this way to form a **giant metallic structure**.

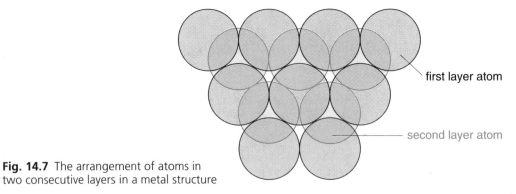

first layer atom

second layer atom

Fig. 14.7 The arrangement of atoms in two consecutive layers in a metal structure

14.10 Explaining the properties of metals

Most metals:

- have high densities;
- have high melting points and boiling points;
- are good conductors of heat and electricity;
- are malleable (can be hammered or bent into different shapes).

These properties can be explained by the close-packed structure of metals.

High density

The close packing of metal atoms gives a *high mass per unit volume*. This results in a high density.

High melting points and boiling points

All atoms are composed of three types of particle – **protons**, **neutrons** and **electrons**. Protons and neutrons are packed tightly in the **nucleus** at the centre of the atom. Protons are positively charged, but neutrons have no charge. Electrons occupy the outer parts of the atom. They have a negative charge (Fig. 14.8).

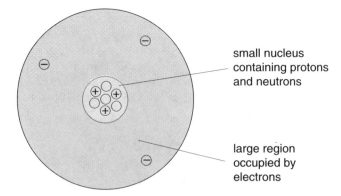

small nucleus containing protons and neutrons

large region occupied by electrons

Fig. 14.8 Protons, neutrons and electrons in a lithium atom

Scientists have discovered that the outer electrons in metal atoms can move around fairly freely. In the metal structure, negative electrons attract the positive nuclei and vice versa. This 'cements' all the atoms together (Fig. 14.9). The strong forces of attraction between the moving electrons and the positive nuclei result in high melting points and high boiling points.

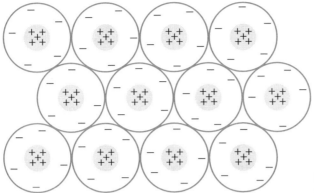

Fig. 14.9 Close-packed atoms with mobile electrons in a metal structure

Good conductivity

When a metal is connected in a circuit, outer electrons in the metal atoms move easily towards the positive terminal. At the same time, electrons can be fed into the other end of the metal from the negative terminal (see Fig. 15.1). This flow of electrons through the metal forms an electric current.

Malleable

The bonds between atoms in a metal are strong, but they are not rigid. When a force is applied to a metal crystal, the layers of atoms can 'slide' over each other. This is called **slip**. After slipping, the atoms settle into position again and the close-packed structure is restored. Fig. 14.10 shows the position of atoms before and after slip. This is what happens when a metal is hammered or bent into different shapes.

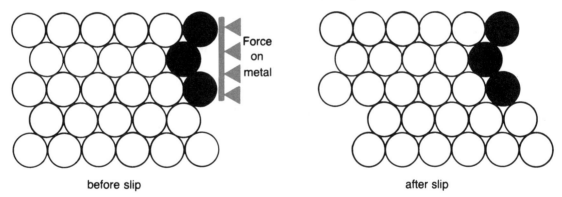

Fig. 14.10 The positions of atoms in a metal crystal before and after slip

Summary

1   Metals can be placed in a **reactivity series** to show their relative reactivity. Metals at the top of the series are more reactive than those lower down.

- metal + oxygen → metal oxide
  (down to copper)
- metal + water → metal oxide + hydrogen
  (down to magnesium)
- metal + dilute acid → metal compound (salt) + hydrogen
  (down to lead)

2   Reactions which give out heat are called **exothermic reactions**. Reactions which take in heat are called **endothermic reactions**.

3   Most **alloys** are mixtures of metals. However, steel (the most common alloy) is a mixture of iron and carbon.

4   Iron is extracted from iron ore (iron(III) oxide) by heating with carbon (coke) in a blast furnace.

5   The chemical reaction during rusting can be summarised as

iron + oxygen + water → hydrated iron oxide (rust)

6   Iron can be protected from rusting by painting, oiling, alloying or coating (plating) with another material.

7   **Oxidation** occurs when a substance combines with oxygen. **Reduction** occurs when a substance loses oxygen. The combination of reduction and oxidation is called **redox**.

8   The extraction of metals involves three stages:
● mining and concentrating the ore,
● converting the ore to the metal,
● purifying the metal.

9   There are three general methods for converting ores to metals:
● heating the ore (for metals below copper in the reactivity series)
● reducing the ore with carbon (for metals between zinc and copper in the reactivity series)
● electrolysis of the molten ore (for metals above zinc in the reactivity series)

10   Metals are **giant structures** made up of millions and millions of **close-packed atoms**.

11   Most metals
● have high densities
● have high melting points and boiling points
● are good conductors
● are malleable

Quick test 14

Questions 1 to 5

Consider the following five alloys labelled A, B, C, D and E.

Alloy	Elements in the alloy	Properties
A	lead and tin	melts at 203 °C
B	bismuth, cadmium, lead and tin	melts at 70 °C
C	carbon, iron and tungsten	unaffected at very high temperatures
D	copper and zinc	golden colour does not tarnish
E	aluminium and lithium	low density, high strength

Which alloy would you use for
1   joining electrical wires?
2   making jewellery?
3   'plugging' an automatic fire sprinkler?
4   making aircraft bodywork?
5   making a drill for bricks and stone?

Questions 6 to 8

Barium comes above calcium but below sodium in the reactivity series. Say how you would expect barium to react in each of the following cases and write a word equation for any reactions which occur.

6   Barium is heated in air.

7   Barium is added to water.

8   Barium is added to dilute hydrochloric acid.

Questions 9 to 11

The table shows how certain metals react with cold water.

Metal	Reaction with cold water
strontium	a steady reaction
vanadium	little reaction
rubidium	a violent reaction
copper	no reaction

9   Place the metals in order of their reactivity, the most reactive first.

10   Give *one* commercial use of copper which depends upon the fact that it does not react with water.

11   Why do you think that the metals sodium and potassium should be removed as a matter of urgency from a laboratory store that had been flooded?

Questions 12 to 17

12   Explain why some metals corrode when they are left in the open air.

13   A student left the following items in the garden for three months to see whether they would corrode. Say whether you would expect each item to corrode *a lot*, *a little* or *not at all*
(a) a stainless steel fork
(b) a new penny
(c) a copper bracelet
(d) an iron nail.

14   What *two* treatments could be used to prevent corrosion of iron?

15   Iron is extracted from its ore in the *blast furnace*. Name *one* ore from which iron may be extracted.

16   What are the *raw materials* needed to make iron in a blast furnace (other than iron ore)?

17   Which chemical reduces iron ore in the top of the blast furnace?

(ULEAC, part question)

Questions 18 to 22

Mineral ores containing metals do not usually conduct electricity.

18   What is done to some ores to make them conduct electricity?

19   Why is it useful to pass electricity through some ores?

20   Iron can be extracted by heating the ore with carbon (coke). Explain why this method will not work with the ores of all metals.

21   Name a metal that does not have to be extracted from an ore.

22   Explain why the metal you have named is not found combined with something else, for example as an ore containing the metal oxide. *(MEG)*

Chapter 15
Electricity and electrolysis

 15.1 Electric currents

Electricity plays an important part in our lives. We use it for lighting, for heating and for cooking. Most of the electricity we use is *mains electricity*. We use this to operate electric lights, electric kettles, hair dryers, etc. Other electrical appliances, like radios, watches, calculators and torches, use electricity from *cells and batteries*.

When an electric current flows through a metal wire, negative electrons on the outside of the metal atoms are attracted to the positive terminal of the battery. At the same time, more electrons are repelled from the negative terminal into the metal wire (Fig. 15.1). **The electric current is simply a flow of electrons.** Electrons flow through the metal, like traffic along a road or water through a pipe.

Electric currents, voltages and circuit diagrams are discussed in detail in Chapter 24.

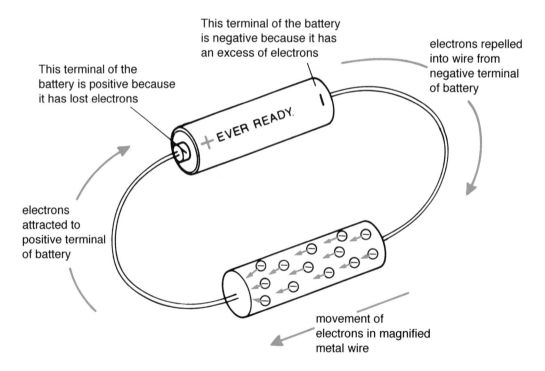

Fig. 15.1 An electric current in a metal wire

15.2 Conduction of electricity by solids and liquids

Which solids conduct electricity?

Experiments show that:

> The only common solids which conduct electricity at low voltages are metals and graphite.

Because of this, metals and graphite are called **conductors** and metals are used for fuses, wires and cables in electrical machines. Solids which do *not* conduct electricity are called **insulators** or non-conductors. Plastics like polythene and PVC are used as insulators for electrical wires and cables.

Which liquids conduct electricity?

Experiments show that **the following liquids will conduct electricity**:

- liquid metals (e.g. molten iron, mercury)
- liquid metal/non-metal compounds (e.g. *molten* sodium chloride)
- aqueous solutions of metal/non-metal compounds (e.g. sodium chloride *solution*)
- aqueous solutions of acids (e.g. sulphuric acid)

Electrolysis

Liquid metals conduct electricity like solid metals. They allow electrons to flow through them.

Unlike metals, liquids and aqueous compounds which conduct electricity are *decomposed* during the process. For example, when liquid (molten) sodium chloride conducts electricity, it is decomposed into sodium and chlorine. This can be summarised by the following word equation:

$$\text{sodium chloride} \xrightarrow{\text{electricity}} \text{sodium} + \text{chlorine}$$

This *decomposition of compounds by electrical energy* is called **electrolysis**. The *compound which is decomposed* is called an **electrolyte**.

The products of electrolysis

When compounds are electrolysed, new substances are produced at the electrodes. For example, when electricity is passed through potassium iodide solution using the apparatus

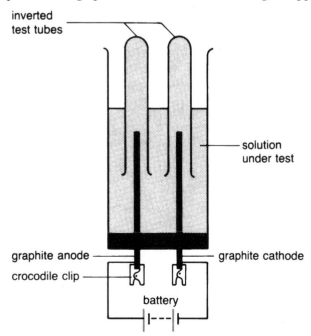

Fig. 15.2 Investigating the products at the electrodes when liquids are electrolysed

in Fig. 15.2, brown streaks of iodine appear near the **anode** (the positive electrode) and bubbles of hydrogen stream off the **cathode** (the negative electrode).

Table 15.1 shows the products formed at the anode and cathode when various liquid and aqueous compounds are electrolysed. Remember that water in the aqueous compounds may give rise to one or both of the products at the electrodes.

Table 15.1 Products at the anode and cathode when various liquid and aqueous compounds are electrolysed

Compound electrolysed	Product at cathode	Product at anode
molten sodium chloride	sodium	chlorine
molten lead bromine	lead	bromine
aqueous potassium iodide	hydrogen	iodine
aqueous sodium chloride	hydrogen	chlorine
aqueous copper sulphate	copper	oxygen
hydrochloric acid	hydrogen	chlorine

Look at the results in Table 15.1. Notice the following patterns in the results.
When metal/non-metal compounds and acids are electrolysed
- an element is produced at each electrode.
- a metal or hydrogen forms at the cathode.
- a non-metal (except hydrogen) forms at the anode.

15.3 Explaining electrolysis

When molten sodium chloride is electrolysed, sodium is produced at the cathode and chlorine at the anode. Sodium particles in the electrolyte have been attracted to the negative cathode, so they are probably positively charged. Scientists write these positively charged sodium particles in sodium chloride as Na^+ (Fig. 15.3). At the same time, chlorine is produced at the positive anode, so the chlorine particles in the electrolyte must be negatively charged. These negatively charged chlorine particles in sodium chloride can be written as Cl^-.

Charged particles, such as Na^+ and Cl^-, which move to the electrodes during electrolysis, are called **ions**.

During electrolysis, Na^+ ions near the cathode combine with negative electrons on the cathode forming neutral sodium atoms:

$$Na^+ + e^- \rightarrow Na$$

At the anode, Cl^- ions lose an electron to the positive anode and form neutral chlorine atoms:

$$Cl^- \rightarrow e^- + Cl$$

The chlorine atoms then join up in pairs to form molecules of chlorine gas, Cl_2.

$$Cl + Cl \rightarrow Cl_2$$
2 chlorine   chlorine
atoms   molecule

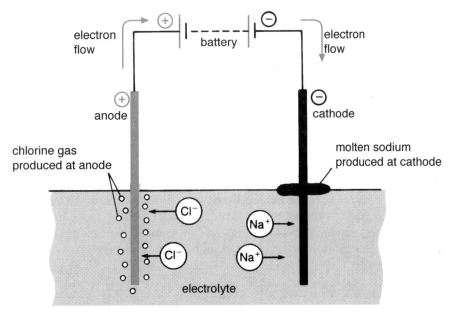

Fig. 15.3 Electrolysis of molten sodium chloride

The movement of ions in the electrolyte and the movement of electrons in the circuit are shown in Fig. 15.3. Notice that the electric current is being carried through the molten sodium chloride by ions. Na⁺ ions remove electrons from the cathode and Cl⁻ ions give up electrons at the anode. The electron flow in Fig. 15.3 has been shown by *drawing an arrow at the side of the circuit*. This is the usual way in which electron flow should be shown in a circuit.

The electrolysis of other molten and aqueous electrolytes can also be explained in terms of ions.

15.4 Charges on ions

xaminer's tip

Remember metals and hydrogen form cations, whereas non-metals (except hydrogen) form anions. Table 15.2 shows the common ions and their charges.

As we saw in Table 15.1, when electrolysis occurs

- metals and hydrogen are produced at the cathode, and
- non-metals (except hydrogen) are produced at the anode.

From these results, we can deduce that:

- **Metals and hydrogen have positive ions**. Positive ions are called **cations** because they are *attracted to the cathode*.
- **Non-metals (except hydrogen) have negative ions**. Negative ions are called **anions** because they are *attracted to the anode*.

Electrolysis experiments show that it requires twice as much electricity (twice as many electrons) to produce a magnesium atom as to produce a sodium atom. Earlier in this chapter, we wrote the formation of sodium during electrolysis as:

$$Na^+ \quad + \quad e^- \quad \longrightarrow \quad Na$$
sodium ion   electron   sodium atom

So, we can write the formation of magnesium as:

$$Mg^{2+} \quad + \quad 2e^- \quad \longrightarrow \quad Mg$$
magnesium ion   2 electrons   magnesium atom

In this way we can build up a list of ions showing their charges, as in Table 15.2.

Table 15.2 Common ions and their charges

				Cations						Anions		
1+			2+			3+		1−			2−	
Hydrogen	H^+	Copper	Cu^{2+}	Aluminium	Al^{3+}	Chloride	Cl^-	Oxide	O^{2-}
Sodium	Na^+	Magnesium	Mg^{2+}	Chromium	Cr^{3+}	Bromide	Br^-	Carbonate	CO_3^{2-}
Potassium	K^+	Calcium	Ca^{2+}	Iron(III)	Fe^{3+}	Iodide	I^-	Sulphide	S^{2-}
Silver	Ag^+	Zinc	Zn^{2+}			Hydroxide	OH^-	Sulphite	SO_3^{2-}
		Iron(II)	Fe^{2+}			Nitrate	NO_3^-	Sulphate	SO_4^{2-}
		Lead	Pb^{2+}						

Examiner's tip

Most metal ions have a charge of 2+.

- The only common metal ions with a charge of 1+ are Ag^+, Na^+ and K^+. (To remember this, say *AgNaK*.)
- The only common metal ions with a charge of 3+ are Cr^{3+}, Al^{3+} and Fe^{3+}. (To remember this, say *CrAlFe*.)

Notice that **iron can form two different ions**, Fe^{2+} and Fe^{3+}. We show this in the names of compounds by writing iron(II) for Fe^{2+} and iron(III) for Fe^{3+}. Thus iron forms two oxides, two chlorides, etc. For example, its two oxides are iron(II) oxide, which is black, and iron(III) oxide, which is red–brown.

15.5 Electrolysis in industry

Electrolysis is very important in industry. Three of its important applications are:

1. the manufacture of aluminium;
2. electroplating; and
3. the manufacture of hydrogen, chlorine and sodium hydroxide from salt.

We will look at the first two of these applications in some detail.

The manufacture of aluminium

Reactive metals such as sodium and aluminium cannot be obtained by reduction of their oxides with coke (carbon) (see 14.8). These metals have to be manufactured by electrolysis of their molten (liquid) compounds. We cannot electrolyse their aqueous solutions because hydrogen from the water is produced at the cathode, *not* the metal. For example, when aqueous sodium chloride is electrolysed, hydrogen is produced at the cathode, *not* sodium.

Aluminium is manufactured by the *electrolysis of molten aluminium oxide*. The aluminium oxide is obtained from *bauxite*. The melting point of pure aluminium oxide is 2045 °C, so it would be very expensive to carry out electrolysis at this high temperature. The aluminium oxide is therefore dissolved in molten *cryolite* (Na_3AlF_6) which melts at less than 1000 °C.

Fig. 15.4 shows a diagram of the electrolytic cell used. Aluminium ions (Al^{3+}) in the electrolyte are attracted to the carbon cathode lining the cell. Here they accept electrons and form aluminium.

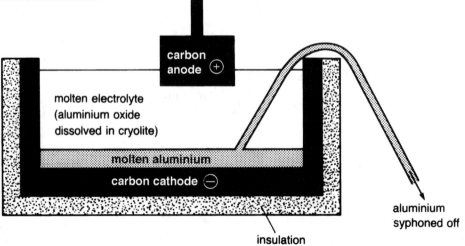

Fig. 15.4 The electrolytic cell for the manufacture of aluminium

Cathode (-) $Al^{3+} + 3e^- \rightarrow Al$

Molten aluminium collects at the bottom of the cell and is siphoned off at intervals.

Oxide ions (O^{2-}) are attracted to the carbon anode. Here they give up electrons and produce oxygen (O_2).

Anode (+) $2O^{2-} \rightarrow 4e^- + O_2$

It takes about 16 kilowatt hours of electricity to produce 1 kg of aluminium. Because of this, plants manufacturing aluminium are usually sited near sources of cheap electricity.

Electroplating

Electroplating is used to protect metals from corrosion, to make articles more attractive and to purify certain metals. Bicycle frames and the steel bodywork of cars are protected from corrosion by copper plating. Kettles are protected in a similar way by chromium plating.

Copper, nickel, chromium and *silver* are the metals most commonly used for electroplating. The metal coating is deposited on the cathode, so the object to be plated must be used as the cathode during electrolysis. The electrolyte must also contain ions of the metal which forms the coating.

Fig. 15.5 shows a steel brooch being electroplated with copper. During electrolysis, copper ions (Cu^{2+}) in the electrolyte are attracted to the cathode (the brooch). Here they gain electrons and form a deposit of copper.

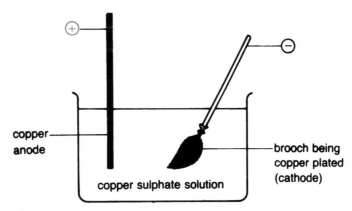

copper anode

brooch being copper plated (cathode)

Fig. 15.5

copper sulphate solution

Cathode (−) $Cu^{2+} + 2e^- \rightarrow Cu$

The anode is a piece of pure copper. Sulphate ions (SO_4^{2-}) in the electrolyte are attracted to the anode, but they do not react in any way. Instead, copper atoms in the anode give up electrons to the anode and go into solution as Cu^{2+} ions.

Anode (+) $Cu \rightarrow Cu^{2+} + 2e^-$

Notice that this process at the anode replaces the copper ions which are removed from the electrolyte at the cathode. Because of this, the process can be used to purify copper. The impure copper is made the anode in the cell, the electrolyte is copper sulphate solution and the cathode is a thin sheet of pure copper. During electrolysis, copper from the impure anode goes into solution as Cu^{2+} ions whilst pure copper is deposited on the cathode.

15.6 Ionic compounds

All metal/non-metal compounds are composed of ions. They are therefore called **ionic compounds**. Ionic compounds include salt (sodium chloride), rust (iron(III) oxide) and limestone (calcium carbonate).

Formulas of ionic compounds

The formulas of ionic compounds can be worked out by *balancing the charges* on the positive ions with those on the negative ions. For example:

- The formula of sodium chloride is Na^+Cl^- or, simply, NaCl. The one positive charge on Na^+ is balanced by one negative charge on Cl^-.
- The formula of magnesium chloride is $Mg^{2+}(Cl^-)_2$ or $MgCl_2$. Here the charges on two Cl^- ions are balanced by one Mg^{2+} ion.
- What is the formula for slaked lime (calcium hydroxide)? Like magnesium ions, calcium ions have a 2+ charge. Two hydroxide ions (OH^-), each 1-, will be needed to balance the charges. The formula is therefore $Ca^{2+}(OH^-)_2$ or $Ca(OH)_2$.

Notice that brackets are required around the OH in $Ca(OH)_2$. The brackets show that OH is a single unit containing one oxygen atom and one hydrogen atom. The 2 means that there are two of these units. (It would be quite wrong to write $CaOH_2$ for the formula. This would imply only one oxygen atom for every two hydrogen atoms in calcium hydroxide.) Other ions such as NO_3^-, SO_4^{2-} and CO_3^{2-} must also be regarded as single units and put in brackets when there are two or three of them in a formula. For example, the formula for iron(III) nitrate is $Fe(NO_3)_3$.

Formation of ionic compounds

Ionic compounds form when metals react with non-metals. During these reactions, *metal atoms lose electrons and form positive ions.* At the same time, *non-metal atoms gain electrons and form negative ions.* Fig. 15.6 represents what happens when sodium reacts with chlorine to form sodium chloride. In this case, one electron is transferred from each sodium atom to each chlorine atom.

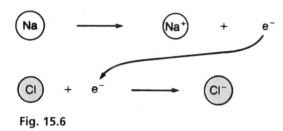

Fig. 15.6

Properties of ionic compounds

In solid ionic compounds, the ions are held together by the attraction between positive and negative charges.

Fig. 15.7 shows the arrangement of ions in a layer of sodium chloride. Notice that Na^+ ions are surrounded by Cl^- ions and vice versa. Layers like this can build up on top of each other to form a three-dimensional structure like that in Fig. 15.8.

Structures, like sodium chloride, in which large numbers of atoms or ions are packed in a regular pattern are called **giant structures**. Metals also form giant structures (see 14.9).

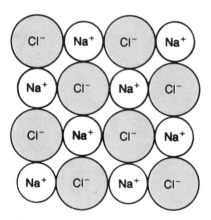

Fig. 15.7 The arrangement of ions in solid sodium chloride

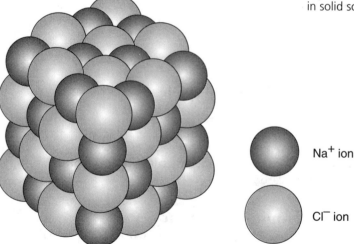

Fig. 15.8 The structure of sodium chloride

In solid sodium chloride, there are strong forces of attraction between oppositely charged ions. These forces are called **ionic bonds**. The strong ionic bonds result in hard materials with high melting points and high boiling points. When ionic substances are hit or knocked, the ions move slightly. If ions with the same charge come next to each other, they repel and the structure breaks apart. This explains why giant ionic structures are brittle.

Ionic substances do not conduct electricity when they are solid because the ions are locked in the structure and cannot move to the electrodes. They do, however, conduct when molten or dissolved in water because the ions are free to move to the electrodes.

15.7 Molecular compounds

When metals react with non-metals, ionic compounds are formed. Non-metals can also react with each other to form compounds, e.g. water (H_2O), carbon dioxide (CO_2) and ammonia (NH_3). These non-metal compounds are composed of *small neutral molecules*. They do *not* contain ions. They are called **simple molecular compounds**.

In simple molecular compounds, like water, there are strong bonds which hold the atoms together *within each molecule*. These are called **covalent bonds**. But, *between the separate molecules* there are only weak forces (Fig. 15.9). These weak forces hold the separate molecules together in liquids such as water and in solids such as sugar and dry ice (solid carbon dioxide). Because of these weak forces, simple molecular structures:

Compare the properties of molecular compounds with those of ionic compounds (Table 15.3)

- are often liquids or gases at room temperature,
- have low melting points and boiling points,
- are soft when solid,
- do not conduct electricity as solids or liquids because they have neither ions (like ionic compounds) nor mobile electrons (like metals).

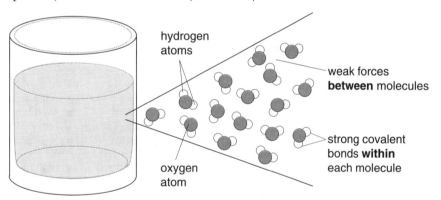

Fig. 15.9 Bonds in simple molecular structures like water – the water molecules are free to move around each other

Giant covalent structures

Diamond is very different from water. It is solid, very hard and it has a very high melting point. Yet diamond has covalent bonds similar to those between hydrogen and oxygen atoms in water. Diamond is pure carbon. A small part of the structure of a diamond is shown in Fig. 15.10 together with a view of a much larger portion. There are millions and millions of carbon atoms in even the smallest diamond.

The structures in Fig. 15.10 are more open than some of the others in this chapter. They will help you to see how the atoms are arranged. They also help you to see the bonds between atoms.

Notice in Fig. 15.10(a) that carbon atoms in the centre of the structure are bonded to four others in a regular tetrahedral arrangement. These bonds are strong covalent bonds which are difficult to break. The covalent bonds hold millions upon millions of carbon atoms together in the whole diamond structure. Because of this, diamond is described as

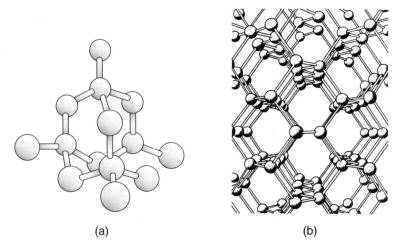

(a)   (b)

Fig. 15.10 The structure of diamond: (a) a small part and (b) a larger portion of the structure

a **giant covalent structure**. The strong covalent bonds in diamond make it hard, difficult to melt and insoluble in water. In addition, diamond will not conduct electricity because it has no electrons or ions to carry the electric current.

Notice, in this section, how substances with covalent bonds form both simple molecular structures and giant structures.

15.8 Comparing different structures

Table 15.3 The bonding and properties in different structures

Type of structure	Type of substance	Bonding	Properties	Structure
Giant metallic	Metals e.g. Al, Fe, Cu and alloys	Atoms are held in a giant structure by the attraction of positive nuclei for outer electrons	• high m.pts. and b.pts. • hard but malleable • conduct electricity • high density	
Giant ionic	Metal/non-metal compounds e.g. lime CaO, limestone $CaCO_3$, iron ore (iron(III) oxide) Fe_2O_3	Attraction between ions with opposite charges	• high m.pts. and b.pts. • hard but brittle • conduct electricity when molten and in acqueous solution • often soluble in water	
Giant covalent	A few non-metals e.g. diamond, graphite, and some non-metal compounds, e.g. sand, polythene	Large numbers of atoms are joined by strong covalent bonds to form a giant structure	• high m.pts. and b.pts. • do not conduct electricity • insoluble in water	
Simple molecular	Most non-metals and non-metal compounds e.g. O_2, Cl_2, H_2O, CO_2, sugar	Atoms are held together in small molecules by strong covalent bonds. Bonds between separate molecules are weak	• low m.pts. and b.pts. • do not conduct electricity soft when solid	

There are four different solid structures and we have now studied each of them – giant metallic, giant ionic, simple molecular and giant covalent. The bonding and properties of these four structures are compared in Table 15.3. Most materials have one of these four structures. The five types of material that we discussed in 12.2 can be assigned as below:

- **metals** – have a giant metallic structure.
- **ceramics and glasses** – have structures which are either giant ionic or giant covalent. Many of these materials, like clay, pottery and most glasses, have a partly ionic and partly giant covalent structure.
- **plastics and fibres** – have a long, single-chain giant structure. These giant covalent structures are called **polymers** (see 18.9).

Summary

1 An electric current is a flow of free electrons in metals and a flow of ions during electrolysis.

2 The only common solids which conduct electricity at low voltages are metals and graphite.

3 Solids which do *not* conduct electricity are called **insulators**.

4 Liquid and aqueous compounds which conduct electricity are called **electrolytes**. The terminals through which electricity enters and leaves the liquid are called **electrodes**. The positive electrode is the **anode**, the negative electrode is the **cathode**.

5 When electrolytes conduct electricity, the compound is decomposed. This decomposition is called **electrolysis**.

6 During electrolysis,
- a metal or hydrogen forms at the cathode,
- a non-metal (except hydrogen) forms at the anode.

7 Charged particles, such as Na^+ and Cl^-, which move to the electrodes during electrolysis are called **ions**. There are forces of attraction between positive and negative charges and forces of repulsion between like charges.

8 Metals and hydrogen have **positive ions** (**cations**).
Non-metals (other than hydrogen) have **negative ions** (**anions**).

9 Ions are formed from atoms by the loss or gain of one or more electrons.

10 Electrolysis can be used
- to manufacture reactive metals like aluminium and sodium,
- to electroplate articles.

11 **Ionic compounds** contain ions. They form when metals react with non-metals.

12 Ionic compounds are composed of giant structures of ions. Most ionic compounds
- are hard,
- conduct when liquid or aqueous,
- have high melting points and boiling points,
- are brittle.

13 **Simple molecular compounds** are composed of small, neutral molecules. Within each molecule, the atoms are held together by strong covalent bonds. Between the separate molecules there are only weak forces.

14 **Simple molecular substances**
- are usually liquids or gases at room temperature,
- have low melting points and boiling points,
- are soft when solid,
- do not conduct electricity.

15 **Giant molecular substances** (giant covalent structures) such as diamond and silica glass are giant structures of millions and millions of atoms joined by strong covalent bonds.

16 **Giant covalent substances**
- are hard,
- have very high melting points and boiling points,
- are insoluble in water,
- do *not* conduct electricity.

Quick test 15

Questions 1 to 6

The apparatus shown below was set up to silver plate a metal spoon.

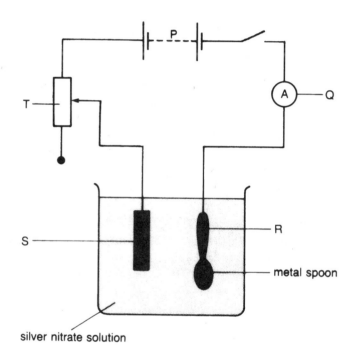

silver nitrate solution

1 Which piece of apparatus (P, Q, R, S or T) is the cathode?
2 What is T used for?
3 What should S be made of?
4 Which *one* of the following would be the safest and most effective conditions for the experiment?

	current	voltage	time
A	20 A	200 V	30 minutes
B	1 A	240 V	30 minutes
C	0.5 A	6 V	30 minutes
D	0.5 A	6 V	1 minute

5 Explain why silver deposits on the metal spoon.
6 Which *one* of the following equation represents the process which coats the spoon?

A $Ag^+ + e^- \rightarrow Ag$
B $Ag \rightarrow Ag^+ + e^-$
C $Ag^{2+} + 2e^- \rightarrow Ag$
D $Ag \rightarrow Ag^{2+} + 2e^-$

Questions 7 to 10

Read these two passages and then answer the questions.

'When food stuck to the frying pan, my grandmother would heat the pan until it was very hot, pour salt into it and rub the salt crystals round the pan with a thick cloth.'

'Sugar melts when heated gently. But if the temperature goes above 160 °C, the liquid goes brown and then black and smells burnt.'

7   Sugar is a carbohydrate. What is the black substance likely to be?
8   What type of bonds hold the particles together in

(a)   a molecule of sugar?
(b)   a crystal of sodium chloride (common salt)?

9   Explain why the salt did not melt even in a very hot pan.
10   What are the particles in solid sodium chloride called?   (*MEG*)

Questions 11 to 13

11   Describe briefly how aluminium is manufactured.
12   Write an equation for the formation of aluminium in the process.
13   Aluminium manufacture often takes place near hydroelectric power stations because
    A   water is needed to clean the ore.
    B   aluminium ore is dissolved in water before it is electrolysed.
    C   the process uses large quantities of electricity.
    D   aluminium cable and alloys are used in the power station.

Questions 14 to 18

    A   one   B   two
    C   three   D   four   E   five

Choose from A to E above
14   the number of charges on a tin(IV) ion.
15   the number of magnesium ions which combine with one sulphide ion.
16   the number of atoms joined together in one sulphate ion.
17   the number of silver ions which combine with one oxide ion.
18   the number of sodium ions which combine with one nitride ion (N^{3-}).

Chapter 16

Acids, bases and salts

16.1 Acids in everyday life

Acids are important in everyday life and in the chemical industry (Chapter 17). They are used to make our clothes, our food and the medicines that protect us from disease.

Acids in our food

Acids are present in many of our foods. For example:

- **Citric acid** is present in all citrus fruits (oranges, grapefruit, etc).
- **Acetic acid** (ethanoic acid) is present in vinegar and in most spicy sauces such as mint sauce, tomato sauce and brown sauce.
- **Ascorbic acid** is vitamin C which is present in fruit and vegetables (Table 3.2).
- **Carbonic acid** is present in all fizzy drinks. It is made by dissolving carbon dioxide in the drink under pressure. The carbon dioxide reacts with water in the drink to form carbonic acid.

$$\text{carbon dioxide} \quad + \quad \text{water} \quad \rightarrow \quad \text{carbonic acid}$$
$$CO_2 \quad + \quad H_2O \quad \rightarrow \quad H_2CO_3$$

Soda water is simply water containing dissolved carbon dioxide and carbonic acid. Coke, Pepsi, lemonade and champagne also contain carbonic acid.

Acids in the soil

The pH (see 16.2) of different soils varies from about 6 to 8, but most soils have a pH between 6.5 and 7.5. In chalk and limestone areas, the soil is usually alkaline with a pH between 7.0 and 7.5. In forests, moorland areas and sandstone regions, the soil is usually acidic (pH 6.5 to 7.0). Peat and clay areas also have acidic soils.

For gardening and arable farming, the best crops are usually obtained with neutral or slightly acidic soil (pH 6.5 to 7.0). Below pH 6.5 the soil is too acidic for most plants, particularly vegetables. However, some heathers and rhododendrons grow best in more acidic soil (i.e. pH less than 6.5).

In areas where the soil is too acidic, it can be improved by treatment with powdered slaked lime (calcium hydroxide). This reacts with acids in the soil and raises the pH to the desired level. Substances like lime which neutralise acids are called **bases** (see 16.4 and 16.5).

Acid rain

Large areas of Scandinavia are covered with lakes and pine forests. During the last 15 years, scientists have noticed more and more damage to the trees and to the organisms in the lakes of Scandinavia. Most scientists think that the damage is caused by acid rain.

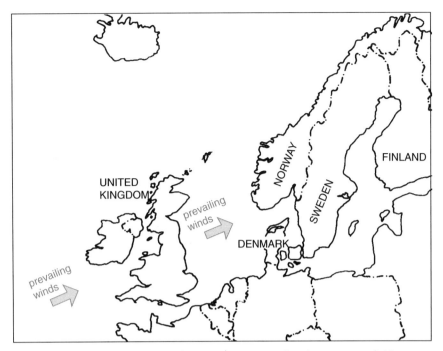

Fig. 16.1 Prevailing winds blow from Britain to Scandinavia. Because of this, many people blame British power stations and factories for the damage to Scandinavian lakes and forests from acid rain.

When fuels burn, sulphur in the fuel forms *sulphur dioxide*. Because of this, city air may contain ten times as much sulphur dioxide as clean air. Sulphur dioxide reacts with water vapour and rain in the air to form *sulphurous acid*.

$$\text{sulphur dioxide} + \text{water} \rightarrow \text{sulphurous acid}$$
$$SO_2 + H_2O \rightarrow H_2SO_3$$

Some of the sulphurous acid (H_2SO_3) is oxidised to sulphuric acid (H_2SO_4). These two acids make the rain much more acidic than normal and this has led to the term **acid rain**. Acid rain causes damage to:

- trees and other plants;
- fish and other organisms in rivers and lakes;
- stonework and metal on buildings and other structures (16.3).

16.2 Measuring acidity

We can use substances called **indicators** to find out whether a solution is acidic or alkaline or neutral. Indicators change colour depending on how acidic or how alkaline a solution is. The most commonly used indicators are **litmus** and **Universal Indicator**.

- Acidic substances dissolve in water to produce solutions which turn litmus red and give a yellow, orange or red colour with Universal Indicator.
- Alkaline solutions turn litmus blue and give a blue, indigo or violet colour with Universal Indicator.

It would be very clumsy if we used the colour of an indicator to describe how acidic something was. So chemists use a scale known as the **pH scale** to measure the acidity or alkalinity of a solution. On this scale:

- acidic substances have a pH below 7 (pH < 7);
- alkaline substances have a pH above 7 (pH >7);
- neutral substances have a pH of 7 (pH = 7).

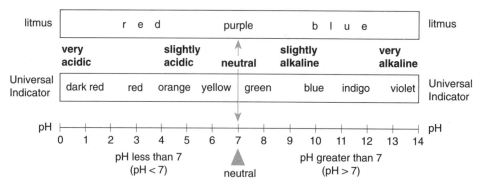

Fig. 16.2 The colours of litmus and Universal Indicator at different pHs

Notice in Fig. 16.2 that Universal Indicator shows different colours along the pH scale. Because of this, it can be used to measure the pH of a solution. It can tell us *how* acidic or *how* alkaline a solution is. It is therefore more useful than litmus which can only tell us whether a solution is acidic, alkaline or neutral.

16.3 The properties of acids

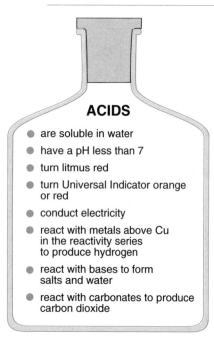

ACIDS

- are soluble in water
- have a pH less than 7
- turn litmus red
- turn Universal Indicator orange or red
- conduct electricity
- react with metals above Cu in the reactivity series to produce hydrogen
- react with bases to form salts and water
- react with carbonates to produce carbon dioxide

Fig. 16.3 The main properties of acids

The main properties of acids are summarised in Fig. 16.3.

Notice in Fig. 16.3 that acids conduct electricity. When this happens, the acids are decomposed by the electric current. This shows that solutions of acids contain ions (see 15.3). All acids produce hydrogen at the cathode during electrolysis. This indicates that they contain **H^+ ions** (Table 16.1).

Table 16.1 The ions in some common acids

Acid	Formula	Ions in the acid
Hydrochloric acid	HCl	$H^+ + Cl^-$
Nitric acid	HNO_3	$H^+ + NO_3^-$
Sulphuric acid	H_2SO_4	$2H^+ + SO_4^{2-}$
Carbonic acid	H_2CO_3	$2H^+ + CO_3^{2-}$
Sulphurous acid	H_2SO_3	$2H^+ + SO_3^{2-}$
Acetic (ethanoic) acid	CH_3COOH	$H^+ + CH_3COO^-$

The H^+ ions in acids are responsible for their chemical reactions with indicators, metals, bases and carbonates. Because of this:

Acids are defined as substances which donate H^+ ions.

Reaction with metals

Acids react with metals above copper in the reactivity series to form a *salt* and *hydrogen* (see 14.2 and 14.3).

metal + acid → salt + hydrogen

An example of this is the reaction of sulphuric acid in acid rain with iron in steel structures to form iron sulphate and hydrogen.

iron in steel + sulphuric acid →   iron sulphate + hydrogen
Fe   + H_2SO_4 → $FeSO_4$ + H_2

This reaction causes steel to corrode more rapidly in areas polluted by acid rain.

Salts are *ionic compounds*. Nearly all salts contain a metal cation (e.g. Fe^{2+}, Na^+, Al^{3+}) and an anion (e.g. Cl^-, SO_3^{2-}, SO_4^{2-}). Three important salts are sodium chloride (NaCl), usually known as common salt or table salt, iron(II) sulphate ($FeSO_4$), used in iron tablets, and ammonium nitrate (NH_4NO_3), the main ingredient in 'Nitram' fertiliser.

Reaction with carbonates

Acids react with carbonates to give a *salt*, *carbon dioxide* and *water*.

carbonate + acid → salt + carbon dioxide + water

Examiner's tip

Learn the key reactions highlighted in green in this section.

A reaction of this kind occurs when sulphuric acid in acid rain reacts with calcium carbonate in buildings made from limestone.

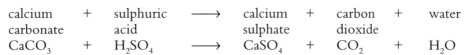

calcium carbonate	+	sulphuric acid	⟶	calcium sulphate	+	carbon dioxide	+	water
$CaCO_3$	+	H_2SO_4	⟶	$CaSO_4$	+	CO_2	+	H_2O

Reaction with bases

Acids react with bases to form a *salt* and *water*.

base + acid → salt + water

These reactions are described as **neutralisations**. They are discussed more fully in 16.5.

16.4 Bases and alkalis

Certain substances can *neutralise acids*. Farmers and gardeners use slaked lime (calcium hydroxide) to neutralise acids in acidic soil. We all use toothpaste to neutralise the acids which are produced from food and which cause tooth decay. You may also have taken indigestion tablets (antacid tablets, e.g. Rennies) to neutralise excess acid produced in your stomach. These substances which neutralise acids are called **bases**.

Bases are the chemical opposites of acids.

Acids give up H^+ ions whereas bases take H^+ ions.

Bases include the oxides, hydroxides and carbonates of metals.

Alkalis

Most bases are insoluble in water, but a few are soluble. These *soluble bases* are called **alkalis**. The Venn diagram in Fig. 16.4 shows the relationship between bases and alkalis.

The commonest alkalis are *sodium hydroxide* (NaOH), *calcium hydroxide* ($Ca(OH)_2$) and *ammonia* (NH_3). Calcium hydroxide is much less soluble in water than sodium hydroxide and ammonia. A solution of calcium hydroxide in water is usually called *lime water*.

Fig. 16.5 summarises the important properties of alkalis.

Sodium oxide and **calcium oxide** react with water to form their hydroxides. These two hydroxides are alkalis.

sodium oxide	+	water	⟶	sodium hydroxide
Na_2O	+	H_2O	⟶	2NaOH

calcium oxide	+	water	⟶	calcium hydroxide
CaO	+	H_2O	⟶	$Ca(OH)_2$

Most other metal oxides and hydroxides are insoluble in water. They are bases, but *not* alkalis.

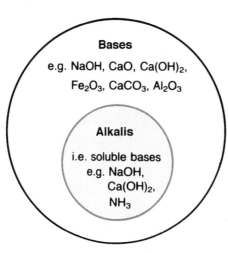

Fig. 16.4 A Venn diagram showing the relationship between bases and alkalis

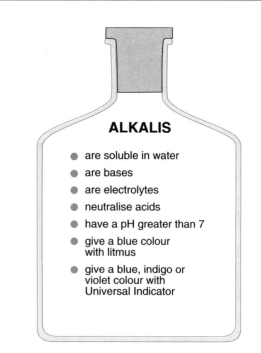

Fig. 16.5 The main properties of alkalis

16.5 Neutralisation

We have already noted some important neutralisation reactions in 16.4: curing indigestion, making soil less acidic and preventing tooth decay. Neutralisation is also used to treat splashes of acid or alkali on skin and clothing and to remove carbon dioxide from the air in air-conditioned buildings. Carbon dioxide is an acidic oxide (when dissolved in water it forms carbonic acid). It is removed from stale air using either sodium hydroxide (soda) or calcium hydroxide (slaked lime) or a mixture of the two (soda lime).

The most important industrial application of neutralisation is in the manufacture of fertilisers. For example, ammonium nitrate fertiliser is manufactured by neutralising nitric acid with ammonia:

$$\text{ammonia} \quad + \quad \text{nitric acid} \quad \longrightarrow \quad \text{ammonium nitrate}$$
$$NH_3 \quad + \quad HNO_3 \quad \longrightarrow \quad NH_4NO_3$$

Ammonium sulphate fertiliser is manufactured by neutralising sulphuric acid with ammonia:

$$\text{ammonia} \quad + \quad \text{sulphuric acid} \quad \longrightarrow \quad \text{ammonium sulphate}$$
$$2NH_3 \quad + \quad H_2SO_4 \quad \longrightarrow \quad (NH_4)_2SO_4$$

The largest group of bases are metal oxides and metal hydroxides such as sodium oxide, aluminium oxide, sodium hydroxide and aluminium hydroxide. These bases neutralise acids to form a salt and water.

Neutralisation is the reaction
base + acid → salt + water

$$\text{e.g. sodium oxide} \quad + \quad \text{hydrochloric acid} \quad \longrightarrow \quad \text{sodium chloride} \quad + \quad \text{water}$$
$$Na_2O \quad + \quad 2HCl \quad \longrightarrow \quad 2NaCl \quad + \quad H_2O$$

$$\text{sodium hydroxide} \quad + \quad \text{hydrochloric acid} \quad \longrightarrow \quad \text{sodium chloride} \quad + \quad \text{water}$$
$$NaOH \quad + \quad HCl \quad \longrightarrow \quad NaCl \quad + \quad H_2O$$

During neutralisation, H^+ ions in the acid react with either oxide ions (O^{2-}) or hydroxide ions (OH^-) in the base to form water.

$$2H^+ + O^{2-} \longrightarrow H_2O \qquad\qquad H^+ + OH^- \longrightarrow H_2O$$
$$\text{(oxide)} \qquad\qquad\qquad\qquad\qquad \text{(hydroxide)}$$

16.6 Alkalis in industry

The most important industrial alkalis are *sodium hydroxide* (**caustic soda**), *calcium hydroxide* (**slaked lime**), *calcium oxide* (**lime**) and *ammonia* (see 17.4).

Fig. 16.6 summarises the manufacture of lime and slaked lime from limestone.

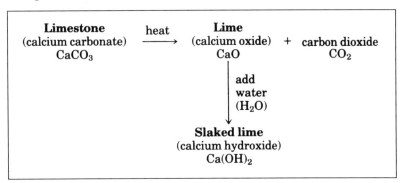

Fig. 16.6 The manufacture of lime and slaked lime from limestone

Lime and slaked lime are used as cheap alkalis in agriculture to neutralise acid soils. They are also used in the manufacture of cement.

Large amounts of sodium hydroxide are used to manufacture soap, paper, rayon and cellulose acetate (Tricel). These processes are illustrated in Figs. 16.7 and 16.8.

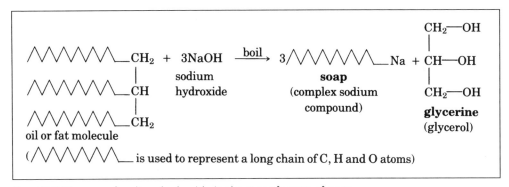

Fig. 16.7 The use of sodium hydroxide in the manufacture of soap

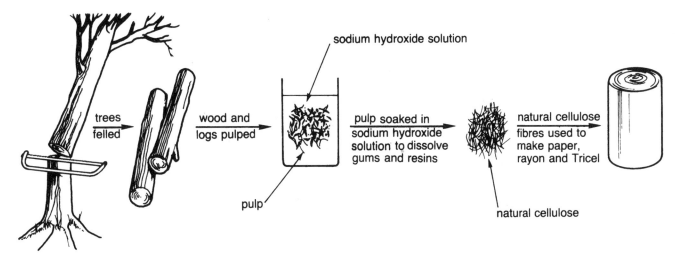

Fig. 16.8 The use of sodium hydroxide in the manufacture of paper, rayon and Tricel

Summary

1 Acids are used to make our clothes, our food and our medicines.

2 **Indicators** can be used to detect acidity and alkalinity.

3 The **pH scale** is used to describe the extent of acidity and alkalinity.
- Acidic substances have a pH below 7.
- Alkaline substances have a pH above 7.
- Neutral substances have a pH of 7.

4 Acids are substances which donate H^+ ions.
- acid (dilute) + metal (above Cu in the reactivity series) → salt + hydrogen
- acid + carbonate → salt + water + carbon dioxide
- acid + base → salt + water

5 Bases are the chemical opposites to acids. Bases take H^+ ions and neutralise acid. Bases include the oxides, hydroxides and carbonates of metals.

6 Alkalis are soluble bases. The commonest alkalis are sodium hydroxide, calcium hydroxide and ammonia.

7 Neutralisation is the reaction

acid	+	base	→	salt	+	water
HCl	+	NaOH	→	NaCl	+	H_2O

The essential reactions in neutralisation are:

	H^+	+	OH^-	→	H_2O
or	$2H^+$	+	O^{2-}	→	H_2O

Quick test 16

Questions 1 to 3

A condensation   D oxidation
B decomposition   E precipitation
C neutralisation

Choose from A to E the type of reaction which occurs when
1 acid soils are treated with lime.
2 sulphur in coal burns to form sulphur dioxide.
3 lime is manufactured from limestone.

Questions 4 to 8

Five liquids, A to E, were found to have the following pHs:

A pH = 1   B pH = 4   C pH = 6   D pH = 8   E pH = 12

Choose from A to E the liquid which
4 is most acidic.
5 would be most suitable for use in preserving food by pickling.
6 would be most suitable for treating indigestion.
7 would be most suitable as an oven grease remover.
8 might be lemonade.

Some power stations are thought to cause acid rain. In January 1985 children from all over Britain took part in a survey to measure the acidity of the acid rain that fell.

9   The children collected rain water and tested it for acidity. Complete the table below using the following:

teat pipette, 1 m^2 polythene sheet, test tube, clean beaker.

Job to be done	Apparatus used
(a) Collect water over a large area	
(b) Store water	
(c) Take a small sample of water for testing	
(d) Put 3 drops of indicator solution into the small sample of water	

10   Why is it important that the beaker is clean?

11   Many lakes in Scotland are very acidic and have to be neutralised by adding limestone which is a carbonate.
   (a) What gas will be given off when the carbonate is added to the acid in the lake?
   (b) What effect does this have on the pH value of the water?

12   Sulphuric acid (H_2SO_4) and nitric acid (HNO_3) are the two main acids in acid rain. What ion is removed when acidic lakes are neutralised?   (*NEAB*)

13   The four substances listed in the table below are all used in the home. The table shows the results for each substance in each of three simple tests.

Substance	Add water then indicator	Action of gentle heat on sample	Action of acid on substance
Sodium carbonate	alkaline	no reaction	odourless gas
Sodium hydrogencarbonate	alkaline	gas evolved	odourless gas
Tartaric acid	acidic	no reaction	no reaction
Calcium hypochlorite	alkaline	no reaction	gas with a strong smell

(a) Devise an identification key to show how this information could be used to identify an unknown solid as one of these substances.

(b) One type of fire extinguisher produces carbon dioxide by reacting a metal carbonate with an acid. The balanced equation for the reaction between sodium carbonate and hydrochloric acid is

$Na_2CO_3 + 2HCl \rightarrow 2NaCl + H_2O + CO_2$

Given the relative atomic masses Na = 23, C = 12 and O = 16,
(i) what is the relative mass of CO_2?

(ii) what is the relative mass of Na_2CO_3?

(c) What mass of CO_2 would be formed by reacting 212 grams of sodium carbonate with excess acid?   (*MEG*)

Chapter 17

The chemical industry

17.1 Choosing an industrial site

Examiner's tip

The four issues raised in 17.1 may be covered in Biology rather than Chemistry lessons.

The chemical industry provides vital materials for our society. Everyday we depend on industrial chemicals for materials such as fertilisers, fibres, foodstuffs, alloys, plastics and paints. Many factors are involved in choosing the site for an industrial plant such as a nuclear power station, an oil refinery, an electrolytic plant or a waste tip. Most of the factors are concerned with:

1 Social issues

- Will it provide employment?
- Is there a readily available and skilled workforce?
- Will it cause a strain on existing social, medical and other community services?
- Will it disrupt or benefit the present community?

2 Environmental issues

- Will it disfigure the countryside with roads, pylons, large buildings, etc?
- Will it produce large amounts of waste or pollution?
- What are the arrangements for waste disposal?
- Will it cause high levels of noise?
- Will it cause dangers to health and safety?

3 Economic issues

- Is there enough cheap land available?
- What is the cost of the raw materials and fuel?
- Will it provide sufficient profits for investors?
- Will the profits benefit the local community?

4 Location issues

- Are the raw materials and fuel available and accessible nearby?
- Are the existing transport facilities (road, rail and/or sea links) suitable for bringing in raw materials and fuel and distributing the products?

17.2 Sulphuric acid – an important industrial acid

The chemical industry is one of the largest manufacturing industries. But, unlike many other industries, its products are used to make other things rather than being used themselves. Sulphuric acid is a very good example of this.

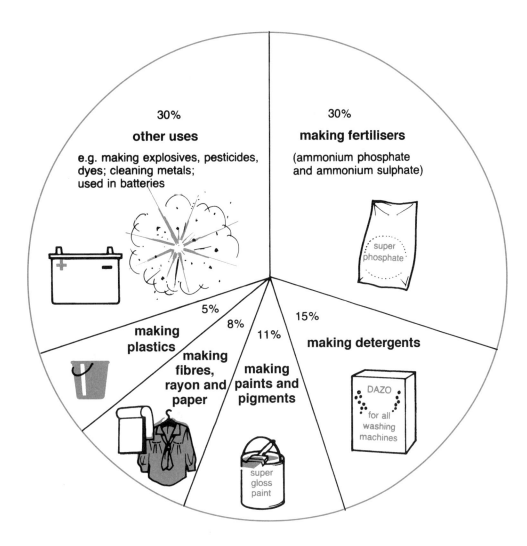

Fig. 17.1 The uses of sulphuric acid

Sulphuric acid is vital to the chemical industry. About 2½ million tonnes are manufactured in the UK each year. Most of this is then used to make a wide variety of other materials (see Fig. 17.1).

Sulphuric acid is used by the chemical industry in two forms – either **dilute** or **concentrated**.

Dilute sulphuric acid contains H^+ and SO_4^{2-} ions in water. It has the typical properties of acids described in 16.3.

Concentrated sulphuric acid contains 98% acid and only 2% water. It contains H_2SO_4 molecules and very few H^+ and SO_4^{2-} ions. Concentrated H_2SO_4 is a strong dehydrating agent, removing water from other materials such as hydrates and carbohydrates. Because of this, it removes water rapidly from living tissues such as the skin and this causes burns.

17.3 Manufacturing sulphuric acid

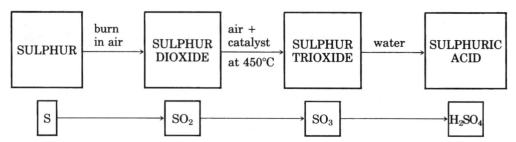

Fig. 17.2 A flow diagram for the manufacture of sulphuric acid

Raw materials

Notice in Fig. 17.2 that the raw materials for the process are **sulphur, air** and **water**. Air costs nothing, water is very cheap and sulphur is relatively inexpensive. This helps to keep down the cost of manufacture. This is important when so much sulphuric acid is needed by industry.

Most of the sulphur used in Britain is imported. It comes from two sources:

- underground deposits of sulphur in the USA, Mexico and Poland;
- 'recovered' sulphur – sulphur which has been removed from crude oil and natural gas.

Chemical processing

Stage 1
Sulphur is burnt in air to produce sulphur dioxide:

$$\text{sulphur} + \text{oxygen} \longrightarrow \text{sulphur dioxide}$$
$$S + O_2 \longrightarrow SO_2$$

Stage 2
The sulphur dioxide is converted to sulphur trioxide by reacting it with oxygen in air. This is called the **Contact Process**. At room temperature, sulphur dioxide and oxygen react very slowly. The reaction is speeded up by using a **catalyst** of vanadium(V) oxide (V_2O_5) and by raising the temperature to 450 °C.

$$\text{sulphur dioxide} + \text{oxygen} \xrightarrow[V_2O_5 \text{ catalyst}]{450\ °C} \text{sulphur trioxide}$$

$$2SO_2 + O_2 \longrightarrow 2SO_3$$

Unfortunately, the reaction of sulphur dioxide with oxygen to form sulphur trioxide is **reversible**. As the SO_3 forms, it starts to decompose and reform SO_2 and O_2. This means that the yield of SO_3 from the reversible process depends on the conditions. The yields of products from other reversible reactions also depend on the conditions. In this case, the reverse reaction gets easier and SO_3 decomposes more easily at higher temperatures. This means that the temperature for the Contact Process must not be too high. The ideal temperature which gives a reasonable rate of forming SO_3 and a slow reverse reaction is found to be 450 °C.

Stage 3
The sulphur trioxide reacts with water to form sulphuric acid.

$$\text{sulphur trioxide} + \text{water} \longrightarrow \text{sulphuric acid}$$
$$SO_3 + H_2O \longrightarrow H_2SO_4$$

17.4 Ammonia – an important industrial alkali

Ammonia, NH$_3$, is an important industrial alkali. It is made from nitrogen and hydrogen. About two million tonnes are manufactured in the UK each year. About three-quarters of this ammonia is used to make fertilisers. The other quarter is used to make a variety of products from nylon, plastics and fibres to dyes and explosives.

The properties of ammonia are summarised in Fig. 17.3. Unlike most bases, ammonia is a **gas**. It has a very pungent smell which you may have smelt in laboratory experiments, or in toilet cleaners which contain ammonia dissolved in water.

Ammonia as a base

Ammonia acts as a base in most reactions. It has typical alkaline reactions with

- indicators,
- acids, forming ammonium salts.

Most fertilisers are made by reacting ammonia with acids. For example, 'Nitram' (ammonium nitrate) is made by reacting ammonia with nitric acid:

$$\text{ammonia} + \text{nitric acid} \longrightarrow \text{ammonium nitrate}$$
$$\text{NH}_3 + \text{HNO}_3 \longrightarrow \text{NH}_4\text{NO}_3$$

**AMMONIA
(NH$_3$)**

- gas at room temperature
- colourless
- pungent smell
- less dense than air
- very soluble in water to give an alkaline solution

Fig. 17.3 Properties of ammonia

17.5 Manufacturing ammonia

Raw materials

The chemical industry uses large amounts of ammonia. Its cost needs to be kept to a minimum. This means that a cheap source of raw materials is essential. Look back at the formula of ammonia in Fig. 17.3. Ammonia contains **nitrogen** and **hydrogen**. These starting materials are obtained from **air**, **water** and **natural gas** (Fig. 17.4).

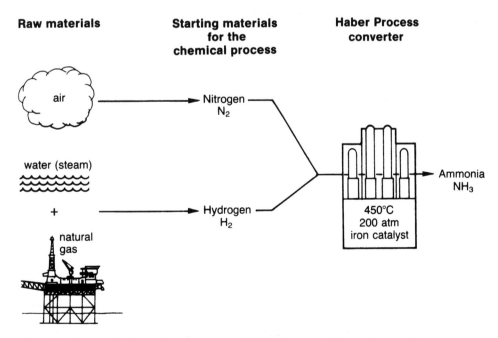

Fig. 17.4 Raw materials and starting materials for the manufacture of ammonia

Chemical processing – the Haber Process

During the last century, the population of Europe rose very rapidly. More crops and other foods were needed to feed more people. To increase production, farmers began to use nitrogen compounds as fertilisers. At first, the main source of fertilisers was sodium nitrate from Chile.

By 1900, the deposits of sodium nitrate in Chile were almost used up. Another source of nitrogen had to be found. The obvious source was nitrogen in the air, but this is very unreactive. No-one had yet found a way of converting nitrogen gas into ammonium salts and nitrates for fertilisers.

The problem was solved by the German chemist, **Fritz Haber** (1868–1934). Haber found the conditions needed to make ammonia from hydrogen and nitrogen. In time, the **Haber Process** became the most important method of manufacturing ammonia.

Nitrogen is so unreactive that it does not combine with hydrogen under ordinary conditions. So, the Haber Process uses high temperature (450 °C), high pressure (200 atmospheres) and a catalyst of iron to make nitrogen and hydrogen combine.

$$\text{nitrogen} \quad + \quad \text{hydrogen} \quad \xrightarrow[\text{iron catalyst}]{450\,°C,\ 200\ atm} \quad \text{ammonia}$$

$$N_2 \quad + \quad 3H_2 \quad \xrightarrow{\hspace{3cm}} \quad 2NH_3$$

Even so, only a fraction of the mixture is converted to ammonia. The reaction is also **reversible**. This means that as soon as the ammonia is formed, it starts to decompose reforming nitrogen and hydrogen and the amount of product (ammonia) is very dependent on the conditions used. If the mixture is left at 450 °C and 200 atmospheres pressure, only 28% of the nitrogen and hydrogen would form ammonia. When this position is reached, nitrogen and hydrogen are reacting to form ammonia, whilst ammonia is breaking up to form nitrogen and hydrogen at the same rate. This can be represented as:

$$N_2 + 3H_2 \rightleftharpoons 2NH_3$$

Notice the symbol $\rightleftharpoons$ in this equation. It shows that the reactants are forming the products at the same rate that the products are reforming the reactants. The mixture is said to be in **equilibrium**.

In order to separate ammonia from the equilibrium mixture, the hot gases are cooled to about −50 °C. This liquefies the ammonia. The unreacted nitrogen and hydrogen remain as gases and can be recycled.

17.6 Fertilisers from ammonia

Plants need certain essential elements in order to grow well (see 2.8). Some of these essential elements are obtained from the air or from water in the soil. Others are obtained from soluble compounds in the soil. Three essential elements which plants obtain from soluble compounds in the soil are nitrogen, phosphorus and potassium. So, if plants are to grow successfully year after year, nitrogen, phosphorus and potassium must be replaced in the soil by adding fertilisers (Table 17.1).

Table 17.1 The role of nitrogen, phosphorus and potassium in plants

Essential element	Role in plant growth	Effect of shortage
Nitrogen	Needed for synthesis of proteins and chlorophyll	Plants are short and stunted
Phosphorus	Needed for synthesis of nucleic acids	Plants grow slowly Seeds and fruit are small
Potassium	Takes part in the synthesis of carbohydrates and proteins	Leaves become yellow and curl inwards

Fertilisers can be used as single compounds such as ammonium nitrate ('Nitram') or as mixtures of compounds containing nitrogen, phosphorus and potassium ('NPK' fertilisers). The proportions of nitrogen, phosphorus and potassium in NPK fertilisers are usually given as percentage nitrogen (N), percentage phosphorus(V) oxide (P_2O_5) and percentage potassium oxide (K_2O).

Nitrogen fertilisers

Nitrogen fertilisers are usually ammonium salts or nitrates. All of these are made from ammonia. **Ammonium nitrate** ('Nitram') is the most widely used fertiliser because

- it is very soluble in water,
- it can be stored and transported as a solid,
- it contains a high percentage of nitrogen (see Table 17.2).

The higher the percentage of nitrogen the better, because a smaller amount of useless material is stored and transported.

Examiner's tip

Questions on ammonia and fertilisers are popular in GCSE exams.

Table 17.2 Calculating the percentage of nitrogen in ammonium nitrate

Fertiliser	Ammonium nitrate
Formula	NH_4NO_3
Relative formula mass	Assuming the relative atomic masses H = 1, N = 14 and O = 16; $NH_4NO_3 = 14 + (4 \times 1) + 14 + (3 \times 16) = 80$
Mass of nitrogen in relative formula mass	14 + 14 = 28
Percentage nitrogen	$\dfrac{\text{Mass of nitrogen}}{\text{Relative formula mass}} \times 100 = \dfrac{28}{80} \times 100 = 35$

⟁Ⓓ 17.7 The nitrogen cycle

We have looked at man-made inorganic fertilisers like ammonium nitrate. Large quantities of **organic fertilisers** are also used by farmers and gardeners (see 10.2 and Table 10.1).

The most widely used organic fertilisers are **animal manure** and **compost** formed from the decaying remains of plants. The nitrogen compounds in manure and compost are decomposed by bacteria in the soil to produce nitrates and ammonium salts. These nitrates and ammonium salts are then absorbed through the roots of plants and used for growth. Animals have to eat plants or other animals in order to get the nitrogen and the proteins which they need. Eventually the animals and plants die and their decaying remains act as organic fertilisers again.

This cycle, involving nitrogen in the air and nitrogen compounds in plants, in animals and in decaying remains, is called the **nitrogen cycle** (Fig. 17.5).

Notice in Fig. 17.5 that some of the nitrogen that plants need is provided by **nitrogen-fixing bacteria**. These bacteria live in nodules on the roots of **leguminous plants** such as peas, beans and clover. The nitrogen-fixing bacteria can convert nitrogen from the air into nitrogen compounds for use by the plants. This conversion of atmospheric nitrogen to nitrogen compounds in plants is sometimes called *natural* nitrogen fixation. The conversion of atmospheric nitrogen to ammonia in the Haber Process is called *industrial* nitrogen fixation.

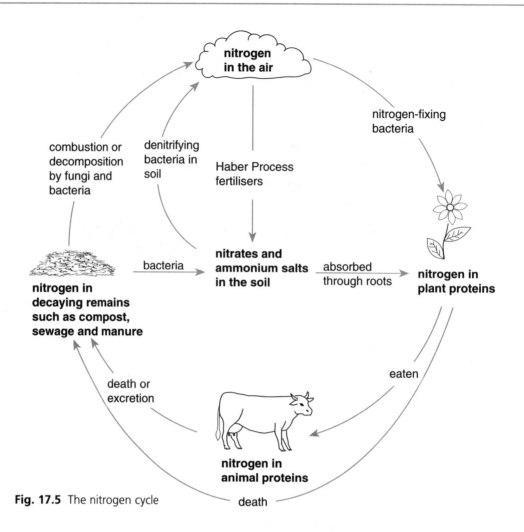

Fig. 17.5 The nitrogen cycle

17.8 Reaction rates and industrial processes

The chemists who work in industry try to produce materials as cheaply as possible. In order to do this they choose conditions which

- increase reaction rates,
- use the cheapest methods and raw materials.
  Reaction rates can be speeded up by:
- **increasing the concentration of the reacting solutions**
  (or increasing the pressure of reacting gases);
- **increasing the surface area** of contact between reacting materials;
- **increasing the temperature** of reactants;
- **using a suitable catalyst.**

Look back at the descriptions of the Contact Process (see 17.3) and the Haber Process (see 17.5). What conditions are used to increase the reaction rate in (i) the Contact Process, (ii) the Haber Process?

17.9 How fast?

Everyday we are concerned about how fast certain reactions occur. We want to know how long it takes to bake a cake, how long it takes to digest a meal and how quickly steel articles rust if they are left outdoors. In fact, there are great variations in the rates at which different reactions take place.

Some reactions are so fast that they are almost instantaneous. Other reactions, like the weathering of limestone on buildings, happen so slowly that it may be centuries before we notice the effect. Most reactions take place at steady rates, somewhere between the extremes of explosions and weathering. The reactions involved in cooking food, in digesting a meal and in burning fuels are good examples of this.

Measuring reaction rates

During a reaction, reactants are being used up and products are forming. So the amounts of the reactants fall and the amounts of the products rise. The reaction rate tells us *how fast the reaction is taking place*. We can calculate the reaction rate by measuring *how much reactant is used up or how much product forms in a given time*.

$$\text{Reaction rate} = \frac{\text{change in amount of a substance}}{\text{time taken}}$$

The rate of the reaction between limestone and acid can be studied using the apparatus shown in Fig. 17.6.

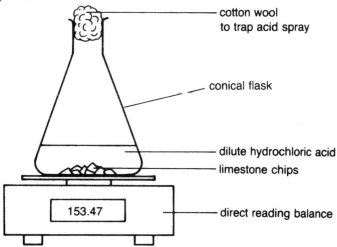

Fig. 17.6 Studying the reaction between limestone and acid

As the reaction occurs, carbon dioxide is produced.

$$CaCO_3(s) + 2HCl(aq) \rightarrow CaCl_2(aq) + H_2O(l) + CO_2(g)$$

The carbon dioxide escapes from the flask as a gas and the mass of the flask and its contents decrease. The decrease in mass is the mass of carbon dioxide produced. The results of one experiment have been plotted on a graph in Fig. 17.7.

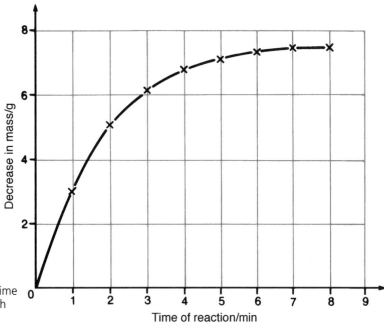

Fig. 17.7 A graph of the decrease in mass against time when limestone reacts with dilute hydrochloric acid

Notice from the graph that there is a decrease in mass of 3 grams in the first minute.
We can calculate the reaction rate as follows:

$$\text{reaction rate in first minute} = \frac{\text{change in mass of carbon dioxide}}{\text{time taken}}$$

$$= \frac{3 \text{ g}}{1 \text{ min}} = \textbf{3 g/min}$$

During the second minute (from time = 1 min to time = 2 min), 2 grams of carbon dioxide
are lost. Therefore,

$$\text{reaction rate in second minute} = \frac{2 \text{ g}}{1 \text{ min}} = \textbf{2 g/min}$$

These calculations and the graph show that the reaction rate is fastest at the start of the
reaction. The faster the reaction, the steeper is the graph. During the reaction, the rate
decreases and the slope of the graph levels off. Eventually, the reaction stops (reaction rate
= 0 g/min) and the graph becomes flat (gradient or slope = 0).

17.10 Factors affecting reaction rates

Think about the following points:
- Large potatoes take longer to boil than small potatoes.
- Milk goes sour more quickly on a hot summer's day.
- Concentrated detergent cleans dishes faster than dilute detergent.
- Stains are removed by soaking a tablecloth in biological detergent.

These points illustrate four important factors which affect the rates of chemical reactions:
- surface area
- temperature
- concentration
- catalysts

Surface area

The surface area of a solid is the area of it which is exposed. If the solid is cut up into smaller
pieces, more surface is exposed and this means it can react faster. This explains why
cut-up potatoes cook faster than whole potatoes. With more surface exposed, the smaller
pieces of potato cook more quickly. Reactions occur when particles collide. When the
potato is cut into smaller pieces, hot water particles collide more frequently with particles
on the surface of the potato. This causes more particles to react per minute, so the potatoes
cook more quickly.

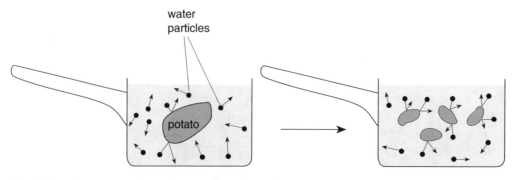

Fig. 17.8 When a potato is cut into smaller pieces, there are more collisions per minute with hot
water particles, so the potatoes cook more quickly

Temperature

Milk sours in a few hours on a hot, sunny day, but it will keep for several days in a cool refrigerator. The chemical reactions which take place when milk goes sour occur more quickly at higher temperatures. At higher temperatures, particles are moving around faster. They therefore collide more frequently and with more energy. This means that the reaction rate increases when the frequency or energy of collision between particles increases.

Concentration

Concentrated detergent removes grease from dishes more quickly than dilute detergent. In general, concentrated solutions react more quickly than dilute ones (Fig. 17.9).

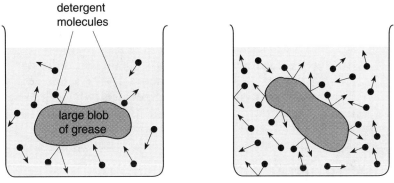

Fig. 17.9 In a concentrated solution there are more collisions per second between the reacting particles, so the reaction proceeds more quickly

Catalysts

Catalysts enable substances to react more easily. They do this by helping bonds between atoms to break and form more easily. The particles need less energy to react, so the reactions proceed more quickly.

For example, catalysts are now used in car exhaust systems. Car exhaust fumes contain poisonous carbon monoxide and nitrogen oxide. These pollutants react together very slowly to form carbon dioxide and nitrogen which are not poisonous.

$$\text{carbon monoxide} \; + \; \text{nitrogen oxide} \longrightarrow \text{carbon dioxide} \; + \; \text{nitrogen}$$
$$2CO \quad + \quad 2NO \quad \longrightarrow \quad 2CO_2 \quad + \quad N_2$$

When the exhaust fumes pass over platinum, the carbon monoxide and nitrogen oxide react together very rapidly. However, *none of the platinum is used up during the reaction*. The mass of the platinum is the same after the reaction as before. The platinum has acted as a **catalyst**.

A catalyst is a substance which alters the rate of a reaction without being used up.

Most catalysts speed up their reactions. However, a few catalysts are used to *slow down* reactions. These are called **negative catalysts** or **inhibitors**.

Catalysts play an important part in industry. Sulphuric acid (see 17.3), ammonia (see 17.5) and petrol (see 18.9) are all produced by processes involving catalysts. These catalysts allow their respective reactions to take place faster and at lower temperatures. Less energy (heat) is therefore needed for the processes and they are more economical.

Catalysts are also vitally important to all living things. Catalysts in biological processes are called **enzymes**. Enzymes are proteins. At this moment, thousands of different chemical reactions are going on in your body. Every one of these reactions is catalysed by a specific enzyme. Without enzymes the reactions in your body would stop and you would die. Reactions in plants, e.g. photosynthesis, are also catalysed by enzymes (see 2.6).

Enzymes are used in biological detergents and washing powders. They break down foods, blood and other biological substances. These biological detergents are more effective than ordinary detergents because they contain enzymes as well as soaps and detergents.

More and more industrial processes are being developed which use enzymes. These processes include baking, brewing and the manufacture of fruit juices, yoghurt, vitamins, cheese and pharmaceuticals. The enzymes for these processes are often extracted from living material such as animal tissues, plants, yeast and fungi.

17.11 The effect of temperature on the rate of enzyme-catalysed reactions

Most catalysed reactions go faster as the temperature rises. This means that the reaction rate increases as expected with temperature. This is also true of enzyme-catalysed reactions at fairly low temperatures, but above about 40 °C their reaction rate decreases rapidly as the temperature rises. This is because the enzymes are proteins and their structure is damaged as the temperature rises above 40 °C. This damage to the protein structure is called **denaturation**. As the protein is denatured, it becomes less and less effective as a catalyst and the enzyme-catalysed reaction gets slower and eventually stops. This explains why enzyme washing powders (which clean by catalysing the breakdown of grease and other stains) cannot be used with very hot water well above 40 °C.

Summary

1 The site for an industrial, chemical, mining or manufacturing plant is determined by four main factors:

- social issues,
- economic issues,
- environmental issues,
- location issues.

2 Sulphuric acid is vital to the chemical industry. It is manufactured from sulphur, air and water.

$$\text{sulphur} + \text{oxygen (in air)} \longrightarrow \text{sulphur dioxide}$$
$$\text{sulphur dioxide} + \text{oxygen} \longrightarrow \text{sulphur trioxide}$$
$$\text{sulphur trioxide} + \text{water} \longrightarrow \text{sulphuric acid}$$

3 Ammonia is an important industrial alkali. It is manufactured from nitrogen and hydrogen.

$$\text{nitrogen} + \text{hydrogen} \xrightarrow[\text{iron catalyst}]{450\,°C,\ 200\ \text{atm}} \text{ammonia}$$

4 When nitrogen reacts with hydrogen to form ammonia, an **equilibrium** mixture is produced. At equilibrium, nitrogen and hydrogen are forming ammonia at the same rate as ammonia is decomposing back to nitrogen and hydrogen.

5 Ammonia is an important material for the manufacture of fertilisers, particularly ammonium nitrate.

$$\text{ammonia} + \text{nitric acid} \longrightarrow \text{ammonium nitrate}$$

6 The **nitrogen cycle** involves a cycle of nitrogen and nitrogen compounds in the air, in fertilisers, in plants, in animals and in decaying remains.

7 The **rates of chemical reactions** can be speeded up by:

- increasing the concentration of reactants (or increasing the pressure of reacting gases),
- increasing the surface area of contact between reactants,

- increasing the temperature of reactants,
- using a suitable catalyst.

8   **Reaction rates** tell us how fast reactions are taking place.

For example, reaction rate $= \dfrac{\text{change in mass of carbon dioxide}}{\text{time taken}}$

9   A **catalyst** is a substance which alters the rate of a reaction without being used up.

10   Negative catalysts which slow reactions down are called **inhibitors**.

11   **Enzymes** are the catalysts in biological processes.

Quick test 17

Questions 1 to 4

The diagram shows five supplies of water (labelled A, B, C, D and E) to a large lake.

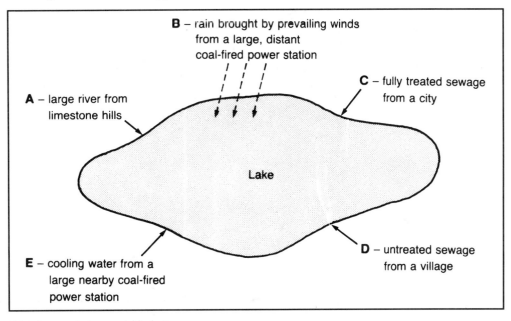

Which supply is most likely to

1   make the water in the lake more acidic?
2   raise the temperature of water in the lake?
3   lead to eutrophication in the lake?
4   neutralise any acidic substances in the lake?

Questions 5 to 7

Consider the following changes which might be made to the reaction between dilute hydrochloric acid and marble chips (calcium carbonate):

A   increasing the temperature
B   diluting the acid further with water
C   using a larger reaction vessel
D   using larger marble chips
E   using smaller marble chips

Which change or changes would

5   increase the rate of the reaction?
6   not affect the rate of the reaction?
7   decrease the rate of the reaction?

Questions 8 to 14

Plants need compounds containing nitrogen in order to grow healthily. These compounds are absorbed through the plant roots from soil water. They enter the soil both by natural processes and with the help of people. This century it has become possible to manufacture ammonia on a large scale by the Haber Process. The ammonia produced is used to make compounds which are used as fertilisers.

8   Why can nitrogen gas in the air in soil *not* be used by most plants?
9   Name one natural process which produces nitrogen compounds that can enter the soil in a form that can be used by plants.
10 Explain why natural sources of nitrogen compounds are not sufficient for repeated crop growing on the same land.
11 What raw materials are used as a source of hydrogen and nitrogen in the production of ammonia in the Haber Process?
12 In the Haber Process, the nitrogen and hydrogen are reacted at 450 °C. Why do you think the reaction is carried out at high temperature instead of ordinary temperature?
13 Ammonia is usually converted into a solid chemical such as ammonium nitrate for use as a fertiliser. Write the word equation for the reaction which is used to make ammonium nitrate from ammonia.
14 The formula of ammonium nitrate is NH_4NO_3. The relative atomic masses of the elements present are: N = 14, H = 1, O = 16. Calculate the percentage by mass of nitrogen in ammonium nitrate.   (*MEG*)

Questions 15 and 16

Ammonia is used to make fertilisers. It is made from nitrogen and hydrogen. The graph shows the percentage of ammonia that can be made from the same mixture of nitrogen and hydrogen at different temperatures and pressures.

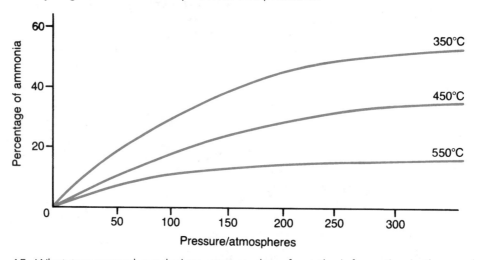

15 What *two* general conclusions can you draw from the information in the graph?
16 Under what conditions of temperature and pressure might you expect that part of a factory producing ammonia to operate?   (*SEB*)

Questions 17 to 20

The diagram of the nitrogen cycle in Fig. 17.5 may help you to answer some of these questions.

17 What do the letters NPK on a bag of fertiliser stand for?
18 How do bacteria in the roots of pea plants take part in the nitrogen cycle?
19 Suggest *two* reasons why most of the nitrates in the soil are not used by plants.
20 Some bacteria in the soil decompose nitrates to nitrogen. These bacteria work best in soil containing little or no air. Suggest conditions in which these bacteria will be most active.

Chapter 18

Energy, fuels and plastics

18.1 Burning and fuels

Burning is probably the most important chemical process. We use burning to keep warm, to cook food, to drive vehicles and to generate electricity.

Burning involves the oxidation of fuels to produce heat.

It is sometimes called **combustion**.

The most important fuels are **coal, oil** and **natural gas**. These are called **fossil fuels** because they have formed from the decay of dead animals and plants. Fossil fuels are mostly **hydrocarbons** – *compounds of hydrogen and carbon*. During burning, the hydrogen and carbon react with oxygen in the air to produce water, carbon dioxide and heat. The water and carbon dioxide escape as waste gases.

$$\underset{\substack{\text{(compound of}\\\text{carbon and hydrogen)}}}{\text{fuel}} + \text{oxygen} \xrightarrow{\text{burning}} \text{carbon dioxide} + \underset{\substack{\text{(hydrogen}\\\text{oxide)}}}{\text{water}} + \text{heat}$$

$$\text{e.g.} \quad \underset{\substack{\text{methane in}\\\text{natural gas}}}{CH_4(g)} + 2O_2(g) \longrightarrow CO_2(g) + 2H_2O(l) + \text{heat}$$

Reactions like this which *give out heat* are called **exothermic reactions**. When fuels burn, a lot of heat is produced. This causes the reactants to burst into flame. Although the burning of fuels can be dangerous, these reactions can be controlled and used in many ways. This happens in a gas cooker or in a Bunsen burner when natural gas reacts steadily with oxygen in the air to produce a flame.

If fuels burn in a limited supply of air, they produce carbon (soot) and *carbon monoxide* as well as carbon dioxide. This is why carbon monoxide is present in car exhaust fumes. Carbon monoxide is very poisonous so you should avoid inhaling exhaust gases.

18.2 Fuels for various processes

Each year in the UK, we need energy equivalent to that which could be provided by about 300 million tonnes of coal. Fig. 18.1 shows the percentages of this energy which we obtain from coal, oil, natural gas, nuclear power and hydroelectric power.

Some fuels, such as coal and coke, are difficult to set alight. Other fuels, like natural gas, burn so rapidly and produce so much heat that they quickly burst into flames. A few fuels, for example hydrogen and petrol vapour, react so rapidly that they can cause explosions.

Because of the dangers of fire and explosion, all fuels must be used and handled with great care.

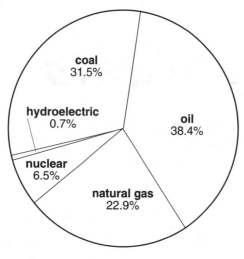

Fig. 18.1 The percentages of our energy needs from different sources (1988)
(Source: BP *Statistical Review of World Energy*, July 1989)

Choosing a fuel

Fuels have different properties. Because of this, different fuels are suitable for different purposes. What is more, industrial chemists have found ways of producing new fuels for specific purposes. These special man-made fuels include firelighters, coke, petrol, GAZ and lighter fuel.

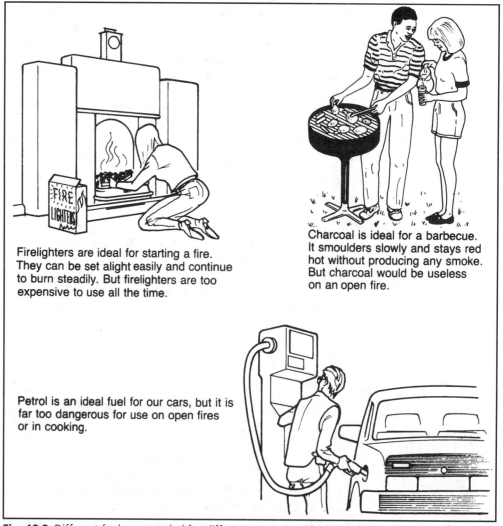

Firelighters are ideal for starting a fire. They can be set alight easily and continue to burn steadily. But firelighters are too expensive to use all the time.

Charcoal is ideal for a barbecue. It smoulders slowly and stays red hot without producing any smoke. But charcoal would be useless on an open fire.

Petrol is an ideal fuel for our cars, but it is far too dangerous for use on open fires or in cooking.

Fig. 18.2 Different fuels are needed for different purposes. Think carefully before choosing a fuel for a particular purpose.

The important criteria to consider in choosing a fuel

- **Cost** Is it important to have a cheap supply of fuel?
- **Availability** Are large amounts of fuel required? If so, how easily can it be obtained?
- **Storage** How easily can the fuel be stored? Will special facilities be needed to store the fuel safely?
- **Transport** How easily can the fuel be transported? Solid fuels are easier to store and transport than liquid fuels. Liquid fuels are easier to store and transport than gaseous fuels.
- **Pollution** Does the fuel produce a lot of ash? Does the fuel produce much smoke?
- **Combustibility** How easily can the fuel be set alight? Does the fuel burn steadily?
- **Safety** Does the fuel pose any risk of fire or explosion?

18.3 Measuring the energy from fuels

Fig. 18.3 shows the apparatus which can be used to find the energy produced when a fuel burns. The heat from the burning fuel is used to heat the water in the metal can. By measuring:

- the volume of water in the can,
- the temperature rise of the water and
- the mass of fuel burnt,

we can calculate the energy (heat) produced when one gram of the fuel burns. The results of one experiment using methylated spirits (meths) are as follows.

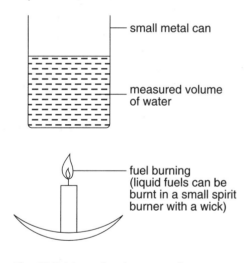

Fig. 18.3 Measuring the energy from a fuel

Volume of water in metal can	300 cm^3
∴ mass of water in can	300 g
Rise in temperature of water	8 °C
Mass of meths burnt	0.5 g

In the experiment, the temperature of 300 g of water was raised 8 °C.

4.2 joules of energy (heat) will warm up 1 g of water by 1 °C.

Therefore 300 × 4.2 joules will warm up 300 g of water by 1 °C,
and 300 × 4.2 × 8 joules will warm up 300 g of water by 8 °C.

This amount of heat (energy) was produced by 0.5 g of meths

⇒ 0.5 g meths produced 300 × 4.2 × 8
= 10 080 joules (J)
= 10.08 kilojoules (kJ)

Therefore, 1 g of meths produces 18.16 kJ of energy on burning.

The measurement of energy in joules is discussed in 21.1.

18.4 Fossil fuels – coal, oil and natural gas

300 million years ago, the Earth was covered in forests and the sea was teeming with tiny organisms. As these plants and animals died, large amounts of decaying material began to pile up. Where the decaying material was in contact with air, it rotted away completely. During this process, complex compounds containing carbon, hydrogen, oxygen and nitrogen in the rotting material reacted with oxygen in the air. The products were carbon dioxide, water and nitrogen.

In some areas, however, the decaying material was covered by the sea, by sediment from rivers or by rocks from earth movements. In these places, the material decayed in the absence of oxygen. It was still attacked by bacteria, but instead of rotting away completely it was compressed by the water and rocks above. Over millions of years this led to the slow formation of coal from plants and to the formation of oil and natural gas from sea creatures.

Conserving fossil fuels

For the last 150 years, industrialised nations have relied on fossil fuels, particularly oil, as sources of energy and for important chemicals. We depend on oil for transport and as the source of chemicals to manufacture important materials like plastics, fibres, paint and antifreeze. Unfortunately, supplies of fossil fuels will not last forever. Coal is still plentiful, but oil and natural gas are likely to run out in fifty to sixty years' time. We need to conserve fossil fuels and prevent the waste of energy. This has led to:

- the use of alternative energy sources (see 18.5);
- improved methods of insulation (see 21.9);
- more efficient use of fuels.

18.5 Alternative energy sources

In time, our supplies of fossil fuels are bound to run out. This means that we must look for alternative energy sources. It is particularly important to find other sources of energy for transport and for generating electricity, both of which rely on oil.

At present, the most viable alternative source of large amounts of electrical energy is nuclear power. This and other alternatives to fossil fuels are summarised in Table 18.1.

Table 18.1 Alternative energy sources

Energy source	How is the energy source used ?
nuclear power	Nuclear fission of uranium-235 produces heat (see 26.8). This heat is used to produce steam which drives turbines generating electricity.
tidal power	As the tides come in and flow out, the water is made to drive turbines which generate electricity.
wind power	The wind is used to drive giant windmills (wind turbines) which generate electricity.
hydroelectric power	Falling water is used to drive turbines which generate electricity. Sometimes the electricity is used to pump water into a high reservoir. In this way, energy can be stored in the water for later use.
solar power	Energy from the Sun is used to heat water in solar panels or to generate electricity using photo cells.
biomass	Material from plants and animals is used to provide fuel for heat, e.g. wood, charcoal, vegetable oils. Sometimes the animal and plant materials (such as manure and compost) are allowed to decompose in the absence of air. This produces **biogas** which is about 60% methane and 40% carbon dioxide.

Fossil fuels and uranium are sometimes described as **non-renewable energy sources**. Once used, they are gone forever. They cannot be replaced. On the other hand, tidal power, wind power, hydroelectric power, solar power and biomass are **renewable energy sources**. They keep on being replaced. However much they are used, the tide continues to rise and fall, the wind continues to blow, etc.

18.6 Crude oil

Crude oil (petroleum) is our main source of fuel and organic (carbon-based) chemicals (Fig. 18.4). The crude oil comes to refineries in the UK from oil wells in the North Sea and the Middle East.

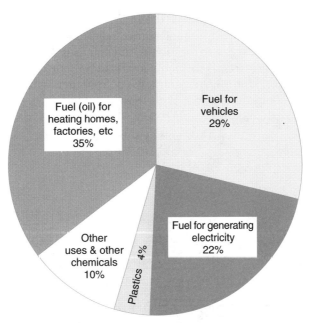

Fig. 18.4 The uses of crude oil

Crude oil is a thick, smelly, dark brown liquid. It is a mixture of hundreds of different compounds. These vary from simple substances like methane (CH_4) to complex substances with dozens of atoms per molecule. Most of the compounds in crude oil are hydrocarbons.

Fractional distillation of crude oil

Crude oil itself is useless. It must be separated into different parts or **fractions** before it is used. Each fraction contains a mixture of hydrocarbons with similar properties. Some of the fractions contain *volatile* hydrocarbons which are easily vaporised. These fractions can be used as petrol. Other fractions are much less volatile. They can be used as fuel for ships or power stations.

The separation of crude oil into fractions is carried out by **fractional distillation**. Fig. 18.5 shows how fractional distillation is carried out at an oil refinery. It also shows the temperatures and products at different heights in the fractionating column.

The crude oil is first heated by a furnace and the vapours pass into the lower part of the fractionating column. As the vapours rise up the column through holes in the trays, the temperature falls. Vapours of different compounds condense at different heights in the column as the temperature falls below their boiling points. Liquids such as petrol (gasoline), which boil at low temperatures, condense high up the column. Liquids such as diesel oil, which boil at higher temperatures, condense lower down.

Each fraction from crude oil contains a mixture of similar compounds with roughly the same number of carbon atoms. Table 18.2 summarises the properties and uses of the different fractions collected at an oil refinery. The uses of the various fractions depend on their properties. For example, refinery gases burn easily at a jet without producing any smoke, so they are ideal for cooking. The residue contains viscous materials which can be used as lubricants or sealants (e.g. bitumen).

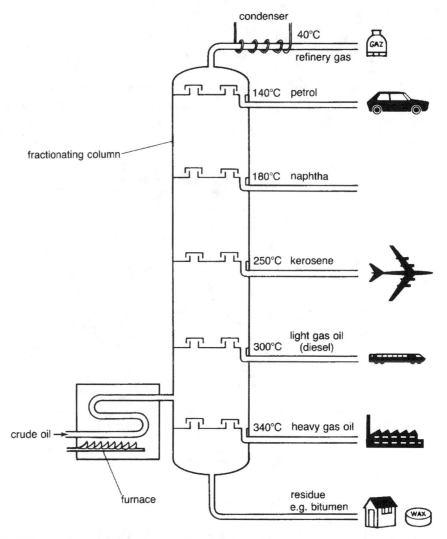

Fig. 18.5 The products and temperatures in a fractionating column at an oil refinery

Table 18.2 The properties and uses of the different fractions produced by fractional distillation of crude oil

Fraction	Boiling range/°C	Number of carbon atoms in molecules	Uses
refinery gas	up to 40	1 – 4	fuel for gas cookers, LPG, GAZ, plastics
petrol (gasoline)	40 – 140	5 – 10	fuel for vehicles, chemicals
naphtha	140 – 180	8 – 12	raw material for chemicals and plastics
kerosene (paraffin)	180 – 250	10 – 16	aircraft fuel, heating and raw material for chemicals
light gas oil (diesel oil)	250 – 300	14 – 20	fuel for trains and lorries, raw materials for chemicals, plastics
heavy gas oil	300 – 340	20 – 30	fuel for ships, factories, central heating
residue	above 340	more than 25	lubricants, waxes, bitumen for roads and roofing

18.7 Chemicals in crude oil – alkanes

Most of the chemicals in crude oil are hydrocarbons. There are various groups of hydrocarbons. The simplest series of hydrocarbons is the **alkanes**.

Table 18.3 describes the first four members of the alkanes. Crude oil and natural gas are the main sources of alkanes. Natural gas is mostly methane (CH_4), with small amounts of ethane (C_2H_6). Propane (C_3H_8) and butane (C_4H_{10}) are the main constituents of 'Calor gas' and GAZ respectively. These are used as fuels by campers and caravaners.

Alkanes with between 5 and 17 carbon atoms are liquids at room temperature. For example, octane (C_8H_{18}) is one of the main constituents of petrol. Alkanes with 18 or more carbon atoms are solids at room temperature.

Table 18.3 The first four members of the alkanes

Alkane	Molecular formula	Structural formula
Methane	CH_4	$\begin{array}{c} H \\ | \\ H-C-H \\ | \\ H \end{array}$
Ethane	C_2H_6	$\begin{array}{c} H\ \ H \\ |\ \ \ | \\ H-C-C-H \\ |\ \ \ | \\ H\ \ H \end{array}$
Propane	C_3H_8	$\begin{array}{c} H\ \ H\ \ H \\ |\ \ \ |\ \ \ | \\ H-C-C-C-H \\ |\ \ \ |\ \ \ | \\ H\ \ H\ \ H \end{array}$
Butane	C_4H_{10}	$\begin{array}{c} H\ \ H\ \ H\ \ H \\ |\ \ \ |\ \ \ |\ \ \ | \\ H-C-C-C-C-H \\ |\ \ \ |\ \ \ |\ \ \ | \\ H\ \ H\ \ H\ \ H \end{array}$

Notice how the alkanes become less volatile and change from gases through liquids to solids as their molecular size increases. Alkanes are typical **simple molecular compounds** (see 15.7). They are:

● gases, volatile liquids or soft solids,
● non-conductors of electricity,
● insoluble in water.

They are also fairly unreactive. Petrol, for example, will not react with sodium or with concentrated sulphuric acid. The most important reaction of alkanes is **combustion**. They burn in air producing carbon dioxide and water.

$$C_3H_8 + 5O_2 \longrightarrow 3CO_2 + 4H_2O$$
propane

These combustion reactions of alkanes are very exothermic, so alkanes in natural gas and crude oil are important as fuels.

18.8 Alkenes

After alkanes, the most important group of hydrocarbons is the **alkenes**. Alkenes are made from alkanes in crude oil. They are used in the manufacture of plastics and other polymers (see 18.9). In alkanes, all the bonds between carbon atoms are single bonds (C—C). Alkenes differ from alkanes because they contain a **double bond** between two of their carbon atoms (C=C). The simplest alkene is ethene (C_2H_4). The next alkene in the series is propene (C_3H_6) (Fig. 18.6).

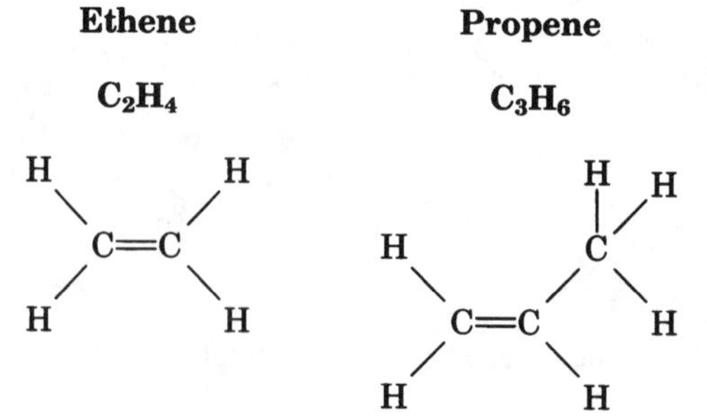

Ethene

C₂H₄

$$C_2H_4$$

Propene

C₃H₆

$$C_3H_6$$

Fig. 18.6 The first two alkenes

Structure and reactions of alkenes

The most stable arrangement for the four bonds to a carbon atom is a tetrahedral one as in alkanes (Fig. 18.7). Because of this structure in which all their carbon atoms have four *single* bonds, alkanes are described as **saturated** hydrocarbons. Alkenes such as ethene, however, contain a *double* covalent bond between two of their carbon atoms and they are described as **unsaturated** hydrocarbons. This makes alkenes much more reactive than alkanes. Other atoms can *add* across the double bond to make two single bonds. So alkenes readily undergo **addition reactions**. Table 18.4 summarises three important addition reactions of ethene.

methane   **ethane**   **ethene**

Fig. 18.7 Models showing the tetrahedral arrangement of atoms bonded to carbon atoms in alkanes (methane and ethane), and the triangular arrangement in an alkene (ethene)

Table 18.4 Three important addition reactions of ethene

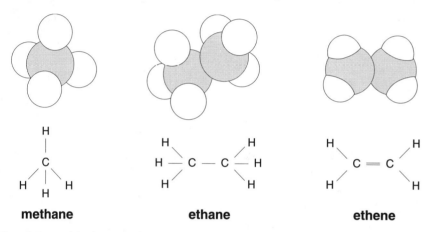

Reaction of ethene	Conditions needed	Equation and product
with bromine or bromine water	reacts easily at room temperature	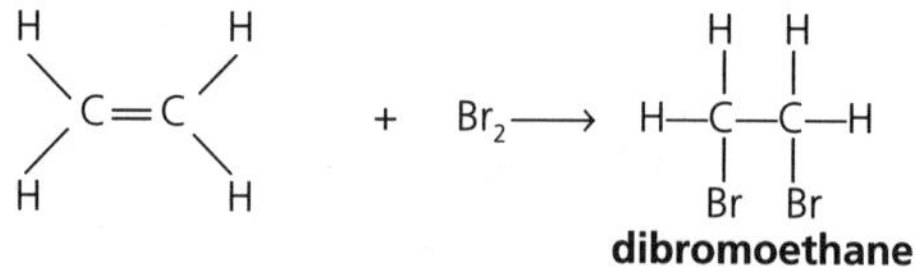 (ethene) + Br₂ ⟶ H—C—C—H with Br Br — **dibromoethane**
with steam	300 °C very high pressure	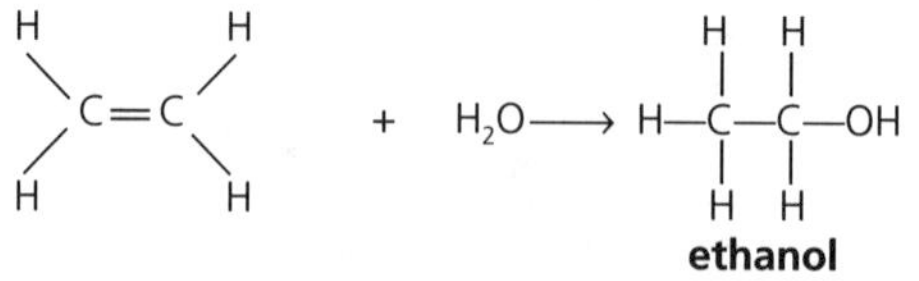 (ethene) + H₂O ⟶ H—C—C—OH — **ethanol**
with itself	high temperatures, high pressures, a suitable catalyst	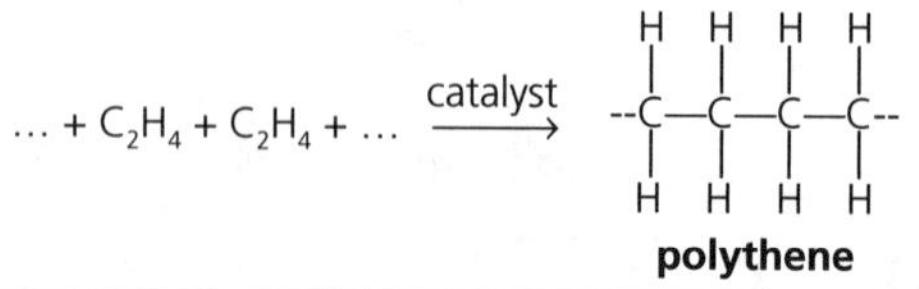 ... + C₂H₄ + C₂H₄ + ... $\xrightarrow{\text{catalyst}}$ — **polythene**

Bromine water is a yellow-orange liquid. During the reaction with ethene it becomes colourless. (The product, dibromoethane, is colourless.) Other alkenes react with bromine water in a similar way so this reaction is used as a **test for alkenes**. The reaction of ethene with steam is important in the manufacture of alcohol and methylated spirits (see 18.10). The reaction of ethene with itself produces polythene (see 18.9).

18.9 Plastics

Polymerisation

Plastics such as polythene, nylon and PVC are **polymers**. They are made by **polymerisation**. This involves joining together small molecules called **monomers**.

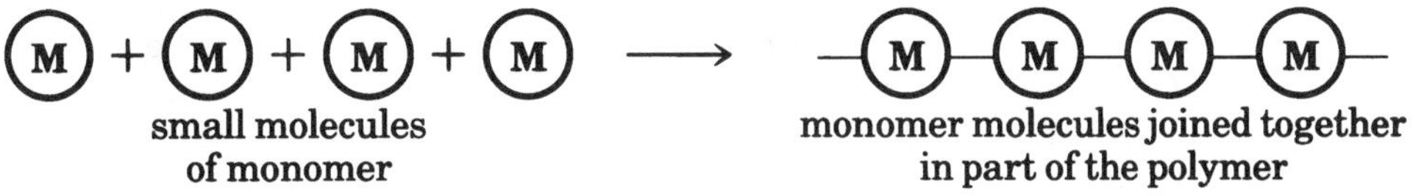

Fig. 18.8 Polymerisation

The most common plastic is **polythene**. This is made by polymerisation of ethene – an addition reaction in which ethene reacts with itself. The process requires high temperature, high pressure and a catalyst.

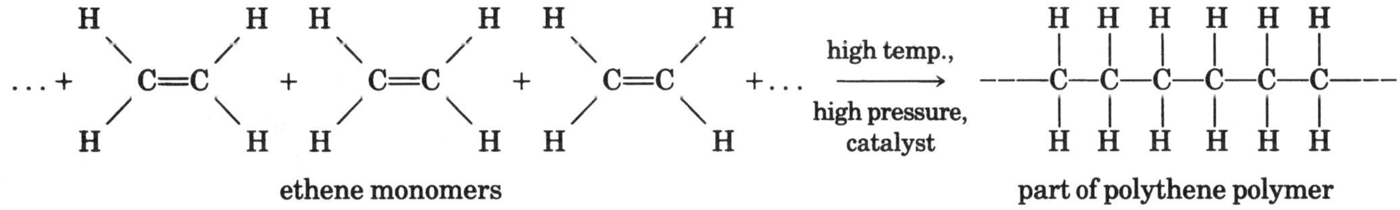

Fig. 18.9 Polymerisation of ethene to form polythene

Polymers from crude oil

Chemists have found ways of obtaining ethene from the heavier fractions of crude oil, such as naphtha and gas oil. These methods involve a process called **cracking**.

During cracking, larger molecules are broken apart forming two smaller molecules. Alkanes, such as decane ($C_{10}H_{22}$) are broken down into smaller alkanes like octane (C_8H_{18}) and alkenes such as ethene (C_2H_4):

$$\text{decane} \longrightarrow \text{octane} + \text{ethene}$$
$$C_{10}H_{22} \longrightarrow C_8H_{18} + C_2H_4$$

Unlike distillation, cracking is a chemical reaction. It involves breaking a bond between carbon atoms to form two new substances. Because of this, it requires high temperatures of about 800 °C.

Ethene and the other alkenes produced during cracking are used to make plastics. The other fragments of cracking, e.g. octane, provide additional supplies of petrol. Larger fragments than octane (molecules with more than eight carbon atoms) can be cracked further.

Some of the important plastics and other products from ethene are shown in Fig. 18.10. Notice that polythene, polystyrene and PVC are all addition polymers. They are made from alkenes – monomers containing a C═C double bond. This is also the case with Perspex, polypropene and Teflon (polytetrafluoroethene, PTFE).

Using plastics

Different plastics have very different properties and therefore different uses. In fact, one of the important advantages of plastics is that by mixing different monomers, or by melting and mixing the final polymers, it is possible to make a plastic with specific properties. Different plastics are chosen for their particular uses because they have a suitable combination of properties. The examples in Table 18.5 show why different plastics are chosen for different uses.

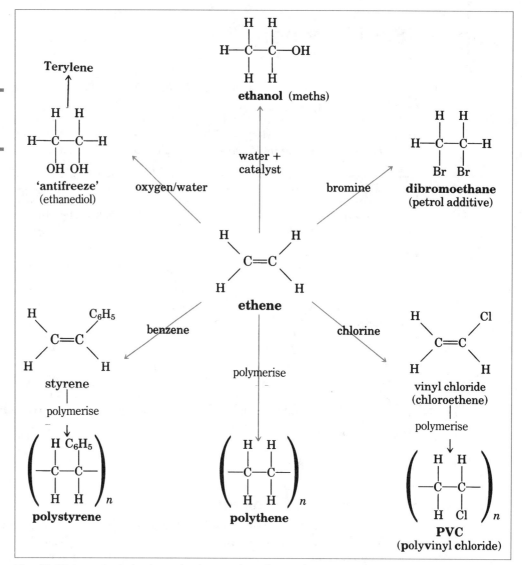

Fig. 18.10 Important plastics and other products from ethene

Table 18.5 The choice of plastics for different uses

	Polythene	PVC (polyvinyl chloride)	Perspex
Important properties	cheap, flexible, light, can be dyed	cheap, strong, easily moulded	strong, clear, easily moulded, resistant to chemicals
Uses	bags, wrappers, cling film	artificial leather for furniture, luggage cases and clothes	safety glasses

18.10 Ethanol

Ethanol is another important product from ethene (Fig. 18.10). The structure of ethanol is shown in Fig. 18.11.

Ethanol is a member of a group of compounds called **alcohols**. All alcohols have an —O—H group in their structure. This is highlighted in Fig. 18.11. Ethanol is by far the most common member of the alcohols. Because of this, it is often called *alcohol*.

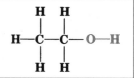

Fig. 18.11

Uses of ethanol

Ethanol has three important uses:

1. **As a solvent** Ethanol is a very good solvent. It will dissolve many different substances. It is also very volatile, so it is used as a solvent in paints, varnishes and perfumes which need to dry quickly when used.

2. **As a fuel** Ethanol burns easily without smoke. This makes it suitable for use in spirit burners for cooking, lighting and heating. The ethanol for this purpose is usually sold as *methylated spirits*, commonly called meths. Meths is approximately 95% ethanol. The other 5% includes colourings and poisonous substances to stop people drinking it. In some countries such as Brazil, ethanol is used as a fuel for vehicles in place of petrol.

3. **In alcoholic drinks** Alcoholic drinks, such as beer, wine and whisky, contain ethanol in varying amounts. The ethanol in these drinks is produced by fermentation of sugars from different sources. The percentage of ethanol and the source of sugar for some different drinks are shown in Table 18.6. There is more about alcoholic drinks and fermentation in 6.7 and 6.8.

Table 18.6 The percentage of ethanol and the source of sugar in different drinks

Drink	Approximate percentage of ethanol	Source of sugar (and flavour)
Beer	4	Barley
Wine	10	Grapes
Sherry	20	Grapes
Whisky	40	Barley
Gin	40	Wheat

Ethanol production

Ethanol is produced by two methods:

1 By fermentation
This method is used to produce alcoholic drinks (see 6.7 and 6.8).

2 From ethene
Most of the ethanol which is used as a solvent or as a fuel is manufactured from ethene. In this process, ethene undergoes an addition reaction with water (steam) (see 18.8). The reaction can be used to illustrate how chemical bonds are broken and then made in chemical reactions.

The first stage in the reaction involves breaking bonds. This requires an *energy input*.

These 2 bonds are broken

The second stage in the reaction involves making bonds. This gives an energy output.

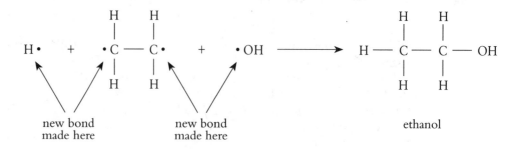

The difference between the energy input for bond breaking and the energy output from bond making gives the overall energy change for the reaction.

Summary

1   **Burning** (combustion) involves the oxidation of fuels to produce heat.

2   The most important fuels are **coal, oil** and **natural gas**. These are called **fossil fuels**.

3   Coal has formed from the decay of plants. Oil and natural gas have formed from the decay of sea creatures.

4   Fossil fuels are mainly composed of **hydrocarbons** – compounds of hydrogen and carbon only.

5   **Exothermic reactions** are those which give out heat.

6   The important criteria in choosing a fuel are:
   - cost
   - availability
   - storage
   - transport
   - pollution
   - combustibility
   - safety

7   4.2 joules of energy (heat) will warm up 1 g of water by 1 °C.

8   Fossil fuels will eventually run out. We need to **conserve** them and prevent waste of energy.

9   Fossil fuels and uranium are **non-renewable energy sources**. Once used, they are gone forever. On the other hand, tidal power, wind power, hydroelectric power, solar power and biomass are **renewable energy sources**. They keep on being replaced.

10 Crude oil can be fractionally distilled to produce different fractions such as refinery gas, petrol and kerosene.

11 **Alkanes** are the simplest series of hydrocarbons. They include methane (CH_4), ethane (C_2H_6) and butane (C_4H_{10}). Alkanes are typical simple molecular compounds.

12 **Alkenes** are hydrocarbons with at least one double bond between two of their carbon atoms. The simplest alkene is ethene ($H_2C = CH_2$).

13 Plastics such as polythene, nylon and PVC are **polymers**. They are made by **polymerisation**. This involves joining together small molecules called **monomers**.

14 **Polythene** is made by polymerising ethene. The ethene is obtained by cracking the heavier fractions from crude oil.

15 During chemical reactions, chemical bonds are first broken and then other bonds are formed. Bond breaking requires an energy input, whereas bond formation gives an energy output.

Quick test 18

Questions 1 and 2

The table below gives information about three different fuels.

Fuel	State (at 20 °C)	Uses	Products of burning
coal	solid	open fire	CO_2, water, ash, SO_2
methane	gas	cooking stove	CO_2, water
petrol	liquid	car engine	CO_2, water, CO

1   Which fuel does least harm to living things in the environment?
2   Give *two* reasons for your answer to question 1.   (*NEAB*)

Questions 3 and 4

The movement of sea water can be used to generate electricity.
3   State *two* different movements of the sea which could be used to generate electricity.
4   Consider the following statements:
    ● Your uncle says that some power stations use 'sea' power.
    ● He says that they are more expensive to build than nuclear or coal-fired power stations.
    ● That is why he thinks there is no point in building any 'sea' power stations.
    Give *three* reasons why you might disagree with your uncle.   (*NEAB*)

Questions 5 and 6

Crude oil contains many useful chemicals which have to be separated before they can be used.
5   (a) How is crude oil separated into the different chemicals?
    (b) Put the missing words into the following sentence.
        This method of separation can be used because chemicals made of larger molecules have ____ boiling points whereas chemicals made of ____ molecules have lower boiling points.
6   Long- and short-chain molecules are obtained when the chemicals in crude oil are separated out, but the short-chain ones are in greater demand and so are easier to sell. Oil companies break some of the spare long-chain molecules into short ones.
    (a) What name is given to the breaking of long-chain molecules from oil into short ones?
    (b) Briefly describe one of the ways in which this is done.   (*NEAB*)

Questions 7 and 8

7   Methane (CH_4) and ethane (C_2H_6) are the main substances in natural gas.

   (a) Complete the table to show the structural formulas of methane and ethane.

Name	Formula	Structural formula
methane	CH_4	
ethane	C_2H_6	
propane	C_3H_8	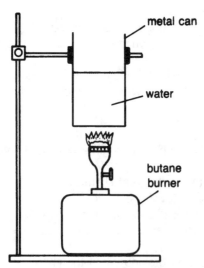

   (b) Draw a diagram to show the tetrahedral arrangement of bonds in methane.

8   Methane, ethane and propane are part of a *homologous series* in which the formulas differ by CH_2.

   How can a homologous series of compounds be compared with a group of elements in the periodic table?

Questions 9 to 13

A pupil wanted to calculate the cost of energy from a portable butane burner. She used the burner to heat water in a metal can. The table below shows the readings she made during the experiment.

mass of empty can	106.3 g
mass of can + water	306.3 g
mass of butane burner at start	467.8 g
mass of butane burner at end	467.2 g
temperature of water at start	21 °C
temperature of water at end	57 °C

In answering the following questions you should show the stages in your working.

9   Calculate the heat energy given out when the butane burns.
   (The specific heat capacity of water is 4200 J/kg/°C. 4200 J will heat 1 kg of water by 1 °C.)

10   Calculate the heat energy given out when 1 kg of butane burns.

11   If butane costs 50p per kg, calculate the cost of producing 100 000 kJ of heat energy.

12   Name the products formed when butane is burnt.

13   Suggest *two* ways of improving the accuracy of this experiment.

                                                                            (ULEAC)

Chapter 19
The periodic table and atomic structure

19.1 Mendeléev's periodic table

During the nineteenth century, several scientists tried to arrange the known elements in a systematic way. The most successful attempt to find a pattern for the elements was made by the Russian chemist, **Dmitri Mendeléev**, in 1869.

> Mendeléev arranged all the known elements in order of their relative atomic masses.

> He wrote the elements in horizontal rows so that elements with similar properties appeared in the same vertical column.

Because of the *periodic* repetition of elements with similar properties, Mendeléev called his arrangement a **periodic table**. Part of Mendeléev's periodic table is shown in Fig. 19.1. Notice that elements with similar properties – for example, sodium and potassium – fall in the same vertical column. Look for other pairs or trios of similar elements which appear in the same column of Mendeléev's table.

> The vertical columns of similar elements in the table are called **groups**.

> The horizontal rows are called **periods**.

	\multicolumn{8}{c}{Group}
	I	II	III	IV	V	VI	VII	VIII
Period 1	H							
Period 2	Li	Be	B	C	N	O	F	
Period 3	Na	Mg	Al	Si	P	S	Cl	
Period 4	K Cu	Ca Zn	* *	Ti *	V As	Cr Se	Mn Br	Fe Co Ni

Fig. 19.1 Mendeléev's periodic table

In setting out his periodic table, Mendeléev made two inspired decisions.

- **He left gaps in the table so that the similar elements were in the same vertical column.** Three of these gaps are shown by asterisks in Fig. 19.1.
- **He predicted the properties of the missing elements.** Mendeléev did this by studying the properties of the elements above and below them in his table. Within fifteen years of his predictions the missing elements had been discovered. They were called scandium, gallium and germanium. Their properties were very similar to Mendeléev's predictions.

The success of Mendeléev's predictions showed that his ideas were probably correct. His periodic table was quickly accepted by scientists as an important summary of the properties of elements.

19.2 Modern periodic tables

Modern periodic tables like the one in Fig. 19.2 are based on Mendeléev's and show all the known elements. Notice in Fig. 19.2 that the elements are numbered along each period, starting with period 1, then period 2, and so on. These numbers are the same as the atomic numbers of the elements (see 19.4). There are some important points to appreciate about modern periodic tables:

1 Modern periodic tables show all elements, arranged in order of increasing atomic number.

2 Moving from left to right across each period, the elements change from metals to non-metals. We have already compared the physical properties of metals and non-metals (Table 12.3) and metal oxides and non-metal oxides (Table 12.7). The important differences in the physical and chemical properties of metals and non-metals are summarised in Table 19.1.

Table 19.1 Comparing the physical and chemical properties of metals and non-metals

Property	Metals e.g. aluminium, copper, iron	Non-metals e.g. oxygen, sulphur, chlorine
Melting and boiling points	usually high	usually low
Conduction of heat and electricity	good	poor (except graphite)
Reaction with air (oxygen)	form metal oxides which are – solids – basic	form non-metal oxides which are – gases – acidic
Ions	form positive ions e.g. Al^{3+}, Cu^{2+}	form negative ions e.g. O^{2-}, Cl^-
Compounds	react only with non-metals to form ionic compounds e.g. Na^+Cl^-	react with metals to form ionic compounds react with other non-metals to form molecular compounds

3 In each group of the periodic table, the elements have similar properties but there is a gradual change in properties from the top to the bottom of the group.

4 Some groups have special names. These names are shown below the group numbers in Fig. 19.2.

5 In modern periodic tables, metals are clearly separated from non-metals. There are about 20 non-metals. These are all found in the top right-hand corner of the table, above the thick green steps in Fig. 19.2. Some elements close to the steps are **metalloids**. Metalloids have some properties like metals and some properties like non-metals.

6 Modern periodic tables show **transition elements** in a different way to Mendeléev. Transition elements are the ten or more elements in the middle of each period. In modern periodic tables, these are taken out of the simple groups. Period 4 is the first period to contain transition elements. These include chromium, iron, copper and zinc.

7 If we exclude the noble gases, elements get more reactive towards the right and left edges of the periodic table.

- The most reactive metals are those in Group I (alkali metals) along the left-hand edge. These include potassium and sodium.
- The next most reactive metals are those in Group II (alkaline–earth metals).
- Transition metals are less reactive again. These are near the centre of the table.
- The most reactive non-metals are the halogens in Group VII near the right-hand edge of the table.

Examiner's tip

Study 19.2 again and make sure you appreciate how the periodic table can be divided into blocks of elements with similar properties.

KEY:

H
Hydrogen
1

▼ symbol
▼ name
▼ atomic number

Transition elements

Group ►	I	II												III	IV	V	VI	VII	O
Period	Alkali metals	Alkaline -earth metals																Halogens	Noble gases
1	**H** Hydrogen 1																		**He** Helium 2
2	**Li** Lithium 3	**Be** Beryllium 4												**B** Boron 5	**C** Carbon 6	**N** Nitrogen 7	**O** Oxygen 8	**F** Fluorine 9	**Ne** Neon 10
3	**Na** Sodium 11	**Mg** Magnesium 12												**Al** Aluminium 13	**Si** Silicon 14	**P** Phosphorus 15	**S** Sulphur 16	**Cl** Chlorine 17	**Ar** Argon 18
4	**K** Potassium 19	**Ca** Calcium 20	**Sc** 21	**Ti** 22	**V** 23	**Cr** Chromium 24	**Mn** Manganese 25	**Fe** Iron 26	**Co** 27	**Ni** 28	**Cu** Copper 29	**Zn** Zinc 30	**Ga** 31	**Ge** 32	**As** 33	**Se** 34	**Br** Bromine 35	**Kr** Krypton 36
5	**Rb** 37	**Sr** 38	**Y** 39	**Zr** 40	**Nb** 41	**Mo** 42	**Tc** 43	**Ru** 44	**Rh** 45	**Pd** 46	**Ag** Silver 47	**Cd** 48	**In** 49	**Sn** Tin 50	**Sb** 51	**Te** 52	**I** Iodine 53	**Xe** 54
6	**Cs** 55	**Ba** 56	57–71 See below	**Hf** 72	**Ta** 73	**W** 74	**Re** 75	**Os** 76	**Ir** 77	**Pt** Platinum 78	**Au** Gold 79	**Hg** Mercury 80	**Tl** 81	**Pb** Lead 82	**Bi** 83	**Po** 84	**At** 85	**Rn** 86
7	**Fr** 87	**Ra** 88	89–103 See below	**Ku** 104	**Ha** 105				not yet named 109									

Lanthanides

La Lanthanum 57	**Ce** 58	**Pr** 59	**Nd** 60	**Pm** 61	**Sm** 62	**Eu** 63	**Gd** 64	**Tb** 65	**Dy** 66	**Ho** 67	**Er** 68	**Tm** 69	**Yb** 70	**Lu** 71

Actinides

Ac Actinium 89	**Th** 90	**Pa** 91	**U** Uranium 92	**Np** 93	**Pu** 94	**Am** 95	**Cm** 96	**Bk** 97	**Cf** 98	**Es** 99	**Fm** 100	**Md** 101	**No** 102	**Lr** 103

Fig. 19.2 A modern periodic table

19.3 Atomic structure

One hundred years ago, scientists believed that atoms were hard, solid particles like tiny snooker balls. Since then, experiments have shown a different structure for atoms. The following statements summarise our present understanding of atomic structure.

- All atoms are composed of just three particles: **protons**, **neutrons** and **electrons**.
- The centre of an atom is called the **nucleus**.
- The nucleus contains protons and neutrons.
- Protons and neutrons have virtually the same mass. Their mass is almost the same as that of a hydrogen atom. So the proton and neutron are given a relative mass of one like the hydrogen atom.
- **P**rotons are **p**ositively charged, but **n**eutrons are **n**eutral.
- The nucleus takes up a minute part of the volume of the whole atom.
- More than 99.9% of the atom is empty space occupied by moving **electrons**.
- Electrons have a mass about 2000 times less than that of protons and neutrons.
- Electrons are negatively charged. The negative charge on one electron just balances the positive charge on one proton.
- The electrons move around the nucleus very rapidly. They tend to remain in layers or **shells** at different distances from the nucleus.

Most of these key points about atomic structure are summarised in Table 19.2.

Table 19.2 Properties of protons, neutrons and electrons

Particle	Position within the atom	Mass relative to a hydrogen atom	Charge
Proton	nucleus	1	+1
Neutron	nucleus	1	0
Electron	'shells'	1/2000	−1

Protons, neutrons and electrons are the building blocks for atoms. Different atoms have different numbers of protons, neutrons and electrons. Hydrogen atoms are the simplest atoms. Each hydrogen atom has only one proton and one electron (Fig. 19.3). The next simplest atoms are those of helium. Each helium atom has two protons, two electrons and two neutrons. After helium comes lithium (three protons, three electrons and four neutrons), then beryllium (Fig. 19.4).

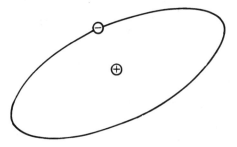 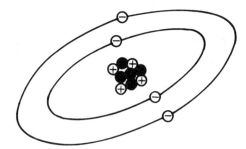

Fig. 19.3 A hydrogen atom has one proton (+) in its nucleus and one orbiting electron (−)

Fig. 19.4 A beryllium atom has four protons and five neutrons (●) in its nucleus, and four orbiting electrons. Two electrons are in a 'shell' close to the nucleus and the other two electrons are in a second 'shell' further away

Some of the heaviest atoms have 100 or more protons, neutrons and electrons. For example, each atom of lead has 82 protons, 82 electrons and 125 neutrons. Notice that in all these examples each atom has the **same number of protons and electrons**. This allows the positive charges on the protons to balance the negative charges on the electrons, so each atom is **neutral** overall.

19.4 Atomic number and mass number

- The only atoms with one proton are those of hydrogen;
- the only atoms with two protons are those of helium;
- the only atoms with three protons are those of lithium, and so on.

Can you see that the number of protons in an atom tells you which element it is?

Because of this, scientists use a special name for the *number of protons in an atom*. They call it the **atomic number**. Thus, hydrogen's atomic number is one, helium's atomic number is two, lithium's atomic number is three, and so on. Notice that the position of an element in the periodic table also tells you its atomic number (Fig. 19.2).

The mass of the electrons in an atom is negligible compared to the mass of protons and neutrons (Table 19.2). In fact, the mass of an atom depends on the number of protons and neutrons in its nucleus. Because of this, scientists use the term **mass number** for *the number of protons plus neutrons* in an atom.

atomic number = number of protons
mass number   = number of protons + number of neutrons

So carbon atoms, with six protons and six neutrons, have an atomic number of six and a mass number of 12. Sodium atoms, with 11 protons and 12 neutrons, have an atomic number of 11 and a mass number of 23.

Sometimes the symbol A is used for mass number and the symbol Z is used for atomic number. So for sodium $A = 23$ and $Z = 11$. Fig. 19.5 shows how the mass number and the atomic number can be shown with the symbol for an element.

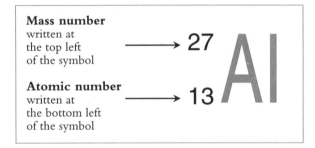

Mass number
written at
the top left
of the symbol

$\longrightarrow$ 27

Atomic number
written at
the bottom left
of the symbol

$\longrightarrow$ 13

Al

Fig. 19.5 Writing the mass number and the atomic number with the symbol for aluminium

19.5 Relative atomic mass and isotopes

Several elements have relative atomic masses which are whole numbers. For example, the relative atomic mass of oxygen is 16.0 and that of aluminium is 27.0, the same as their mass numbers. This is what we might have expected because the mass of an atom depends on its protons and neutrons, both of which have a relative mass of 1.0. For example, we can find the relative atomic mass of $^{27}_{13}$Al as follows:

$^{27}_{13}$Al atoms have:
13 protons, relative mass	= 13.0
13 electrons, relative mass	= 0.0
14 neutrons, relative mass	= 14.0
therefore, relative atomic mass of $^{27}_{13}$Al	= 27.0

Isotopes

Unlike oxygen and aluminium, some elements have relative atomic masses that are *not* whole numbers. For example, the relative atomic mass of neon is 19.2 and that of magnesium is 24.3. These unexpected results were explained in 1919 when F.W. Aston discovered that one element could have atoms with different masses.

Atoms of the same element with different masses are called **isotopes**. Each isotope has a relative mass which is a whole number, but the average atomic mass for the mixture of isotopes is not always a whole number.

Let's look at chlorine as an example. Naturally occurring chlorine has two isotopes, $^{35}_{17}Cl$ and $^{37}_{17}Cl$. Each of these isotopes has 17 protons and 17 electrons and therefore both have an atomic number of 17. However, one isotope ($^{35}_{17}Cl$) has 18 neutrons and the other isotope ($^{37}_{17}Cl$) has 20 neutrons. Their mass numbers are therefore 35 and 37, respectively. They are referred to as **chlorine–35** and **chlorine–37**.

Isotopes are atoms with the same atomic number, but different mass numbers.

Table 19.3 The isotopes of hydrogen

	Hydrogen-1	Hydrogen-2 (also called **deuterium** or heavy hydrogen)	Hydrogen-3 (also called **tritium**)
Symbol	^1_1H	^2_1H	^3_1H
Number of protons	1	1	1
Number of neutrons	0	1	2
Number of electrons	1	1	1
Atomic number	1	1	1
Mass number	1	2	3

Table 19.3 illustrates these points by looking at the isotopes of hydrogen. The three isotopes of hydrogen have *identical chemical properties* because they have the same number of electrons. However, they have *different physical properties* because they have different numbers of neutrons and therefore different masses. Samples of hydrogen–1, hydrogen–2 and hydrogen–3 have different densities, different melting points and different boiling points. The similarities and differences between isotopes of the same element are summarised in Table 19.4.

Table 19.4 The similarities and differences between isotopes of the same element

Isotopes have the same	Isotopes have different
• number of protons • number of electrons • atomic number • chemical properties	• numbers of neutrons • mass numbers • physical properties

The relative atomic mass of an element is the **average mass** of one atom. This can be calculated from the relative masses and the relative proportions of the different isotopes. Table 19.5 shows how the relative atomic mass of chlorine can be calculated.

Table 19.5 Calculating the relative atomic mass of chlorine

Naturally occurring chlorine contains three chlorine-35 atoms for every chlorine-37 atom:

relative atomic mass of $^{35}_{17}Cl$ = 35

relative atomic mass of $^{37}_{17}Cl$ = 37

$$\text{Relative atomic mass of chlorine} = \frac{(3 \times 35) + 37}{4}$$

$$= \frac{105 + 37}{4} = \frac{142}{4}$$

$$= 35.5$$

19.6 Electron structures and the periodic table

During chemical reactions, changes occur in the number of electrons belonging to atoms. Some atoms gain electrons, some lose electrons and others share electrons. Once these changes in electron structure have taken place, the atoms or ions are usually more stable, i.e. less reactive.

Some atoms, such as those of helium and neon, never react. This indicates that atoms of helium and the other noble gases must have very stable electron structures. Scientists have therefore concluded that atoms and ions will have very stable electron structures if they have 2 electrons (like helium), 10 electrons (like neon), 18 electrons (like argon) and so on. These stable electron structures are closely related to the way in which electrons are arranged in layers or **shells**. We now know that:

* the first shell is stable when it contains **2** electrons;
* the second shell is stable when it contains **8** electrons;
* the third shell is stable when it contains **8** or **18** electrons.

Neon atoms, with 10 electrons, have 2 electrons in their first shell and 8 electrons in their second shell. The electron structure of neon is therefore written as 2,8.

Argon, the next noble gas, is stable because its atoms have 18 electrons: 2 in the first shell, 8 in the second shell and 8 in the third shell. The electron structure of argon is written as 2,8,8.

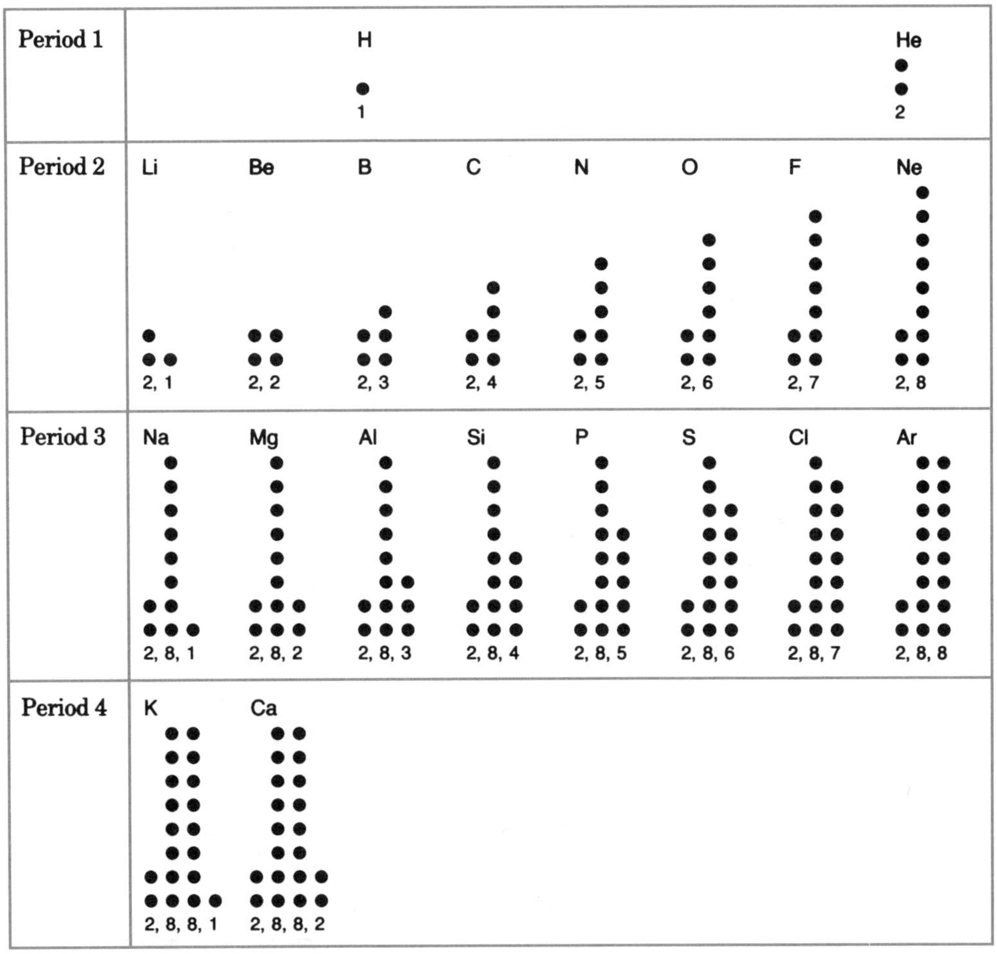

Fig. 19.6 Electron structures of the first 20 elements in the periodic table

Fig. 19.6 shows the electron structures of the first 20 elements in the periodic table. After the first shell is full (at helium), electrons go into the second shell. So the electron structure of lithium is 2,1, beryllium is 2,2, boron is 2,3 and so on. Once the second shell is full (at neon), electrons go into the third shell. So the electron structure of sodium is 2,8,1, etc.

Using these electron structures, we can explain why elements in the same group of the periodic table have similar properties (see 19.7 and 19.8).

19.7 Group I – the alkali metals

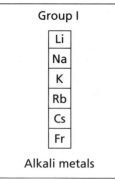

Group I

Li
Na
K
Rb
Cs
Fr

Alkali metals

The elements in Group I include sodium and potassium. They are called **alkali metals** because they react with water to form alkaline solutions. The alkali metals are very reactive. Because of this, they are stored under oil to protect them from oxygen and water vapour in the air.

Reactions of the Group I metals

Table 19.6 summarises the properties of alkali metals and of lithium, sodium and potassium in particular.

Table 19.6 The properties of alkali metals

Property	Character
Appearance	Shiny, but quickly form a dull layer of oxide
Strength	Soft metals, easily cut with a knife
M.p and b.p	Low compared with other metals
Density	Less than 1.0 g/cm³. The metals float on water
Reaction with air	Burn with increasing vigour from Li down the group to form white oxides sodium + oxygen → sodium oxide $4Na + O_2 \rightarrow 2Na_2O$
Reaction with cold water	Lithium reacts steadily, sodium vigorously, potassium violently. The products are hydrogen and an alkaline solution of the metal hydroxide; e.g. sodium + water → sodium hydroxide + hydrogen $2Na + 2H_2O \rightarrow 2NaOH + H_2$
Colour of compounds	Solid compounds are white and their solutions are clear unless the negative ion is coloured
Valency (combining power)	All the metals have a valency of one; their ions are Li^+, Na^+, K^+, etc. Oxides are Li_2O, Na_2O, K_2O, etc.

Notice two points from Table 19.6:

1. The elements have very similar properties.
2. Their reactions with air and water show that these reactions get more vigorous down the group from lithium to potassium.

These points illustrate an important feature of the periodic table (point 3, 19.2).

Although elements in a group have similar properties, there is a gradual change in the properties of the elements from the top to the bottom of a group.

We can use this to predict the properties of the different elements in a group.

Each alkali metal appears immediately after a noble gas in the periodic table. So, alkali metals have one electron in their outer shell (Table 19.7). By losing this outer electron, their atoms form **positive ions** (e.g. Li^+, Na^+, K^+) with stable electron structures like a noble gas. For example, Na^+ ions have the same electron structure as neon (2,8) and K^+ ions have the same electron structure as argon (2,8,8).

Table 19.7 The electron structures of the atoms and ions of the first three alkali metals

Alkali metal	Atom		Ion	
Lithium	Li	2,1	Li^+	2
Sodium	Na	2,8,1	Na^+	2,8
Potassium	K	2,8,8,1	K^+	2,8,8

All Group I metals:
- form ions with a charge of 1+,
- are very reactive because they are keen to lose the single electron in their outer shell.

The uses of sodium compounds

In hot countries, impure sodium chloride is left when sea water evaporates. Sodium chloride is also obtained from salt beds beneath the Earth's surface. Impure salt is used for de-icing roads. Pure salt is used for cooking. The elements, sodium and chlorine, can be produced by electrolysing molten salt (15.3). Liquid sodium is used as a coolant in fast nuclear reactors and sodium vapour provides the yellow glow in street lighting.

19.8 Group VII – the halogens

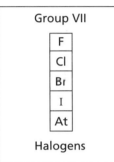

Group VII

F
Cl
Br
I
At

Halogens

The elements in Group VII are called **halogens**. The common elements in the group are chlorine (Cl), bromine (Br) and iodine (I). The halogens are so reactive that they never occur naturally as uncombined elements. They always occur with metals in **salts**, e.g. sodium chloride (NaCl), magnesium bromide ($MgBr_2$) and calcium fluoride (CaF_2). This is the reason for the name 'halogens' which means 'salt formers'.

In these salts, the halogens occur as **negative ions**, e.g. chloride (Cl^-), bromide (Br^-) and iodide (I^-). The commonest chlorine compound is sodium chloride (NaCl). This occurs in rock salt and in sea water. Every kilogram of sea water contains about 30 grams of sodium chloride. Sea water is also the commonest source of bromine. The bromine is present in sea water as bromide ions. Sea water also contains traces of iodides, but the main source of iodine is sodium iodate ($NaIO_3$), which is mined in Chile.

Some of the important uses of fluorine, chlorine and their compounds are summarised in Table 19.8.

Table 19.8 Important uses of fluorine, chlorine and their compounds

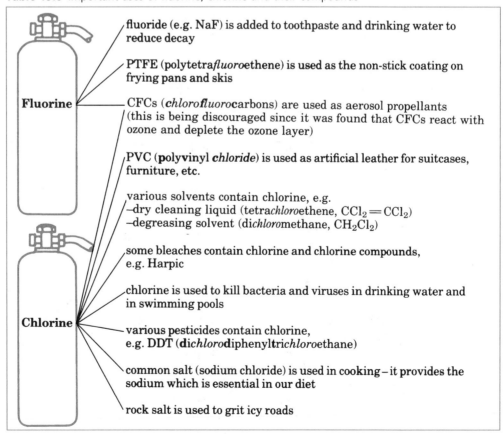

Fluorine

fluoride (e.g. NaF) is added to toothpaste and drinking water to reduce decay

PTFE (polytetra*fluoro*ethene) is used as the non-stick coating on frying pans and skis

CFCs (*chlorofluoro*carbons) are used as aerosol propellants (this is being discouraged since it was found that CFCs react with ozone and deplete the ozone layer)

PVC (**polyvinyl** *chloride*) is used as artificial leather for suitcases, furniture, etc.

various solvents contain chlorine, e.g.
–dry cleaning liquid (tetra*chloro*ethene, $CCl_2 = CCl_2$)
–degreasing solvent (di*chloro*methane, CH_2Cl_2)

some bleaches contain chlorine and chlorine compounds, e.g. Harpic

chlorine is used to kill bacteria and viruses in drinking water and in swimming pools

Chlorine

various pesticides contain chlorine, e.g. DDT (**di***chloro***diphenyltri***chloro***ethane**)

common salt (sodium chloride) is used in cooking – it provides the sodium which is essential in our diet

rock salt is used to grit icy roads

Properties of the halogens

Look closely at Table 19.9. This shows that the halogens are a typical group in the periodic table. They have similar properties to one another, but there is a gradual change in the properties of the elements from the top to the bottom of the group.

Table 19.9 Some properties of chlorine, bromine and iodine

Halogen	Relative atomic mass	Structure	Colour and state at room temperature	Melting point/°C	Boiling point/°C
Chlorine	35.5	Cl_2 molecules	pale green gas	−101	−35
Bromine	79.9	Br_2 molecules	orange-red liquid	−7	58
Iodine	126.9	I_2 molecules	dark purple solid	114	183

Note how the following properties of the halogens in Table 19.9 change as their relative atomic masses increase:
- state at room temperature
- melting point
- boiling point
- colour

All the halogens have **simple molecular structures** with **diatomic molecules**, i.e. Cl_2, Br_2, I_2. Strong bonds hold the two atoms together as a molecule, but the bonds between separate molecules are weak. This means that their molecules are easily separated, so their boiling points are relatively low.

Moving down the group, the halogen molecules get larger and heavier. Therefore, from chlorine to iodine, they are gradually more difficult to melt and vaporise. This is reflected in increasing melting and boiling points.

Reactions of the halogens

The chemical reactions of the halogens are also similar within the group, with gradual changes from one element to the next down the group. Fluorine is the most reactive of all non-metals. Chlorine is also very reactive, but iodine is only moderately reactive. Table 19.10 summarises the reactions of chlorine, bromine and iodine with cold water and hot iron. Notice how the elements get less reactive as we go down the group from chlorine to iodine. Compare this with Group I where the elements get more reactive as relative atomic mass increases.

Table 19.10 Some reactions of chlorine, bromine and iodine

Halogen	Reactions with cold water	Reaction with hot iron
Chlorine	forms a mixture of hydrochloric acid and hypochlorous acid the solution is very acidic and a strong bleach (the bleaching of damp indicator paper is used as a test for chlorine)	reacts rapidly and vigorously forming iron(III) chloride ($FeCl_3$)
Bromine	forms a mixture of hydrobromic acid and hypobromous acid the solution is acidic and a bleach	reacts slowly forming iron(III) bromide ($FeBr_3$)
Iodine	reacts slightly with water the solution is slightly acidic and a very mild bleach	reacts very slowly forming iron(II) iodide ($Fe I_2$)

Electron structures

The reactions of halogens can be related to their electron structures. In the periodic table, each halogen comes just before a noble gas. This means that they have seven electrons in their outer shell (see Table 19.11). By gaining one electron, halogens form **negative ions** with stable electron structures like a noble gas. Therefore, all the halogens form stable ions with one negative charge (e.g. F^-, Cl^-, Br^-).

Table 19.11 The electron structures of the atoms and ions of the first three halogens

Halogen	Atom	Ion
Fluorine	F 2,7	F^- 2,8
Chlorine	Cl 2,8,7	Cl^- 2,8,8
Bromine	Br 2,8,18,7	Br^- 2,8,18,8

19.9 The transition metals

Fig. 19.7 shows some of the common transition metals in the periodic table. Notice that the transition metals come between the reactive metals in Groups I and II and poor metals in the triangle below the steps separating metals from non-metals.

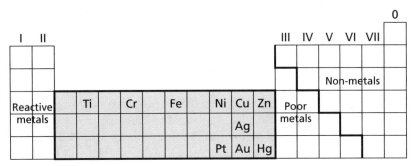

Fig. 19.7 Some of the common transition metals in the periodic table

The transition metals have very similar properties. Unlike other parts of the periodic table, there are similarities across the periods of transition metals as well as down their groups.

The most important transition metals are iron and copper. Iron is by far the most widely used metal. More than 700 million tonnes of iron are produced each year. It is used almost entirely as steel in girders and supports for buildings, in vehicles, in engines and in tools.

After iron and aluminium, copper is the third most widely used metal. About 8 million tonnes are manufactured each year. Copper is used mainly for electrical wires and cables and in hot water pipes and radiators. The uses of copper are also increased by **alloying** (see 14.4). Alloying copper with zinc produces brass, which is harder and stronger than pure copper. Alloying copper with tin produces bronze, which is stronger and easier to mould than pure copper.

Characteristic properties of transition metals and their compounds

Some properties of iron and copper are listed in Table 19.12.
You should compare these with the properties of alkali metals in Table 19.6.

Table 19.12 Some properties of iron and copper

Element	Appearance	M.p. /°C	B.p. /°C	Density /g cm⁻³	Reaction with water	Valency (combining power)	Colour of compounds
Iron	Shiny, grey and hard	1540	2860	7.9	Does not react with pure water (reacts slowly with steam)	+2 and +3 Ions are Fe^{2+} and Fe^{3+}	Fe^{2+} salts – green Fe^{3+} salts – yellow or brown
Copper	Shiny and hard	1080	2560	8.9	Does not react with water or steam	+1 and +2 Ions are Cu^{+} and Cu^{2+}	Cu^{+} salts – white Cu^{2+} salts – blue or green

The information in Table 19.12 illustrates the characteristic properties of transition metals and their compounds.

1. Hard strong metals.
2. High melting points and boiling points.
3. High densities, greater than 7.0 g/cm³.
4. Fairly unreactive metals. Transition metals do *not* react with cold water. (Iron will, however, rust when it can react with *both* water and oxygen.)

⑤ More than one valency.

⑥ Coloured compounds.

⑦ Catalytic properties. Transition metals and their compounds can act as catalysts. Iron or iron(III) oxide (Fe_2O_3) are catalysts for the Haber Process (17.5), vanadium(V) oxide (V_2O_5) is the catalyst for the Contact Process (17.3) and platinum is used in the catalytic converters in car exhaust systems (17.10).

19.10 Group 0 – the noble gases

Group 0
He
Ne
Ar
Kr
Xe
Rn

The noble gases

Four of the noble gases (neon, argon, krypton and xenon) occur in the atmosphere. In fact, argon makes up almost 1% of pure dry air, but the other three are present in very small amounts. Small quantities of helium occur as a constituent of natural gas, although the element was first identified in the Sun's atmosphere. The sixth noble gas, radon, is formed during the radioactive decay of the element radium.

Properties of the noble gases

The noble gases are all colourless and odourless gases at room temperature with low melting points and boiling points. As expected, their melting points, boiling points and densities show a steady rise as their relative atomic mass increases. Fig. 19.8 shows the steady increase in boiling points with relative atomic mass.

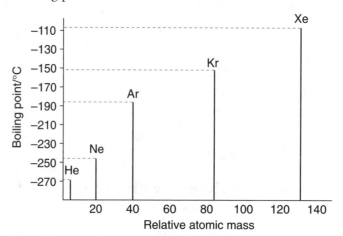

Fig. 19.8 A graph showing the boiling points of the noble gases as their relative atomic masses increase

The noble gases all exist as separate single atoms. Until 1962, no compounds of the noble gases were known. Chemists thought they were totally unreactive and they were called the **inert** gases. Several compounds are now known and the name 'inert gases' has been replaced by the name 'noble gases'.

Uses of the noble gases

Table 19.13 lists the important uses of noble gases, with a reason for these particular uses.

Table 19.13 Important uses of noble gases

Noble gas	Use	Reasons for this use
Helium	• In meteorological balloons	Very low density, non-flammable
	• Mixed with oxygen as the gas breathed by divers	Helium causes fewer problems if the diver has to come to the surface quickly
Neon	In neon lights	Neon produces a bright glow when an electric discharge (spark) passes through it
Argon	During welding processes	Argon provides an inert atmosphere so that the metal being welded does not react with oxygen in the air
Argon and krypton	In electric light bulbs	The white hot tungsten filament will not react with argon or krypton

19.11 Chemical bonding

When elements react to form compounds, there are changes in the number of electrons in their outer shells. Elements tend to gain, lose or share electrons so as to obtain a very stable structure – like that of a noble gas.

Ionic bonds – transfer of electrons

Fig. 19.9 shows what happens when sodium chloride (Na^+Cl^-) is formed from sodium and chlorine atoms.

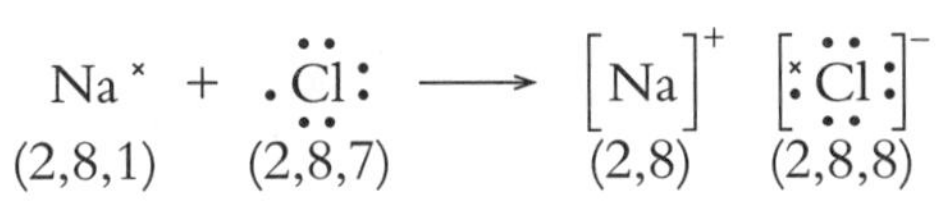

$$Na^{\times} + \cdot\overset{\cdot\cdot}{\underset{\cdot\cdot}{Cl}}\colon \longrightarrow \left[Na\right]^+ \left[\overset{\cdot\cdot}{\underset{\cdot\cdot}{\colon\!\!Cl\!\!\times}}\colon\right]^-$$
$$(2,8,1) \quad (2,8,7) \qquad (2,8) \quad (2,8,8)$$

Fig. 19.9 Electron transfer in the formation of sodium chloride

The electron structure of each atom and ion is shown below its symbol. In addition, the number of electrons in the outer shell of each atom is shown by dots or crosses around its symbol. Each sodium atom loses the one electron in its outer shell to form a sodium ion (Na^+) with an electron structure of 2,8 (like neon). The electron lost by the sodium atom is gained by a chlorine atom to form a chloride ion (Cl^-) with an electron structure of 2,8,8 (like argon).

So the formation of NaCl involves the complete *transfer* of one electron from each Na atom to each Cl atom forming Na^+ and Cl^- ions. *The attraction between these oppositely charged ions results in ionic bonding.*

Transfer of electrons to form ionic compounds is typical of the reactions between metals and non-metals. Fig. 19.10 shows the electron transfer that takes place in the formation of sodium oxide.

$$Na^{\times} + \overset{\cdot\cdot}{\underset{\cdot\cdot}{O}}\colon + Na^{\times} \longrightarrow \left[Na\right]^+ \left[\overset{\cdot\cdot}{\underset{\cdot\cdot}{\times\!\!O\!\!\colon}}\right]^{2-} \left[Na\right]^+$$
$$(2,8,1) \quad (2,6) \quad (2,8,1) \qquad (2,8) \quad (2,8) \quad (2,8)$$

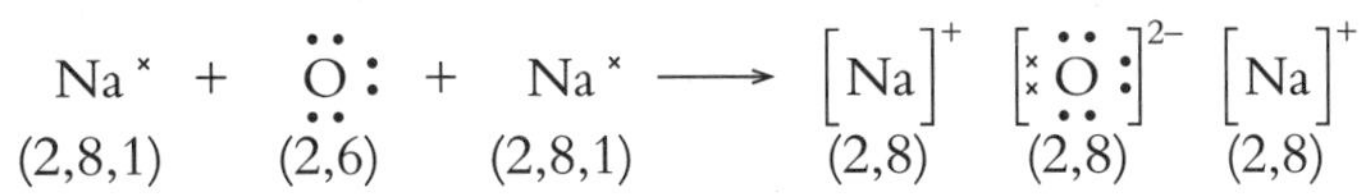

Fig. 19.10 Electron transfer in the formation of sodium oxide

Notice, in this case, that each oxygen atom gains two electrons, one from each of two sodium atoms, to obtain an electron structure of 2,8 (like neon).

Covalent bonds – sharing electrons

When non-metal atoms form molecules, they become more stable by sharing electrons. Fig. 19.11 shows how this happens when a hydrogen atom and a chlorine atom form hydrogen chloride.

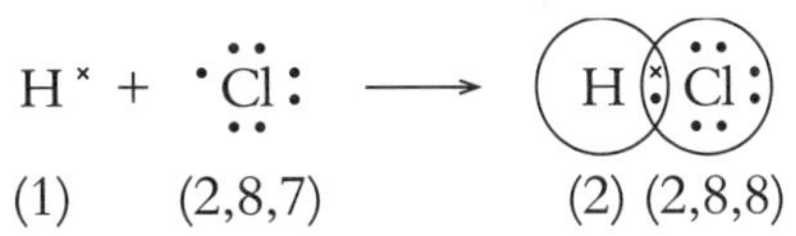

$$H^{\times} + \cdot\overset{\cdot\cdot}{\underset{\cdot\cdot}{Cl}}\colon \longrightarrow \left(H\overset{\cdot\cdot}{\underset{\cdot\cdot}{\colon Cl}}\colon\right)$$
$$(1) \quad (2,8,7) \qquad (2) \; (2,8,8)$$

Fig. 19.11 Electron sharing in the formation of hydrogen chloride

When the hydrogen and chlorine atoms come close together, the electrons in their outer shells can overlap. By doing this, one pair of electrons is shared by each atom (Fig. 19.11). *The shared pair of electrons is attracted by the positive nucleus of both hydrogen and chlorine forming a covalent bond.* In hydrogen chloride, the hydrogen atom gains an electron structure like the noble gas helium (2) and chlorine has an electron structure like argon (2,8,8).

The atoms in molecular compounds (simple molecular and giant covalent) are held together by covalent bonds. The structure, bonding and properties of molecular substances were discussed earlier (see 15.7). Fig. 19.12 shows how electrons are shared in the formation of two other molecular compounds, H_2O and CO_2.

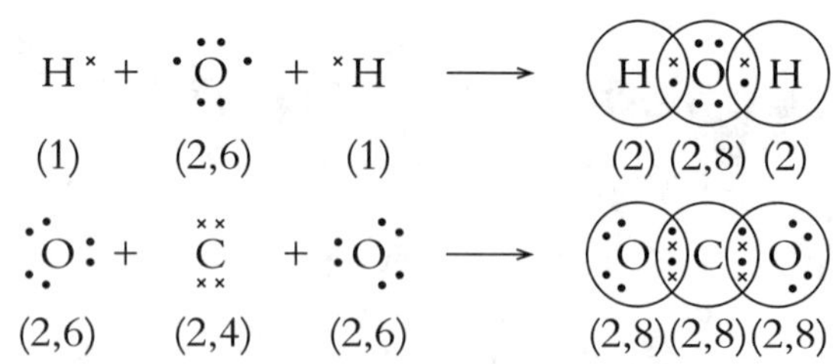

$$H^\times + \cdot \overset{\cdot\cdot}{\underset{\cdot\cdot}{O}} \cdot + {}^\times H \longrightarrow H(\overset{\times\cdot}{\underset{\times\cdot}{O}})H$$

(1)   (2,6)   (1)   (2) (2,8) (2)

$$\overset{\cdot\cdot}{\underset{\cdot\cdot}{O}}\!: + \overset{\times\times}{\underset{\times\times}{C}} + :\overset{\cdot\cdot}{\underset{\cdot\cdot}{O}} \longrightarrow \overset{\cdot\cdot}{\underset{\cdot\cdot}{O}}(\overset{}{}C)\overset{\cdot\cdot}{\underset{\cdot\cdot}{O}}$$

(2,6)   (2,4)   (2,6)   (2,8)(2,8)(2,8)

Fig. 19.12 Electron sharing in the formation of water and carbon dioxide

Summary

1   In the **periodic table**, elements are arranged in order of ascending atomic number. The vertical columns of similar elements are called **groups**. The horizontal rows are called **periods**.

2   In each group of the periodic table, the elements have similar properties, but there is a gradual change in properties from the top to the bottom of a group.

3   Moving from left to right across each period, the elements change from metals to non-metals.

4   Atoms are composed of **protons**, **neutrons** and **electrons**. Protons and neutrons occupy the **nucleus**. Electrons move rapidly around the nucleus in **shells** at different distances from the nucleus.

5   **Atomic number** = number of protons
    Mass number = number of protons + number of neutrons

6   **Isotopes** are atoms with the same atomic number but different mass numbers. Isotopes have the same number of protons and electrons and the same chemical properties, but different numbers of neutrons and different physical properties.

7   Elements in the same group have similar chemical properties because they have the same number of electrons in their outer shell.

8   With non-metals, the elements get less reactive with the increase in relative atomic mass down a group. On the other hand, metals get more reactive with the increase in relative atomic mass down a group.

9   Unlike other parts of the periodic table, there are similarities across the periods of transition metals as well as down their groups.

Quick test 19

Questions 1 to 7

A   Group I   D   Group 0
B   Group IV   E   Transition metals
C   Group VII

1   Which set of elements are also known as the noble gases?
2   Which set contains elements used in jewellery?
3   Which set contains an element which is used as a germicide?
4   Which set of elements contains a metalloid which boils above 3000 °C?
5   Which set contains elements that react with water forming a solution of pH 12?
6   Which set contains a pale green element with diatomic molecules?
7   Which set contains an element with no known compounds?

Questions 8 to 11

The table gives information about some elements.

Atom	Number of protons	Number of neutrons
W	6	6
X	6	8
Y	7	8
Z	8	9

8 What is the mass number of element X?
9 What is the atomic number of element Y?
10 How many electrons will one atom of element Z contain?
11 How many different elements are shown in the table?

Questions 12 to 15

In the table below, the halogens are arranged in the same order as they appear in Group VII of the periodic table.

Element	Symbol	Melting point/°C	Colour	Formula of compound with hydrogen	Reaction with hot iron
Fluorine	F	−220	very pale yellow	HF	very fast
Chlorine	Cl	−101	pale green	HCl	fast
Bromine	Br	−7	reddish	HBr	slow
Iodine	I	114	nearly black	H I	very slow
Astatine	At				

12 As you go down the Group VII elements from fluorine to iodine, what happens to
 (a) their melting points,
 (b) their colours,
 (c) their reactions with hot iron?
13 What pattern can you see in the formula of their compounds with hydrogen?
14 Astatine lies below iodine in Group VII. Complete the last row of the table by making a prediction of its properties.
15 A sample of iodine contains 80% $^{127}_{53}$I and 20% $^{131}_{53}$I.
 (a) What is the mass number of $^{127}_{53}$I?
 (b) What is the mass number of $^{131}_{53}$I?
 (c) What is the relative atomic mass of iodine in the sample?

Chapter 20
Forces and motion

20.1 Forces

A force is a push or a pull. If you wanted to exert a force on something you could, for example, push it, pull it, twist it or squeeze it. Five important kinds of force are:
The following are examples of some important forces.

1. **Gravitational forces** caused by the pull of the Earth on objects.
2. **Frictional forces** try to stop things moving. They cause the *friction* or *drag* which stops objects slipping over each other or sliding past each other.
3. **Contact forces** are produced when two objects are pushed together. The contact force from the starting block pushes a sprinter away at the start of a race.
4. **Magnetic forces** act on magnetic materials. The magnetic strip in a magnetic door catch pulls the door to the frame and keeps the door closed.
5. **Electric forces** act between electric charges. Electric forces (*static*) sometimes make your hair cling to a plastic comb.

Notice that forces can:

- make things move,
- stop things moving,
- change the speed and/or direction of moving objects,
- change the shape of objects.

20.2 Force, weight and mass

Forces vary enormously in size – from the tiny forces needed to remove a cataract from someone's eye, to huge forces to cut through rock. So, it is important that we can measure the size of a force. **Forces are measured in newtons (N)**. This name was chosen in honour of Sir Isaac Newton, the famous physicist (1642–1727). It requires a force of about one newton (1 N) to lift an average-sized apple or orange.

Everyone experiences one important force all their lives. This is the **force of gravity** which is caused by the pull of the Earth on our bodies.

Experiments show that every object in the universe attracts all other objects. These attractions are called **gravitational forces**. The gravitational forces between relatively small objects like tables, chairs and people are too small to have any effect. But if one object is as large as the Earth, the gravitational force is very strong.

The gravitational force between the Earth and an object is usually called the **weight** of the object. It is important to understand the difference between weight and **mass**.

Weight is the force of gravity on an object, measured in newtons (N).
Mass is the amount of matter (or stuff) in an object,
measured in kilograms (kg).

On Earth, a mass of 1 kg has a weight of 10 N. So, an apple with a mass of 0.1 kg (100 g) has a weight of 1 N. A person with a mass of 50 kg has a weight of 500 N.

If we could get the apple and this person to the moon, their masses would stay the same because they still contain the same amount of matter. However, their weights would be only one-sixth of their weights on Earth. This is because the moon is smaller than the Earth and its gravitational pull is only one-sixth of the Earth's (Fig. 20.1).

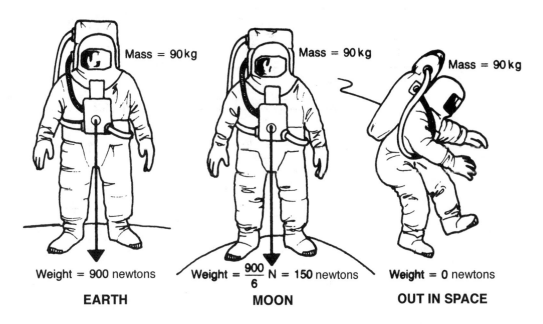

Mass = 90 kg   Mass = 90 kg   Mass = 90 kg

Weight = 900 newtons   Weight = $\frac{900}{6}$ N = 150 newtons   Weight = 0 newtons

EARTH   **MOON**   **OUT IN SPACE**

Fig. 20.1 Gravity on Earth, on the moon and in outer space

Examiner's tip

Make sure you appreciate the difference between weight and mass and that weight is a force.

When an astronaut is far out in space, there is no gravitational pull from the Earth, the moon or any stars or planets. He or she just floats around in a *weightless* state.

Using the international system (SI), the correct unit for mass is the kilogram (kg). However, many people measure masses in grams (g) and even in ounces (oz), pounds (lb) and stones.

$$1000 \text{ g} = 1 \text{ kg} = 2.2 \text{ pounds}$$
$$1000 \text{ kg} = 1 \text{ tonne}$$

20.3 Stretching forces

When we hang weights from a spring, the spring extends (stretches). The force of gravity pulling on the weight pulls on the spring and this causes it to extend. The spring can support the weights due to the forces of attraction between particles in the spring. The pull in the spring which supports the weights is called a **tension**.

Fig. 20.2 shows the apparatus we can use to investigate the stretching forces acting on a spring. The results are given in Table 20.1 and plotted on a graph in Fig. 20.3.

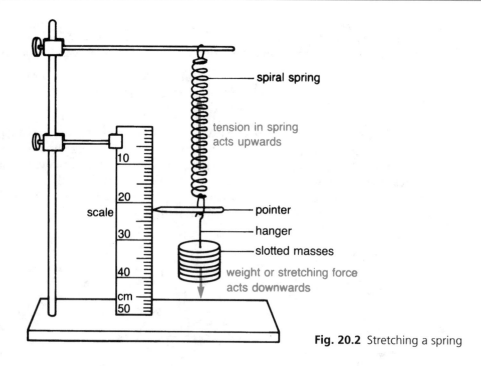

Fig. 20.2 Stretching a spring

Table 20.1 The results of an experiment using the apparatus in Fig. 20.2

Weight added, stretching force on spring/N	Position of pointer on scale/cm	Extension of spring/cm
0	10.0	0
2	13.9	3.9
4	18.1	8.1
6	22.0	12.0
8	25.9	15.9
10	30.0	20.0

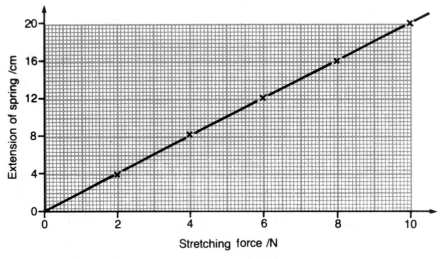

Fig. 20.3 Extension of a spring against stretching force (load)

The graph of extension against stretching force is a straight line. When the stretching force is doubled, the extension doubles, and so on. The extension is said to be **proportional** to the stretching force. Using the symbol ∝, which means 'proportional to', this can be summarised as:

$$extension \propto stretching\ force$$

This result is usually known as **Hooke's Law** after the scientist Robert Hooke who first investigated springs during the 17th century. Other materials, such as wires, elastic bands, wood and even concrete, are also stretched by forces.

Elasticity

Some materials *return to their original length when the force is removed*. These materials are said to be **elastic**. As the stretching force increases, a point is reached when a material remains deformed even when the force is removed. This *extent of elasticity* varies greatly from one material to another.

The elastic properties of springs are put to use in kitchen and bathroom scales and springs in mattresses, chairs and other furniture. Although the elasticity of wood and concrete is much less than most metals, it allows buildings to move slightly when there are minor earthquakes rather than fall down.

20.4 Frictional forces

If you have waded knee-deep in water you will know how difficult it is to make progress. Your movement through the water is slowed down by **friction**. Frictional forces (friction) are the *forces which prevent motion*. These forces prevent an object moving over a surface or through a fluid (liquid or gas).

Fig. 20.4 Forces on a shopping trolley

Fig. 20.4 shows Simon pushing a heavy trolley over a rough floor. Notice that there are ten forces acting on the trolley and that these forces act in different directions.

- The force of gravity pulls the trolley down, causing a weight of 200 N.
- The floor pushes up on each trolley wheel with a force of 50 N. The total upward force is therefore 4×50 N = 200 N. This overall upward force of 200 N from the floor just balances the downward force (weight) so the trolley does not move up or down. Forces like these are called **balanced forces** because they produce no change in the movement of an object.
- Simon pushes the trolley to the right with a force of 60 N.
- A frictional force of 20 N (5 N on each wheel) acts on the trolley to the left and this impedes its movement.

The **resultant (overall) force** on the trolley is therefore 60 – 20 = 40 N to the right. It is the size and direction of this resultant force which affects the movement of the trolley. Simon's push on the trolley to the right and the frictional forces to the left are examples of **unbalanced forces**. Unbalanced forces change the speed and/or the direction of moving objects.

What causes friction?

Friction occurs when the molecules of one object get very close to the molecules of another surface or the molecules in a fluid. The forces of attraction between the molecules must be overcome in order to move one surface over another or through another.

The effects of friction

Friction has three major effects:

1. it prevents objects moving or slows them down;
2. it produces heat when two objects rub against each other (you will notice this if you rub your hands vigorously or if you slide down a rope);
3. it wears things out as surfaces rub against each other (e.g. tyres lose their tread because of the friction between the tyres and the road).

Reducing friction

Friction can be reduced by the use of

- bearings,
- lubrication,
- streamlining.

Two of these methods are illustrated in Fig. 20.5. Bearings and lubrication are used to reduce friction between a wheel and its axle. The ball bearings reduce the area of contact between the moving surfaces. The oil between the bearings, wheel and axle acts as a lubricant by separating the moving surfaces with a thin layer of liquid.

One of the latest attempts to reduce friction is *air lubrication*. This is very useful in machine tools, in hover mowers, hovercraft and aerotrains. Air is forced between the surfaces in contact at high pressure. This forces the surfaces apart and keeps friction to a minimum.

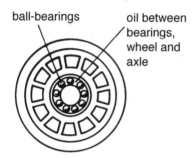

Fig. 20.5 Reducing friction between a wheel and its axle

Lubrication is also important in our bodies. Synovial fluid is the lubricant which allows bones to slide over one another.

When objects move through fluids, like air and water, the frictional forces which resist their motion are usually called **drag**. Streamlining of cars, trains, aircraft and rockets reduces drag to a minimum. The vehicles can then get to higher speeds with less fuel.

Using friction

Friction is often a nuisance, but sometimes it is essential. Have you ever tried to walk on ice? If so, you will know that movement is very difficult when friction is reduced to a minimum. We depend on friction between the soles of our shoes and the ground to stop and start and walk around easily. The tyres and brakes on vehicles also depend on friction for starting, moving and stopping.

If there was no friction, pens and pencils would not be able to leave marks on paper, anything on a slope would move downhill and screws would become loose.

20.5 Turning forces

It is much easier to hold a heavy book close to your chest than at arms length. The force of gravity pulling on the book causes a turning effect. So, forces can also cause objects to turn. The turning effect is greater when the book is held at arms length. We usually call this turning effect the **moment of the force**.

Tools like levers, bottle openers and spanners are useful because they increase the turning effects of forces. It may be impossible to undo a tight nut with your fingers. Using a spanner, the job could be easy, even though you use the same force (Fig. 20.6).

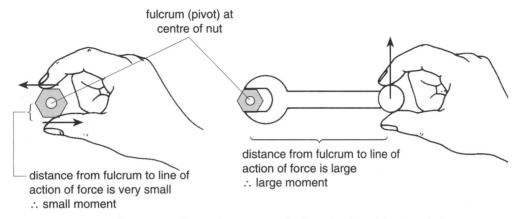

fulcrum (pivot) at centre of nut

distance from fulcrum to line of action of force is very small ∴ small moment

distance from fulcrum to line of action of force is large ∴ large moment

Fig. 20.6 Increasing the turning effect with a spanner. The line of action of the force is shown as →.

Notice that the moment of a force depends on both the size of the force and the distance of its line of action from the pivot or **fulcrum**.

moment of a force = force × distance from fulcrum to line of action of force

Seesaws and crowbars also depend on the application of moments. In Fig. 20.7, Toya and Jenny both produce a moment on the seesaw.

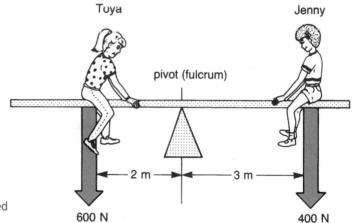

Toya

Jenny

pivot (fulcrum)

2 m

3 m

Fig. 20.7 Moments produced on a seesaw

600 N

400 N

Toya's weight acts down on the left and Jenny's weight acts down on the right. The point through which a weight acts is called its **centre of mass**.

Toya's weight tries to turn the seesaw anticlockwise. Jenny's weight tries to turn the seesaw clockwise.

Toya's moment = 600 N × 2 m = 1200 Nm
Jenny's moment = 400 N × 3 m = 1200 Nm
So, Toya's moment = Jenny's moment

In this case, the seesaw does not turn because the turning moments caused by their weights balance.

i.e. Anticlockwise moment = clockwise moment

This is called the **Principle of Moments** and we say that the seesaw is in equilibrium.

20.6 Force and pressure

Why is it easy to push a drawing pin into a piece of wood, but impossible to push your finger into a piece of wood? The answer is that the force on the drawing pin is concentrated on a small area (the point of the pin). When you press your finger on the wood, the force is spread out over a much larger area (the area of skin touching the wood).

Scientists use the word **pressure** to describe how concentrated a force is. If the force is concentrated on a small area, pressure is high. If the force acts on a large area, pressure is low (Fig. 20.8).

Pressure is defined as the force per unit area.

$$\text{Pressure} = \frac{\text{force}}{\text{area}}$$

So, the units for pressure are newtons per square metre (N/m²) or pascals (Pa), i.e. 1 N/m² = 1 Pa.

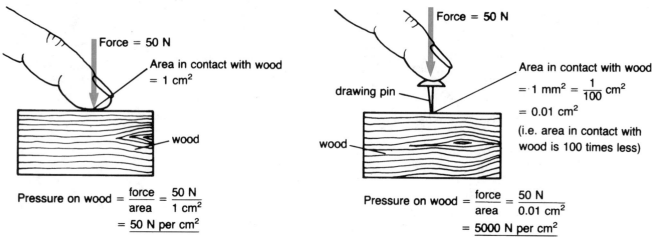

Fig. 20.8 The pressure on the wood below the point of the drawing pin is 100 times greater than the pressure from the finger

20.7 Pressure in liquids

The force of gravity pulls a liquid down in its container. This exerts pressure on the container and on objects in the liquid.

Pressure increases with depth

As we go deeper into a liquid, the mass of liquid pushing down increases. The force from the liquid is therefore greater and so is the pressure. Because of this, dams are built with thicker walls at their base (Fig. 20.9).

Pressure acts in all directions

A liquid pushes on every surface in contact with it, whichever way the surface is facing. This helps to explain why there is an upward force (**upthrust**) on an object in a liquid. If this upthrust is large enough, it can balance the weight (force) of the object downwards. Under these conditions, the object will float (Fig. 20.9).

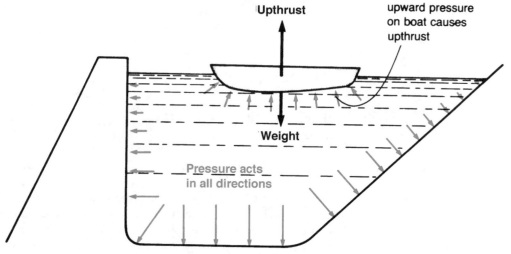

Fig. 20.9 Pressure in liquids. Pressure increases with depth and this is shown by arrows of increasing length

Hydraulic machines

Hydraulic machines use liquids under pressure to transmit forces. Liquids have two important properties which make hydraulic machines possible.

1 Unlike gases, **liquids cannot be compressed easily**. *In a gas*, the particles are widely spaced so they are easily pushed closer together (compressed). *In liquids*, the particles are close together so they cannot be pushed together (compressed) easily.

2 **Pressure on a trapped liquid can be transmitted through the whole liquid**.

Hydraulic machines are important in hydraulic jacks, car brakes, fork-lift trucks and chair-lifts for the physically disabled.

The principle on which these machines work is shown in Fig. 20.10. Check the calculations at the side of Fig. 20.10. These show that when a force of 100 newtons is applied to piston A, the pressure transmitted through the liquid is 100 000 newtons per square metre (N/m^2). This creates a force on piston B of 10 000 N. This could lift a car of mass 1 tonne (1000 kg). Notice that 'newtons per square metre' is written as N/m^2. The slanting line stands for 'per'.

Hydraulic jacks, car brakes, fork-lift trucks and chair-lifts all rely on arrangements similar to that shown in Fig. 20.10. By using pistons with different cross-sectional areas, they can magnify forces.

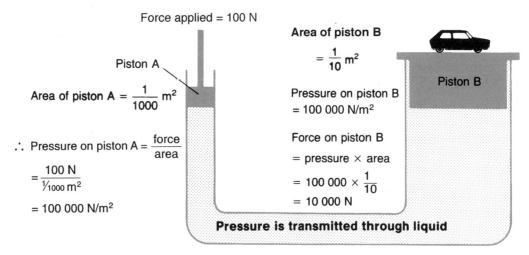

Fig. 20.10 Hydraulic machines can magnify forces. A force of 100 N on piston A transmits a pressure through the liquid to produce a force on piston B of 10 000 N

20.8 Distance and displacement

Fig. 20.11 shows a map of John's route to school. Altogether, John walks a total distance of 600 metres (200 m + 300 m + 100 m). But John has not walked 600 metres in a straight line. He has gone east, then north, then east again. John has only been *displaced* 424 metres from his starting point in a north-east direction. We can say that John has walked a total *distance of 600 metres*, but his **displacement** is only *424 metres north-east*.

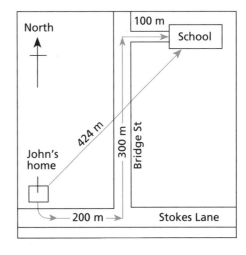

Fig. 20.11   John's walk to school

Distance = total path taken whatever the direction
Displacement = distance moved in a particular direction

20.9 Speed and velocity

As well as measuring how far John has moved, we may want to know how fast he has moved. We can calculate John's speed if we know the time he takes to walk to school.

$$\text{speed} = \frac{\text{distance moved}}{\text{time taken}}$$

Suppose John walks to school in ten minutes, what is his speed in metres per second (m/s)?

$$\text{John's speed} = \frac{\text{distance moved}}{\text{time taken}} = \frac{600 \text{ metres}}{10 \times 60 \text{ seconds}}$$

$$= \frac{600 \text{ metres}}{600 \text{ seconds}}$$

$$= 1.0 \text{ m/s}$$

Notice that 'metres per second' is written as m/s. Remember that the slanting line stands for 'per'. When we are describing motion, **per means 'in one'**. So, a speed of '2 m/s' means 'two metres per second' or 'two metres in one second'.

The **SI units** for distance and time are the metre and the second, respectively. So, speed is measured in metres/second or m/s in SI (the International System of Units). However, many other units are in everyday use such as miles per hour (mph) and kilometres per hour (km/h).

Although John walks 600 metres to school in 10 minutes, he is moving in different directions during those 10 minutes. His speed is 1.0 m/s, but it has no particular direction. If we calculate John's *speed in a particular direction*, this is called his **velocity**.

$$\text{velocity} = \frac{\text{displacement}}{\text{time taken}}$$

In our example, John's velocity $= \dfrac{424 \text{ metres north-east}}{10 \times 60 \text{ seconds}}$

$$= 0.7 \text{ m/s } \textbf{north-east}$$

Notice that whenever a velocity is given, its direction must always be stated as well as its size.

Quantities that have *both size and direction*, such as displacement and velocity, are called **vectors**. Quantities that have *size but no direction*, such as distance and speed, are called **scalars**. Another example of a vector is **weight**. The weight of an object always acts in a *downward direction*.

20.10 Distance–time graphs

Katie sets off from home on her bicycle to the newsagents 330 metres away. The first part of her journey is along a narrow, bumpy lane. The second part is along a road. Table 20.2 shows the distance Katie has travelled after every 10 seconds.

Table 20.2

Time taken/s	0	10	20	30	40	50	60	70	80	90	100
Distance/m	0	20	40	60	80	130	180	230	280	330	330

Fig. 20.12 shows a distance–time graph of Katie's journey. The first part of the journey is 80 metres along the bumpy lane. This takes 40 seconds. On the graph it is shown as a straight line. We can find the gradient (slope) of the line as follows:

$$\text{Gradient (slope) of line} = \frac{\text{distance moved}}{\text{time taken}} = \frac{80 \text{ metres}}{40 \text{ seconds}} = 2 \text{ m/s}$$

So, the gradient of a distance–time graph = speed.

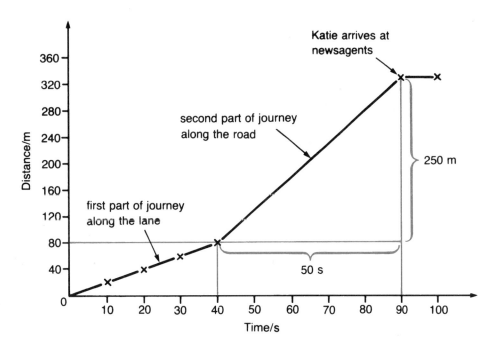

Fig. 20.12 A distance–time graph

During the second part of the journey, Katie's speed increases. Here she travels 250 metres in 50 seconds. So, her speed is 250/50 = 5 m/s.

Notice that the gradient (slope) of the distance–time graph increases (gets steeper) as speed increases.

20.11 Average speed

The first part of the graph in Fig. 20.12 shows a constant speed of 2 m/s. The second part shows a constant speed of 5 m/s. Finally, the speed between 90 and 100 seconds is zero. Notice how the speed changes during the journey. If you want the speed at any moment, the best way is to find the gradient of the graph at that time. Of course, if you were travelling in a car, you could find its speed at any moment by looking at the speedometer. This works by measuring the rate at which the wheels are rotating.

Average speed is obtained from the *total* distance moved and the *total* time taken:

$$\text{Average speed} = \frac{\text{total distance moved}}{\text{total time taken}}$$

For the journey described in Fig. 20.12,

$$\text{average speed} = \frac{330 \text{ metres}}{100 \text{ seconds}} = 3.3 \text{ m/s}$$

20.12 Changing speed – acceleration

The makers of a sports car claim that it will increase its speed from 0 to 40 m/s in 10 seconds. When a moving object increases its speed, we say it accelerates. The *rate at which an object increases its speed* is called **acceleration**.

$$\text{acceleration} = \frac{\text{change in speed}}{\text{time taken}} = \text{change in speed per unit time}$$

e.g. the sports car's acceleration $= \frac{(40 - 0)\text{m/s}}{10 \text{ s}} = \frac{4 \text{ m/s}}{\text{s}}$

So the car accelerates by 4 metres per second every second. This means that it increases its speed by 4 metres per second every second (i.e. **4 m/s²**).

Suppose the car is travelling at 40 m/s. The driver suddenly applies the brakes and the car stops in 2 seconds. What is the acceleration this time?

$$\text{acceleration} = \frac{\text{change in speed}}{\text{time taken}}$$

$$= \frac{\text{final speed} - \text{initial speed}}{\text{time taken}}$$

$$= \frac{0 - 40 \text{ m/s}}{2 \text{ s}} = -20 \text{ m/s}^2$$

In this case, the car is *slowing down*, not speeding up. **Negative acceleration** of this kind is called **deceleration**.

20.13 Speed–time graphs

Look at Fig. 20.13. This shows the speed of a rocket during the first five seconds after take-off.

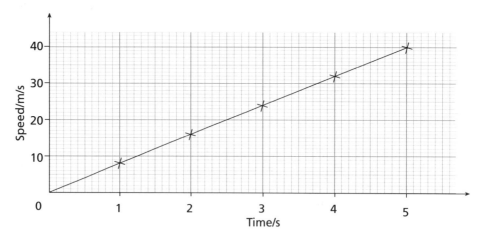

Fig. 20.13 A speed–time graph for a rocket just after take-off

At take-off (i.e. zero time), speed of rocket = 0 m/s
After 1 second, speed of rocket = 8 m/s
After 2 seconds, speed of rocket = 16 m/s
After 3 seconds, speed of rocket = 24 m/s
After 4 seconds, speed of rocket = 32 m/s

So, the acceleration of the rocket is 8 m/s².

The straight line of the graph shows that the speed is increasing at an even rate (i.e. that acceleration is constant). Acceleration is found by calculating the gradient (slope) of the graph.

$$\text{Gradient of the speed–time graph} = \frac{\text{change in speed}}{\text{time taken}} = \text{acceleration}$$

If we were asked how far the rocket travels in the first four seconds, we must first calculate its average speed in this time:

speed at time 0 seconds = 0 m/s

From the graph, Fig. 20.13:

speed after 4 seconds = 32 m/s

therefore average speed in first 4 seconds $= \dfrac{0 + 32}{2} = 16$ m/s

therefore distance travelled in 4 seconds $= 16 \times 4 = 64$ metres

Notice that:

$$\text{distance moved} = \text{average speed} \times \text{time taken}$$

Examiner's tip

In sections 20.8 to 20.13, the key words to understand are distance, displacement, speed, velocity and acceleration.

20.14 Newton's laws of motion

Newton's first law of motion

If you roll a stone or a ball over a flat, icy surface it seems to move on and on and on because there is so little friction. If we could reduce friction and air resistance (drag) to zero, the stone would go on rolling forever. These simple ideas were first summarised by Sir Isaac Newton in his **first law of motion**:

If an object is stationary it will remain so, and if it is moving it will continue to move with constant speed in a straight line, unless external forces act upon it.

In practice, most moving objects slow down because external frictional forces act on them. If, however, the frictional forces on a moving object are just balanced by other forces causing the object to move, then the object will continue to move with constant velocity.

Newton's second law of motion

Newton's first law is concerned with objects at rest or those moving at constant speed. His second law is concerned with the motion of accelerating and decelerating objects.

If you have ever tried to push a vehicle along a flat road, you know that it accelerates away faster if two people push instead of one. When accurate investigations are made, the results show that the *acceleration doubles when the force doubles* and acceleration trebles when the force trebles, etc. This means that the **acceleration is proportional to the force applied**, i.e.

acceleration ∝ force

In symbols this is written

$$a \propto F \qquad\qquad\qquad\qquad (Equation\ 1)$$

Experience may also have taught you that a small car is easier to push and accelerate than a large van. Accurate experiments show that if you push *double the mass*, with the same force, *the acceleration is only half* what it was. These results can be summarised by saying that acceleration is *inversely proportional* to mass.

$$\text{acceleration} \propto \frac{1}{\text{mass}}$$

$$a \propto \frac{1}{m} \qquad\qquad\qquad\qquad (Equation\ 2)$$

Equations 1 and 2 can be combined to give:

$$a \propto \frac{F}{m}$$

(Equation 3)

or
$$F \propto m \times a$$

Equation 3 is the mathematical form of **Newton's second law of motion**, which says:

> The acceleration of an object is inversely proportional to its mass and directly proportional to the force acting on it.

The equation for Newton's second law can also be written as

$$F = k \times m \times a$$

where k is a constant. However, the unit of force (one newton) was chosen so that k equals one, so we can write

Force $=$ mass $\times$ acceleration   *(Equation 4)*

$$F \quad = \quad m \quad \times \quad a$$

Using equation 4,

> one newton is the force which gives a mass of 1 kg an acceleration of 1 m/s².

When using equation 4, remember

- F must be in newtons
- m must be in kilograms
- a must be in metres per second per second.

Example

A car of mass 1.5 tonnes accelerates from rest to 20 m/s in 4 seconds. What is
(a) the average acceleration?
(b) the force causing the acceleration?
(c) the distance travelled in the 4 seconds?

First, put all measurements in the correct units:

mass of car = 1.5 tonnes = 1500 kg
initial speed of car = 0 m/s
final speed of car = 20 m/s
time of acceleration = 4 s

(a) Average acceleration $= \dfrac{\text{change in speed}}{\text{time taken}}$

$$= \frac{20 \text{ m/s}}{4 \text{ s}} = 5 \text{ m/s}^2$$

(b) Force causing acceleration, $F = m \times a$
$$= 1500 \times 5 = 7500 \text{ N}$$

(c) Distance travelled in 4 s = average speed $\times$ time

$$= \frac{20 \text{ m/s}}{2} \times 4 \text{ s} = 40 \text{ m}$$

Newton's third law of motion

Newton's third law explains what happens when objects push against each other and collide:

> When one object pushes against another, the second object pushes back with an equal and opposite force.

So, when you stand on the floor, you push against the floor with a force equal to your weight. The floor pushes back with an equal and opposite force. If this were not so, you would move down with the floor or through the floor.

20.15 Falling under gravity

When an object is dropped, it falls to the ground and accelerates due to the force of gravity. In air, a penny falls faster than a bit of paper. But in a vacuum, when the air is removed, both the penny and the paper fall at the same rate (Fig. 20.14).

The difference in air is due to air resistance (drag). This affects the fall of less dense objects like paper more than dense objects like the penny.

Careful experiments confirm that when air resistance is negligible, all objects accelerate to the ground at the same rate. The apparatus which can be used to measure acceleration due to gravity is shown in Fig. 20.15. It consists of an electromagnet, connected to a battery via a two-way switch. The current in the electromagnet holds a small ball bearing about one metre above a hinged trap door. When the switch is moved to position 2, the current in the electromagnet stops and the ball starts to fall. At the same time the circuit to the timer is completed and it starts counting. After falling through about one metre, the ball hits the hinged trap door. This breaks the contact at C and stops the clock.

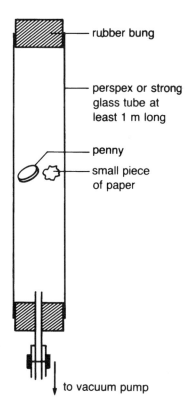

rubber bung

perspex or strong glass tube at least 1 m long

penny

small piece of paper

to vacuum pump

Fig. 20.14 Experiment to show that a penny and a bit of paper fall at the same rate in a vacuum

Results
Height through which ball falls = 1.25 m
Time of fall = 0.50 s

Calculations

$$\text{Average speed during fall} = \frac{\text{distance fallen}}{\text{time taken}} = \frac{1.25 \text{ m}}{0.5 \text{ s}} = 2.5 \text{ m/s}$$

Initial speed = 0 m/s
Final speed = 2 × average speed = 5 m/s

$$\text{Therefore, acceleration during fall} = \frac{\text{increase in speed}}{\text{time taken}} = \frac{5 \text{ m/s}}{0.5 \text{ s}} = 10 \text{ m/s}^2$$

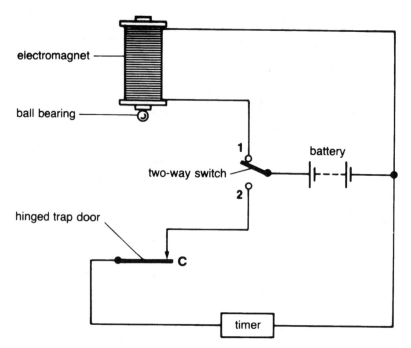

Fig. 20.15 Measuring the acceleration due to gravity

Accurate experiments show that **acceleration due to gravity is 9.8 m/s²**, but its value is usually approximated to 10 m/s². It is usually given the symbol g.

This result means that the speed of a falling object increases by 10 m/s every second. Acceleration due to gravity also means that if an object is thrown upwards, its velocity will *decrease* by 10 m/s every second until it reaches its highest point. After that, its velocity will increase downwards at the rate of 10 m/s every second.

Example

A stone is dropped from the top of a cliff and takes three seconds to reach the beach below. Calculate:

(a) the speed of the stone as it hits the beach,

(b) the height of the cliff.

(a) Initial speed of stone = 0 m/s
Acceleration of stone = 10 m/s² (acceleration due to gravity)
Therefore, speed after 3 s (as stone hits beach) = 3 × 10 = 30 m/s

(b) Average speed of stone = $\dfrac{0 + 30}{2}$ = 15 m/s

Therefore, height of cliff = distance fallen by stone
= average speed × time
= 15 m/s × 3 s
= 45 m

Weight and gravity

Weight is the force exerted by a mass as a result of acceleration due to gravity.
Remember, force = mass × acceleration

so **weight = mass × acceleration due to gravity**

So, the weight of a 9 kg mass is given as

weight = mass × acceleration due to gravity
= 9 kg × 10 m/s² = 90 N

Terminal velocity

When objects fall, air resistance (drag) increases as they move faster. Eventually the air resistance acting upwards equals the weight of the object acting downwards. The overall force on the object is then zero (i.e. the forces acting on the falling object are exactly balanced) and it continues to *fall with a constant velocity*. This speed is called the **terminal velocity**. It depends on the size, the shape and the weight of the falling object.

Summary

1   **Forces** can make things move, stop them moving, change their movement and change their shape.

2   **Weight** is the force of gravity on an object, measured in newtons (N).

3   **Mass** is the amount of matter (or stuff) in an object, measured in kilograms (kg). On Earth, a mass of 1 kg has a weight of 10 N.

4   The size and direction of the **resultant force** on an object affects its movement.

5   When elastic materials are stretched:

   extension ∝ stretching force.

   This is Hooke's Law.

6   **Friction** hinders the movement of objects, produces heat and causes wear.

7   **The moment of a force** = force × distance from fulcrum to line of action of force.

8   **The Law of Moments** says: Anticlockwise Moment = Clockwise Moment, in equilibrium

9   **Pressure** $= \dfrac{\text{Force}}{\text{Area}}$

10   In a fluid (liquid or gas) pressure increases with depth and acts in all directions.

11   Unlike a gas, a liquid cannot be compressed easily, so pressure can be transmitted through a trapped liquid.

12   **Distance** = total path taken whatever the direction.
   Displacement = distance moved in a particular direction.

13   **Speed** $= \dfrac{\text{distance}}{\text{time taken}}$, **velocity** $= \dfrac{\text{displacement}}{\text{time taken}}$

14   Velocity is a vector quantity. It has size and direction, i.e. 3 m/s *west*.

15   On a distance–time graph, the gradient = speed.

16   **Acceleration** $= \dfrac{\text{change in speed}}{\text{time taken}}$ = change in speed per unit time

17   On a speed–time graph, the gradient = acceleration.

18   **Newton's first law of motion** says: If an object is stationary it will remain so, and if it is moving it will continue to move with constant speed in a straight line, unless external forces act upon it.

   When balanced forces act on a moving object, its velocity does not alter.

19   **Newton's second law of motion** says: The acceleration of an object is inversely proportional to its mass and directly proportional to the force acting on it.

   i.e. $a = \dfrac{F}{m}$ or $F = m \times a$, Force = mass × acceleration

20   When two bodies collide, the forces they exert on each other are equal and opposite.

Quick test 20

Questions 1 to 5

What is the correct SI unit for
1   force,
2   distance,
3   mass,
4   acceleration,
5   pressure?

Questions 6 to 7

Tony and Zubair decide to walk from a youth hostel to a mountain lodge. On their map, the distance is 12 km north-east. The path which they follow is 16 km and they take 4 hours.
6   What is their average speed for the walk?
7   What is their average velocity for the walk?

Questions 8 to 10

A car travels at 40 km/h for 15 minutes and then at 30 km/h for 30 minutes.
8   How far does it travel in the first 15 minutes?
9   How far does it travel in the next 30 minutes?
10 What is the average speed of the car?

Questions 11 to 14

Questions 11 to 14 relate to the graph which shows the speed of a car at different times.

Choose the letter(s) from A to L which show where
11 the car is stationary,
12 the car is accelerating,
13 the car is decelerating,
14 the car is travelling at constant speed.

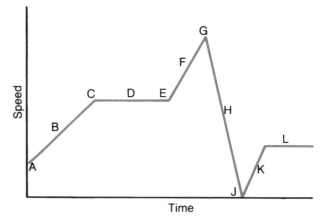

Questions 15 to 19

A cyclist and a runner had a race. The graph shows their movement during the race.
15 What distance did they race?
16 How long did the cyclist take for the race?
17 When is the runner running the fastest?
18 What is the average speed of the runner during the race?
19 Who accelerates more quickly at the start of the race?

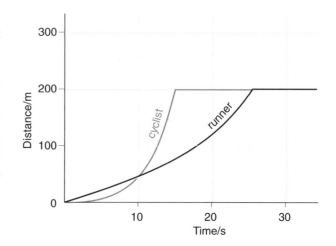

Questions 20 to 21

An astronaut has a mass on Earth of 90 kg and a weight of 900 N. He then travels to the moon where the gravitational field strength is only 1.5 N/kg.

20 What is his mass on the moon?

21 What is his weight on the moon?

Questions 22 to 25

A stone dropped from a helicopter takes 10 seconds to hit the sea below.

22 What is the acceleration of the stone in m/s^2?

23 What is the final speed of the stone during the fall?

24 What is the average speed of the stone during the fall?

25 What is the height of the helicopter above the sea?

Questions 26 to 28

26 Which *one* of the following would help a car to stop more quickly in an emergency?

    A extra luggage   D well-worn tyres

    B slower speed   E wet road surface

    C smooth road surface

27 A gas exerts a pressure because the gas particles

    A pass energy to the container.

    B want to get out of the container.

    C try to push each other out of the container.

    D exert a force when they hit the walls.

28 If the pressure is reduced in all the tyres of a car

    A the pressure exerted by the tyres on the ground increases.

    B the force exerted by the tyres on the ground increases.

    C the area of contact between the tyres and the ground increases.

    D the weight of the tyres and car on the ground increases.

Chapter 21
Energy transfers

21.1 Doing work and using energy

Clare is a fitness freak. She uses weight training to tone up her muscles and keep fit. Everytime Clare lifts the weights, she is doing **work**. The amount of work that Clare does depends on:

- how far she lifts the weights,
- how heavy the weights are.

Remember that weight is a force caused by the pull of the Earth. Work is defined by the following formula:

$$\text{Work} = \text{Force} \times \text{Distance}$$

In fact, **work is done whenever a force causes something to move**. We do work when we throw a stone, push a trolley or lift a bag. Vehicles do work when they climb hills, overcoming the force of gravity. When a vehicle travels along a flat road, it does work overcoming the force of friction.

Work is measured in **joules** (J). One joule of work is done when a force of one newton moves something through a distance of one metre.

$$
\begin{array}{ccccc}
\text{Work} & = & \text{Force} & \times & \text{Distance} \\
\text{in joules} & & \text{in newtons} & & \text{in metres} \\
1\,\text{J} & = & 1\,\text{N} & \times & 1\,\text{m}
\end{array}
$$

Example
How much work does Clare do if she lifts two masses of 0.5 kg through 50 cm (Fig. 21.1)?

$$\text{mass lifted} = 2 \times 0.5\,\text{kg} = 1\,\text{kg}$$
$$\text{therefore weight lifted} = 10\,\text{N (see 20.2)}$$
$$\text{distance lifted} = 50\,\text{cm} = 0.5\,\text{m}$$
$$\text{therefore work done} = \text{force} \times \text{distance}$$
$$= 10\,\text{N} \times 0.5\,\text{m}$$
$$= 5\,\text{J}$$

Energetic people like Clare can usually do lots of work. We might say that Clare has 'plenty of energy' which she transfers to the weights. Scientists use the word *energy* in the same way. When we do work, we transfer energy. When machines do work, they also transfer energy.

Energy helps us to get jobs done
– it enables us, and the machines we use, to transfer energy and do work.

Energy can be measured in terms of the amount of work done. Therefore, the units of energy, like those of work, are **joules**.

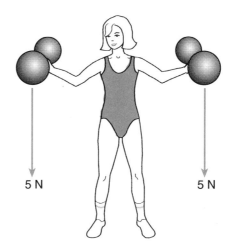

Fig. 21.1 When Clare lifts the weights she is doing work. If she holds them still, her arms get tired because her muscles use energy to hold the weights up – but she is *not* doing any work because the weights are not moving.

21.2 Forms of energy

There are several forms of energy. Some of these are summarised in Table 21.1.

Table 21.1 Different forms of energy

Form of energy	What form does the energy take?	Examples
potential energy (gravitational potential energy)	Anything lifted above the ground gains potential energy – its extra height gives it the *potential* to do work when it falls. Pot. energy = weight × height lifted 　　　　(J)　　　(N)　　　　(m) 　　　　　= $m \times g \times h$	Weight lifted above the floor; someone who has climbed some stairs; water stored in a high-level reservoir
strain energy	Material that has been stretched and is under *strain* is storing energy, which can be released if the strain is relieved.	A stretched bow ready to shoot an arrow; a tuned (tightened) violin string; a wound-up watch spring; a stretched rubber band
kinetic energy	Moving objects can do work if they hit something. The energy which they possess is called kinetic energy. Kin. energy = ½ × mass × (speed)² 　　　　(J)　　　(kg)　　　(m/s) 　　　　　= $\frac{1}{2}mv^2$	Any moving object, e.g. a falling stone, falling water, a moving car, you running
heat (thermal energy)	Molecules in any material move faster when heated. The hot, fast-moving molecules possess kinetic energy which can be used to do work.	Hot materials, e.g. hot water, steam, red hot charcoal
electrical energy (electricity)	An electric current is a flow of electrons. The moving electrons can do work.	Electric currents
chemical energy	Chemical energy is locked in the bonds between atoms. When fuels and foods react with oxygen, this stored energy can be converted into heat or into kinetic energy.	The chemicals in fuels and in foods
nuclear energy	Energy is stored in the nuclei of all atoms. This energy is released, mainly as heat and light, when a nuclear reaction occurs, e.g. in a power station or in a nuclear explosion.	All atoms contain nuclear energy. The nuclear energy in radioactive atoms is so great that they break up.
wave energy (see Chapter 22)	Waves carry energy. This can be made to do work, e.g. wave energy from the sun causes photosynthesis.	Light waves, radio waves and sound waves

Does Ben (mass 50 kg) have greater energy after he has climbed into a tree 5 m above the ground or when he is running at 5 m s⁻¹?

$$\text{Potential energy in the tree} = \text{weight} \times \text{height gained}$$
$$= 500 \text{ N} \times 5 \text{ m} = 2500 \text{ J}$$
$$\text{Kinetic energy running} = \tfrac{1}{2} \times \text{mass} \times (\text{speed})^2$$
$$= \tfrac{1}{2} \times 50 \times 5^2$$
$$= 625 \text{ J}$$

So Ben gains far more energy in climbing the tree than he does when running.

When we do work or when a machine does work, energy is transferred. However, the energy is *not used up*; it is *not lost*. Instead, the energy is converted from one form to another. Some important examples of **energy transfers** are shown in Fig. 21.2.

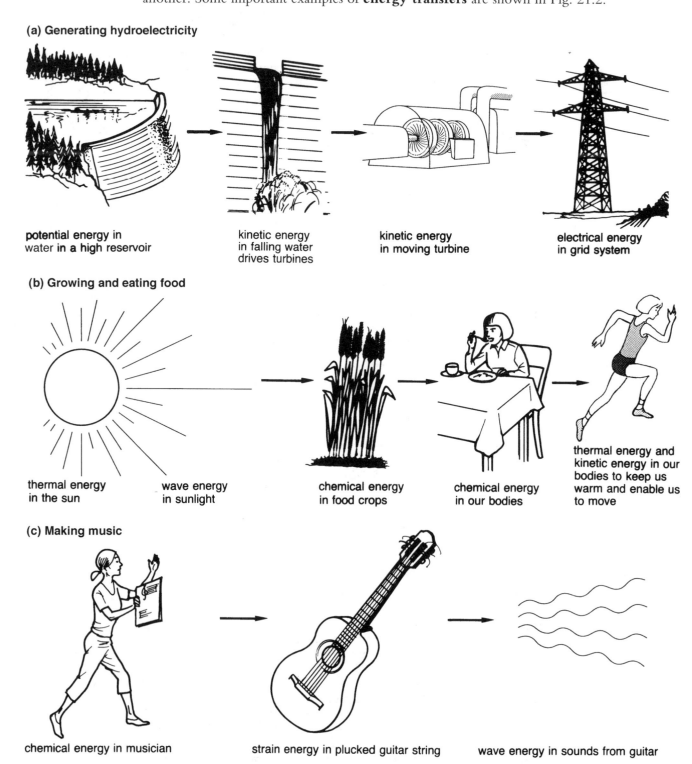

(a) Generating hydroelectricity

potential energy in water **in a high reservoir**

kinetic energy in falling water drives turbines

kinetic energy in moving turbine

electrical energy in grid system

(b) Growing and eating food

thermal energy in the sun

wave energy in sunlight

chemical energy in food crops

chemical energy in our bodies

thermal energy and kinetic energy in our bodies to keep us warm and enable us to move

(c) Making music

chemical energy in musician

strain energy in plucked guitar string

wave energy in sounds from guitar

Fig. 21.2 Some important energy transfers

Notice that energy is being converted from one form to another in all the events shown in Fig. 21.2. For example, the chemical energy of food in the musician is converted into strain energy in the stretched guitar string. This strain energy is then transferred to wave energy in sounds when the guitar string is released.

Notice also that energy is *not* lost when these energy conversions occur. It is simply changed from one form of energy into another form. We say that the energy has been conserved. This important point is summarised in the **law of conservation of energy**. This states that:

Energy cannot be made or lost,
it can only be changed from one form into another.

21.3 Efficiency of energy conversions

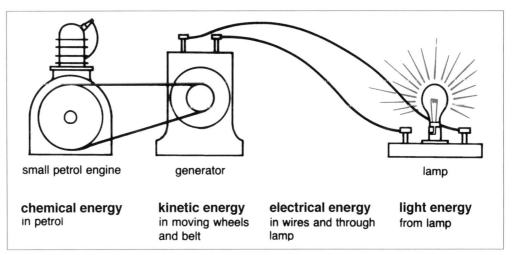

Fig. 21.3 A small petrol engine generating electricity to light a lamp

When a musician plucks a guitar (Fig. 21.2), only about 25% of the musician's chemical energy is being converted into strain energy in the guitar strings. The rest of the energy is converted into heat to keep the musician warm and into heat from friction between her fingers and the guitar strings. None of the chemical energy in the musician is lost, but only 25% is converted into useful strain energy in the strings (which will go on to produce music). This means that the **efficiency** of converting the musician's chemical energy into strain energy in the strings is only 25%.

Look at Fig. 21.3. This shows the energy conversions which occur when a small petrol engine is used to drive a generator which produces electricity to light a lamp. At each stage in Fig. 21.3, some energy is wasted (dissipated) as heat. The petrol engine, the generator and the lamp all get warm.

We can show these energy changes in a flow diagram such as Fig. 21.4. Some energy is transferred usefully from one stage to the next. The rest of the energy is wasted, often as heat. Both the useful and the wasted (dissipated) energy should be shown at each stage in an energy flow chart.

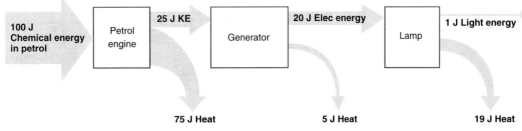

Fig. 21.4 A flow diagram showing the energy changes which occur when a petrol engine and generator are used to light a lamp

From the energy transfers in Fig. 21.4, we can calculate the efficiency of each machine:

$$\text{Efficiency} = \frac{\text{useful energy (or work) out of machine}}{\text{energy (or work) put into machine}} \times 100\%$$

Example

What is the efficiency of the generator in Fig. 21.4?

useful energy out of generator = 20 J
energy put into generator = 25 J

$$\therefore \text{efficiency} = \frac{\text{useful energy output}}{\text{energy input}} \times 100 = \frac{20}{25} \times 100 = 80\%$$

Human efficiency

Fig. 21.1 showed Clare lifting weights. While she does this her body uses 10 000 J every minute. In one minute, Clare raises two 5 N weights through 0.5 metres sixty times. What is Clare's efficiency?

Energy output in lifting two 5 N weights through 0.5 m = force × distance
= 2 × 5 N × 0.5 m
= 5 J

energy output in 1 minute = 5 J × 60 = 300 J

so, Clare's efficiency = $\dfrac{\text{useful energy output}}{\text{energy input}} \times 100$

$$= \frac{300}{10\ 000} \times 100 = 3\%$$

21.4 Power

Engineers and athletes often talk about power. Engineers are concerned about the power of machines. Athletes are interested in the power they can develop in running, jumping and throwing. We can understand the power of a machine by considering a crane lifting cargo onto a ship. Suppose the crane is lifting a weight of 50 000 N through a height of 10 m onto a ship (as in Fig. 21.5).

Fig. 21.5

We can easily calculate the work done by the crane in lifting the cargo:

Work done by crane = force × distance
= 50 000 N × 10 m = 500 000 J = 5×10^5 J

It is all very well to know this, but the crane would be useless if it took several hours to lift the load onto the ship. In order to appreciate the usefulness of the crane, we need to know how quickly it can do the work of lifting the cargo. Suppose the crane lifts the cargo in five seconds:

$$\text{Work done by crane per second} = \frac{5 \times 10^5 \text{ J}}{5 \text{ s}} = 10^5 \text{ J/s}$$

The *work done* by the crane *per second* is known as its **power. Power is defined as the rate of working or the rate of transferring energy**. It can be calculated using the following formula:

$$\text{power} = \frac{\text{work done}}{\text{time taken}} = \frac{\text{energy output (energy transferred)}}{\text{time taken}}$$

Power can be expressed in *joules per second* (as in the crane example), but we usually use the word **watt** (W) in place of joules per second. The name 'watt' is used to honour the Scottish scientist, James Watt (1736–1819). Watt was the first person to investigate the power of machines. One watt is a rate of working of one joule per second.

Human power

Linford measured his power output by running up a flight of stairs. The flight of stairs was 12 m high and he ran up in 4.2 seconds. Linford's mass is 56 kg; therefore his weight is 560 N.

$$\text{work done} = \text{force} \times \text{distance} = \text{weight} \times \text{height of stairs}$$
$$= 560 \text{ N} \times 12 \text{ m} \quad = 6720 \text{ J}$$
$$\text{power} = \frac{\text{work done}}{\text{time taken}}$$
$$= \frac{6720 \text{ J}}{4.2 \text{ s}} = 1600 \text{ W}$$

We can say that Linford's working rate is 1600 watts. In other words, he can convert chemical energy into potential energy at the rate of 1600 watts.

21.5 Energy transfers in a power station

Fig. 21.6 shows the important energy transfers which take place during the production of electricity in a power station. Some of our power stations use coal as their source of

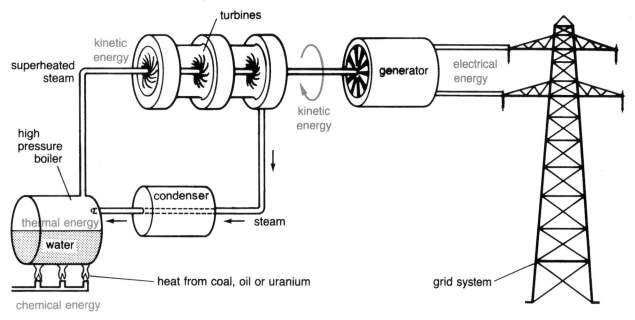

Fig. 21.6 The production of electrical energy in a power station

energy. Other stations use natural gas, oil or uranium. A few power stations in Scotland use falling water to drive the turbines. The electricity generated in this way is called hydroelectricity.

The main transfers of useful energy in the power station are:

- chemical energy in coal or oil
  or
  nuclear energy in uranium } → thermal energy in water/steam and kinetic energy in steam

- kinetic energy
  in superheated steam → kinetic energy
  in rotating turbines

- kinetic energy
  in rotating turbines → kinetic energy of rotating coils
  in generator

- kinetic energy of rotating coils
  in generator → electrical energy
  in grid system

21.6 How do we use our sources of energy?

Fig. 21.7 shows how Britain uses its energy supplies. Notice the following points:

- The main users of energy are industry, transport and homes.
- Industry uses most of the country's energy production. This energy is used to convert raw materials like coal and crude oil into useful commodities like plastics and electricity.
- Within industry, the main user of energy is the energy industry itself. Refining oil, mining coal and generating electricity need large amounts of energy.
- Most of the fuel consumed in Britain is used to generate electricity. Unfortunately power stations are only about 30% efficient. The other 70%

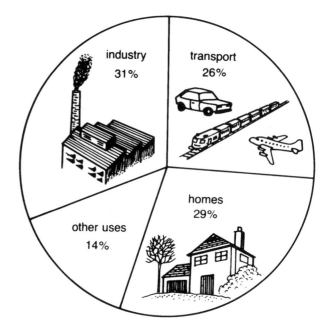

Fig. 21.7 How we use our sources of energy

of the energy in the fuel is wasted as heat when the fuel burns, as heat in the cooling towers and turbines or as heat due to friction in the generators.

In fact, energy is wasted as heat and spread out into the surroundings in many processes. The heat is shared out amongst millions of particles. This spread out energy cannot be transferred on in a useful way or used to work machines. Just contrast this dissipated (spread out) energy with foods and fuels which are stores of concentrated and useful chemical energy.

Conserving our sources of energy

In 18.4 and 18.5 we considered the importance of conserving fossil fuels and the search for alternative energy sources. The information in Fig. 21.7 can lead to further suggestions for conserving energy:

- **Saving energy in industry** by improving the efficiency of industrial processes. For example, it should be possible to improve the efficiency of power stations by reducing the energy wasted as heat and by using the thermal energy which would otherwise be wasted to heat homes, offices and factories.
- **Saving energy in the home** by reducing our energy demands. This could be achieved in almost every home by better insulation (21.11).
- **Saving energy in transport** by using fuel as economically as possible. This might involve using different methods of transport, e.g. travelling by train or coach, or sharing cars for journeys rather than travelling on our own. We should also drive cars at a steady speed so that fuel is used most economically. Car manufacturers are also designing cars with lower petrol consumption.

21.7 Heat as a form of energy

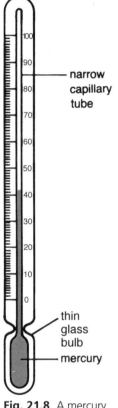

narrow capillary tube

thin glass bulb

mercury

Fig. 21.8 A mercury thermometer for measuring temperatures between 0 and 100 °C. What temperature does the thermometer show?

Heat is a form of energy. When materials are heated, they gain energy and their particles move faster (see 13.3). Thus heat (thermal energy) shows itself in the movement of particles.

It is important not to confuse 'heat' and 'temperature'.

- 'Heat' tells us how much thermal energy is contained in a body. Heat is measured in joules (J).
- 'Temperature' tells us how hot something is. Temperature is measured in degrees Celsius (°C) or kelvin (K).

When water is heated up, it requires 4200 J to heat 1 kg of water by 1 °C. Scientists summarise this by saying that the **specific heat capacity** of water is 4200 J per kg per °C. In contrast, the specific heat capacity of copper is only 385 J per kg per °C.

Thermometers

Temperature is measured using a **thermometer**. The most common type is the mercury thermometer (Fig. 21.8). When the temperature rises, mercury in the bulb expands and moves further up the narrow capillary tube.

Most thermometers have a scale marked in degrees Celsius (°C). This is known as the **Celsius scale** after the Swedish scientist who suggested it. The temperature in degrees Celsius is sometimes referred to as *degrees centigrade* because the Celsius scale has one hundred divisions between 0 °C (the temperature at which water freezes) and 100 °C (the temperature at which water boils).

21.8 Heat transfer

Examiner's tip

There are four processes by which heat is transferred from one place to another – **conduction**, **convection**, **evaporation** and **radiation**.

Differences in temperature can lead to a transfer of energy in the form of heat.

If you walk around in bare feet, you will notice that your feet feel much colder walking on tiles than on carpet. Your feet feel cold because they are losing energy. Energy associated with the movement of particles in your feet is being transferred to particles in the tiles. This transfer of energy as heat from your feet to the tiles is an example of **conduction**.

Conduction is the transfer of heat through a material from places of higher temperature to places of lower temperature without the material moving as a whole.

A second way in which heat can be transferred from one place to another is illustrated by electric heaters and radiators (see Fig. 21.9). Air near the heater is warm. This causes it to expand, become less dense and rise. As the air rises, cooler air falls and moves in to replace it. This flow of air is an example of **convection**. Notice that convection, like conduction, involves energy being transferred through the movement of particles.

Convection is the transfer of heat by movement of a liquid or gas due to differences in density caused by differences in temperature.

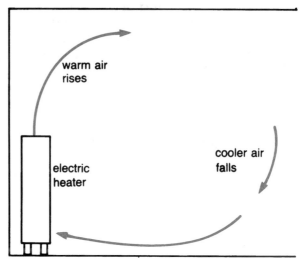

Fig. 21.9 Convection currents of air caused by an electric heater

A third process in which heat can be transferred by the movement of particles is **evaporation**. In this case, particles escape from the surface of a liquid and move off into the air as a gas. This is discussed further in 13.4.

Sunbathing and photosynthesis rely on probably the most important method of heat transfer. Sunbathing and photosynthesis both require energy from the Sun. This energy has travelled millions of miles from the Sun to the Earth as electromagnetic waves (see 22.11). This is an example of **radiation**.

Radiation is the transfer of energy (heat) from one place to another by means of electromagnetic waves.

Notice that radiation, unlike conduction, convection or evaporation, does not require the movement of particles for the transfer of energy. In the case of radiation, energy is transferred by electromagnetic waves.

21.9 Preventing heat transfer

The conductivity of a material is a measure of how well it transfers energy by conduction. Look closely at Table 21.2 which shows the relative **conductivities** of various materials.

Table 21.2 The relative conductivities of some common materials

Material	Relative conductivity	
copper	16 000	good
aluminium	8800	conductors
steel	3100	
concrete	175	
glass	35	
water	25	
brick	23	
breeze block	9	
wood	6	
felt	1.7	
fat	1.5	
wool	1.2	poor
air	1.0	conductors

Notice the following points from Table 21.2:

- Metals are much better **conductors** than any other materials. Because of this they are used for kettles, saucepans and radiators.
- Poor conductors, such as air and wool, are used to *reduce heat transfer* from hotter to colder objects. These poor conductors are called **insulators**.
- Air is the worst conductor of the materials in Table 21.2. It is an excellent insulator. Materials which trap air, e.g. hair, feathers, fibreglass and wool, are also used as insulators. They are used in winter clothing, cavity wall insulation, roof insulation and in lagging for refrigerators, ovens and pipes.

Keeping ourselves warm

Fat, wool and air are the best insulators in Table 21.2. They play an important part in keeping warm-blooded animals, including ourselves, alive during the cold winter months. For example:

- Seals have a thick layer of fat (blubber) surrounding all their body. We have only a thin layer of fat. Seals can live all winter in icy Arctic waters where we would not survive more than a few minutes.

- Birds have feathers; other animals have thick fur. Fur and feathers are poor conductors. They reduce heat transfer by trapping a layer of air. In cold weather birds fluff out their feathers to trap more air. (This is also why the fine hairs on your arms 'stand up' when you are cold.)

- On cold days, we wear layers of clothing made from fabrics such as wool. These fabrics trap air which acts as an insulator to keep us warm.

If we did not wear clothes, we would lose lots of heat by convection (Fig. 21.10). By wearing clothes, we trap a layer of air around our bodies. This prevents convection currents and the trapped air also acts as an insulator.

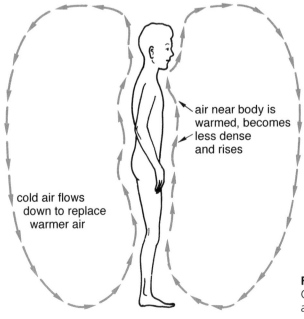

air near body is warmed, becomes less dense and rises

cold air flows down to replace warmer air

Fig. 21.10
Convection currents around a naked person

Keeping our homes warm

Insulation is also important in several methods which we use to keep our houses warm (Fig. 21.11). For example:

- **draught excluders** stuck around doors and windows prevent convection currents and loss of warm air to the outside.
- **cavity wall insulation** – mineral wool or polystyrene in the cavity traps air and prevents circulation of convection currents. The air acts as an insulator.
- **double glazing** – the layer of air between glass sheets acts as an insulator. The layer must be thin to prevent convection currents.
- **loft insulation** – mineral wool or vermiculite traps air which acts as an insulator.

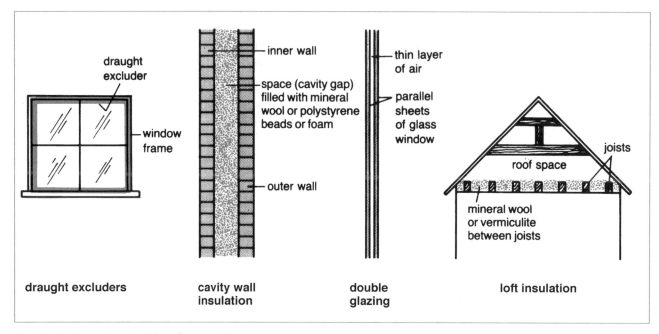

Fig. 21.11 Preventing heat loss from our homes

Summary

1 **Work** (J) = Force (N) × Distance (m)

2 **Energy transferred** = work done.

3 **Gravitational potential energy** = weight × height lifted, i.e. PE = mgh

4 **Kinetic energy** = $\frac{1}{2}$ mass × (speed)^2, i.e. KE = $\frac{1}{2}mv^2$

5 The **law of conservation of energy** says that:

Energy cannot be made or lost, it can only be changed from one form into another.

6 Efficiency = $\dfrac{\text{energy output}}{\text{energy input}} \times 100 = \dfrac{\text{work got out}}{\text{work put in}} \times 100$

7 Power is defined as the rate of working or the rate of transferring energy.

∴ **Power** (W) = $\dfrac{\text{work done (J)}}{\text{time taken (s)}} = \dfrac{\text{energy transferred (J)}}{\text{time taken (s)}}$

8 Foods and fuels are concentrated sources of chemical energy.

9 **Heat** is a form of energy. It tells us how much thermal energy a material has.

10 **Temperature** tells us how hot something is. It is measured in °C or K.
$x\,°\text{C} = (x + 273)\,\text{K}$

11   Differences in temperature can lead to the transfer of energy in the form of heat.

12   During energy transfers, energy is often wasted as heat and dissipated into the surroundings.

13   When materials are heated, they may expand, change state or react/change in some way.

14   The **specific heat capacity** of a substance is the amount of heat required to raise the temperature of 1 kg of it by 1 °C.

15   **Conduction** is the transfer of heat through a material from places of higher temperature to places of lower temperature without the material moving as a whole.

16   **Convection** is the transfer of heat by movement of a liquid or gas due to differences in density.

17   **Radiation** is the transfer of energy (heat) from one place to another by means of electromagnetic waves.

18   In conduction, convection and evaporation, energy is transferred by the movement of particles. In radiation, energy is transferred by electromagnetic waves.

19   **Insulation** can reduce the transfer of energy from hotter to colder objects. Insulation is important in keeping ourselves warm and in keeping our homes warm.

Quick test 21

Questions 1 to 3

A small electric motor is used to lift a load. A meter is used to measure the amount of energy supplied to the motor. The motor is switched on for 10 seconds and the meter shows that 1000 joules of energy has been supplied. During this time the motor does 600 joules of work lifting the load.
1   How fast is energy being supplied to the motor?
2   Work out the power output of the motor.
3   How many joules of energy does the motor waste each second?   (*NEAB*)

Questions 4 to 7

The diagram below shows how energy from fuel is used in power stations.

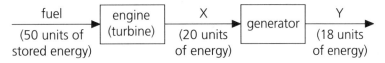

4   Name the forms of energy labelled X and Y in the diagram.
5   How many units of energy are 'lost' from the engine?
6   What has happened to this 'lost' energy?
7   An engineer showing you around the power station tells you that the generator is more efficient than the engine. What does he mean by this statement?   (*NEAB*)

Questions 8 to 9

A girl uses a force of 80 N to push a lawnmower 20 metres across a garden in 5 seconds.
8   How much work does the girl do?
9   How much power does she develop?

Chapter 22
Sound and waves

22.1 Introduction

Waves play an important part in our lives. They affect our leisure activities, our work and our home life. For example:

- waves on the sea help us to enjoy swimming, surfing and sailing;
- radiowaves enable us to transmit information and messages from one place to another;
- microwaves provide energy for cooking;
- X–rays and gamma rays have important medical uses.

These examples illustrate two important properties of waves:

1 Waves carry energy.

2 Waves carry information.

At the present time, various experiments are being carried out to see if the energy of water waves can be converted into useful energy. One experiment involves floating rafts which move up and down with the waves. The movement of the rafts is made to drive a generator and produce electricity.

The most important applications involving waves carrying information are radar, radio and television broadcasts and, of course, the light and sound that carry messages to our eyes and ears.

22.2 Sound waves

Sound plays an important part in our lives. It enables us to talk to each other, to enjoy music and to communicate using radios and telephones. Sounds are produced when you speak, when you beat a drum, when you pluck a guitar or blow into a recorder.

All sounds are produced by something vibrating.

The vibrating material might be the vocal chords in your throat, a drumskin, a guitar string or even the air inside a recorder.

Fig. 22.1 shows how sound waves are produced by a guitar. As the string on the guitar vibrates, it causes the air to move backwards and forwards in the direction of the sound. As the guitar string moves to the right, it *compresses* the air on the right-hand side of it. When the string moves to the left, the air on the right expands (is *decompressed*). As the string vibrates, it pushes out a series of **compressions** (C) and **decompressions** (D), one after the other. In a compression, the air pressure is higher than atmospheric pressure. The decompressions are sometimes called **rarefactions**.

When the compressions and decompressions reach your ears, they cause your ear drums to vibrate (see 7.3). The movements of your ear drums are then transferred to nerves. These nerves send electrical impulses to your brain and you 'hear' the sound.

Notice that the air itself does *not* move from the guitar string to your ear. Each bit of air is repeatedly compressed and then decompressed. It is the repeated compressions and decompressions which make up the sound waves (Fig. 22.2).

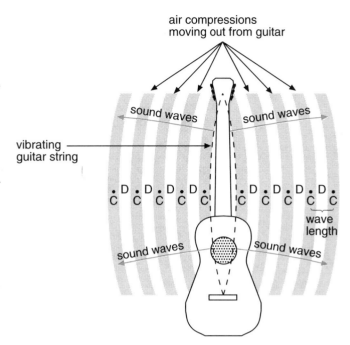

Fig. 22.1 Sound waves from a guitar. The Cs indicate compressions and the Ds indicate decompressions

As the sound waves travel outwards, air molecules are pushed together in a compression and then move apart in a decompression. The molecules in the air are therefore vibrating backwards and forwards in the *same* direction as the wave. Waves like these are called **longitudinal waves**. In longitudinal waves, the bits or the particles in the transmitting material vibrate in the same direction as the wave.

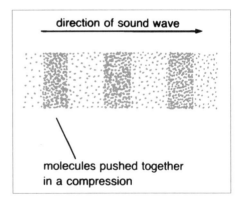

Fig. 22.2 Compressions and decompressions of air molecules in a sound wave

22.3 Hearing sounds

If you sit still and listen, you will hear sounds from all directions. The sounds may travel to you through glass windows, through wooden doors, even through brick walls. This shows that sound waves can travel through all materials. However,

sound waves cannot travel through a vacuum.

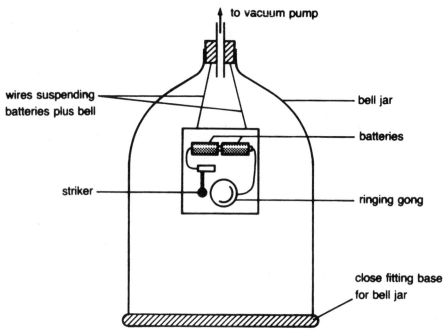

Fig. 22.3 An experiment to investigate whether sound waves can travel in a vacuum

The experiment shown in Fig. 22.3 can be used to prove that sound cannot travel through a vacuum. As the air is pumped out of the bell jar the sound of the bell gets softer. Eventually, you can no longer hear the bell at all, even though the striker continues to hit the gong.

Sound waves are transmitted by particles vibrating and knocking into one another. In a vacuum, there are no particles, so sound cannot be transmitted.

The speed of sound depends on the material the sound travels through. In solids and liquids the particles are packed more tightly than in gases. This allows sound to travel faster through liquids and solids than through gases.

When sound waves hit a material, three things can happen:

❶ the sound waves can be **reflected** off the material. The reflected noise is called an **echo** (see 22.4 and 22.5).
❷ the sound waves can be **transmitted** through the material.
❸ the sound waves can be **absorbed** by the material.

Hard, compact materials, such as glass, brick and wood, reflect about 99% of the sound energy that hits them.

Loose, soft materials, such as carpets, curtains, foam and polystyrene, reflect 50% or less of the sound energy that hits them. The rest is absorbed. Because of this, these materials are useful in soundproofing.

22.4 Echoes – the speed of sound in air

Have you noticed echoes when you have been near cliffs, near large buildings or in mountainous areas? Using echoes, you can easily measure the speed of sound in air.

Stand 50 to 100 metres from a large building and clap your hands. Listen for the echo. Now try to clap your hands continuously so that each clap coincides with the echo from the previous clap. When you do this, the **sound travels to the wall and back in the time between the two claps**. Whilst you are clapping, get a friend to time ten of your claps.

Suppose you stood 80 metres from the building and you clapped ten times in five seconds:

distance travelled by sound between claps = 2 × 80 m = 160 m

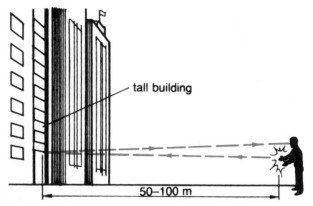

Fig. 22.4 Measuring the speed of sound in air

$$\text{time between claps} = \frac{5\text{ s}}{10} = 0.5\text{ s}$$

From this information we can say that sound travels 160 m in 0.5 seconds,

therefore the *speed of sound in the air* $= \dfrac{\text{distance}}{\text{time}} = \dfrac{160\text{ m}}{0.5\text{ s}} = 320\text{ m/s}$

22.5 Echoes and ultrasound waves

Echoes have some important uses. They have been used to search for oil and to estimate the thickness of the polar ice cap. In these investigations, explosives are detonated at ground level sending waves through the Earth. These sound waves are partly reflected when they meet a boundary between different materials such as rock and oil or ice and soil. By timing the echo and knowing the speed of sound through the Earth, scientists can estimate the depth of an oil well or the thickness of ice.

Bats also use echoes to detect objects. The sound waves that bats produce are caused by vibrations at a rate of more than 20 000 per second. The frequency of these waves is so high that we cannot hear them. We use the term **ultrasound waves** (ultrasonics) to describe sound waves like these with very high frequencies that cannot be detected (heard) by the human ear.

Ultrasound waves are used to measure the depth of the sea, to detect shoals of fish and to hunt for submarines (Fig. 22.5). Ultrasound waves also have important medical uses. They are used to 'look at' unborn babies (Fig. 22.6). They can be used to scan for tumours in the body. Unlike X-rays, ultrasound waves are perfectly safe.

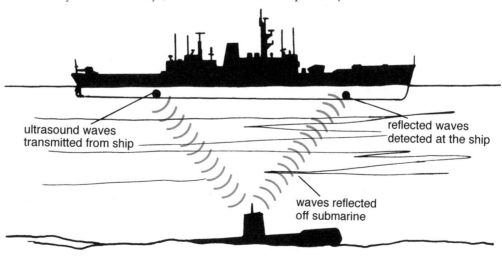

ultrasound waves
transmitted from ship

reflected waves
detected at the ship

waves reflected
off submarine

Fig. 22.5 Ultrasound waves being used to detect a submarine

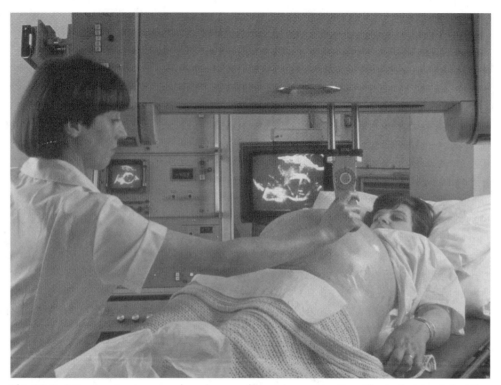

Fig. 22.6 A pregnant woman undergoing an ultrasonic examination. The technician is holding the probe (which produces the ultrasound waves) to the woman's abdomen, An image of the fetus appears on the screen. This can be interpreted like an X-ray picture. Ultrasonic examinations are used to monitor growth and diagnose possible abnormalities in the fetus.

22.6 Describing waves

Have you ever tried to rescue a ball or a boat from a still pond by making waves? This method is never very successful. The waves move across the surface of the pond, but the water only moves up and down. This means that articles floating on the pond do not move across it with the waves. They only bob up and down.

As the water moves up and down, the wave carries energy from one place to another without the water being carried along. This illustrates another important characteristic of waves:

Waves carry energy from one point to another without transferring matter.

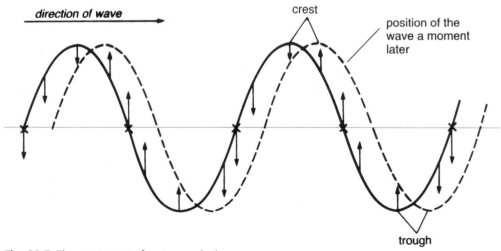

Fig. 22.7 The movement of water producing a wave

Fig. 22.7 shows the general shape of water waves. At the points marked by a cross, the water is passing through the *average undisturbed position*. Arrows on the wave show how the water is moving at various points. The dashed curve shows the position of the water and the wave a moment later. The peaks in the waves are called **crests** and the dips in the waves are called **troughs**.

Wavelength

If possible, try the following experiment. Fill a tank or bath with water to a depth of 5 cm. Now make waves by dipping a horizontal ruler in and out of the water at intervals of about half a second.

Try to estimate *the distance between one crest and the next*. This distance is called the **wavelength** (Fig. 22.8). The wavelength is represented by the symbol λ (a Greek letter, pronounced *lambda*).

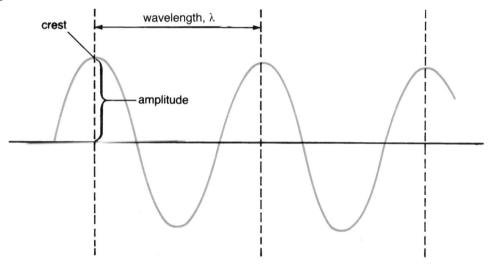

Fig. 22.8 Measuring a wave

Amplitude

Try to estimate *the height of a crest from the undisturbed position of the water*. This is called the **amplitude** of the wave. Think of the amplitude as the height of a hump (crest) in the wave from the undisturbed position. (It is *not* the vertical distance from the top of a crest to the bottom of a trough). As the amount of energy carried by a wave increases, its amplitude also increases. We all know that big waves carry more energy and therefore can do more damage than small waves!

Frequency

Carry on dipping the ruler in and out of the water. Try to estimate the number of wave crests passing a point just in front of the ruler in ten seconds. Suppose you count thirty crests in ten seconds. This means that three waves pass the point each second. We say that the **frequency** of the waves is 3 waves per second or 3 hertz. Frequency is *the number of crests which pass a point in one second*. The symbol for frequency is *f*. The unit of frequency is the **hertz (Hz)**. One hertz is a frequency of one wave per second.

Speed

The speed of a wave is *the distance travelled by the wave in one second*. Suppose that three waves pass a particular point in one second (i.e. frequency, f = 3 Hz). Suppose also that the wavelength, λ is 4 cm. This wave is illustrated in Fig. 22.9. Each crest moves forward by three whole waves every second. So over one second the crest at X will have moved to Y.

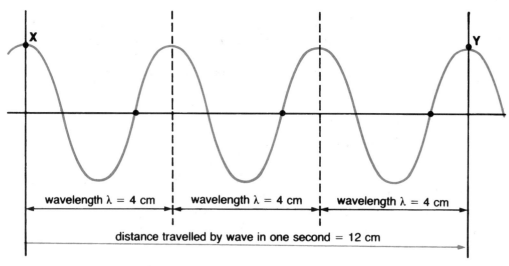

Fig. 22.9

Distance moved by a crest in one second = 12 cm,
therefore *speed of wave* = 12 cm per second.

Notice that the speed of a wave can be obtained from the following equation:

$$\text{Speed} = \text{wavelength} \times \text{frequency}$$
$$v = \lambda \times f$$

This is called the **wave equation**.

Example

Red light has a frequency of 4×10^{14} Hz and a wavelength of 7.5×10^{-7} m. What is its speed?

$\lambda = 7.5 \times 10^{-7}$ m, $f = 4 \times 10^{14}$ Hz

Therefore, the speed of red light = wavelength × frequency
$$v = 7.5 \times 10^{-7} \text{ m} \times 4 \times 10^{14} \text{ per second}$$
$$= 30 \times 10^{7} = 300\ 000\ 000 \text{ m/s}$$

Compare this with the speed of sound which is only 320 m/s. Light travels about one million times faster than sound.

Resonance

The term resonance is used to describe what happens when a vibrator is forced to vibrate at its *natural frequency*. An example of resonance is when a car or a washing machine vibrates quite violently at one particular speed. In these cases, the frequency of a rotating part (e.g. motor, wheel, drum) is equal to the natural frequency of vibration of the body of the car or the washing machine. When resonance occurs in this way:

- the amplitude of the vibrations of the driven vibrator increases,
- the maximum amount of energy is transferred from the forcing vibrator to the driven vibrator.

22.7 Measuring sounds

The distance between one compression and the next gives the **wavelength** of a sound wave. The number of compressions per second is the **frequency**.

$$\text{speed of sound} = \text{wavelength} \times \text{frequency}$$
$$v = \lambda \times f$$

Using a microphone connected to a **cathode-ray oscilloscope**, it is possible to 'see' the wave nature of sounds. The sounds reaching the microphone make its cone vibrate. These vibrations are turned into electrical vibrations by the microphone and they appear as a wave pattern (waveform) on the screen of the cathode-ray oscilloscope.

The quality of sounds

Fig. 22.10 shows the waveforms on a cathode-ray oscilloscope when the note A is produced from a tuning fork, a piano and a violin.

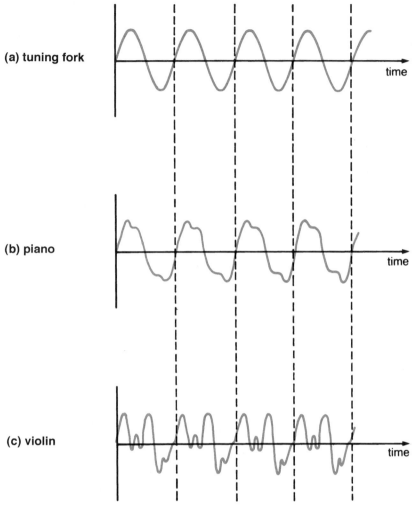

Fig. 22.10 Waveforms on a cathode-ray oscilloscope when note A is obtained from (a) a tuning fork, (b) a piano and (c) a violin

Notice two things from Fig. 22.10.

1. Waveforms with the same frequency have roughly the same shape.
2. Only the tuning fork produces a pure note with a smooth waveform. The piano and the violin have 'squiggles' on their waveforms. This is because other notes with different frequencies and wavelengths are mixed in with note A.

The **quality** of a note depends on the extent to which other notes are mixed in with it. Thus, note A on the tuning fork is purer in quality than note A on the piano. In turn, note A on the piano is purer in quality than note A on the violin. Different instruments produce different mixtures of notes. This gives each instrument its own special sound. This is why note A on a piano sounds quite different from note A on a violin or note A on a guitar.

Loudness

Fig. 22.11 shows the waveforms of the same note produced quietly then loudly. Notice that the two sounds have the *same wavelength*, but **the louder sound has greater amplitude**. This is what we might have expected because the louder sound transmits more energy.

Loud sounds cause a greater pressure change on our eardrums than soft sounds. During normal conversation, your ear drum will experience a pressure change of about one newton per square metre (1 N/m^2 or 1 **pascal**). This is tiny in comparison with atmospheric pressure (100 000 pascals). Loud noises can cause pressure waves with an amplitude of 100 pascals or more. These sounds are painful and can damage your hearing. There are now laws which limit the noise level from industrial machinery and aeroplanes. People who work with noisy machines should wear ear protectors.

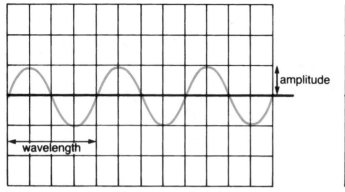

(a) quiet sound from a tuning fork

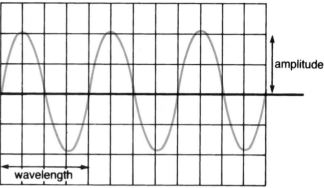

(b) loud sound from same tuning fork

Fig. 22.11 Waveforms on a cathode-ray oscilloscope when the same note is produced from a tuning fork (a) quietly and (b) loudly

Pitch

We use the word 'pitch' to describe how a note or a noise sounds. Bass notes are low in pitch, treble notes are high in pitch. Some men have very low-pitched voices, whereas young children usually have high-pitched voices.

> The pitch of a note depends on its frequency.
> High-pitched notes have a greater frequency than low-pitched notes.

Fig. 22.12 shows the wave patterns on a cathode-ray oscilloscope from tuning forks of different pitch. (Note that the amplitude of the two waveforms is the same, so these notes are being produced at the same volume.)

We hear sounds because sound waves cause our ear drums to vibrate. This then causes vibrations in the inner ear and messages are passed to the brain via the auditory nerve. Different people have different sensitivity to different sounds and so have different ranges of hearing.

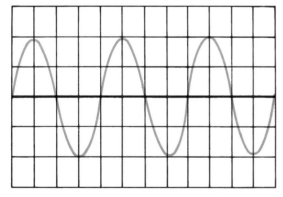

(a) low-pitched tuning fork with low frequency

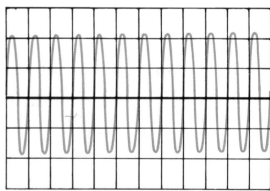

(b) high-pitched tuning fork with high frequency

Fig. 22.12 Wave patterns on a cathode-ray oscilloscope of notes produced from tuning forks of different pitch

22.8 Reflection and refraction of waves

When waves hit materials, three things can happen.

❶ **The waves can be reflected**. When waves are reflected from a flat surface, *the angle of incidence (i) is equal to the angle of reflection (r)* (see 23.2 and Fig. 22.13).

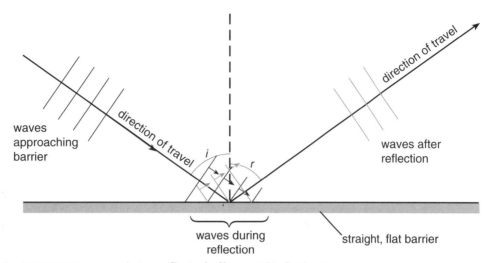

Fig. 22.13 Water waves being **reflected** off a straight, flat barrier

2 **The energy in the waves can be absorbed**. This causes the material to get warmer. This is what happens in a microwave oven. Energy in the microwaves is absorbed by the food which is heated and cooked.

3 **The waves can pass through the material**. As waves pass into a different material, their *speed changes*. This can change the direction of the wave. The *change in direction* is called **refraction** (see 23.3 and Fig. 22.14). Notice in Fig. 22.14 that the frequency of the waves is the same in shallow and in deep water, but the wavelength is shorter in shallow water. This means that the wave speed is lower in shallow water.

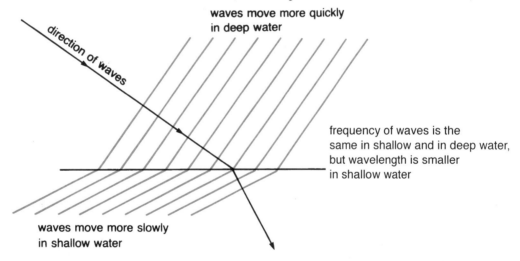

Fig. 22.14 Water waves being **refracted** as they move into shallower water

Under some circumstances, all three of these phenomena can happen at the same time. Part of a wave is reflected, part is absorbed and part of the wave passes through the material.

22.9 Transverse and longitudinal waves

One of the best ways to study waves is to watch ripples on the surface of water. When a stone hits the surface of a pond, kinetic energy in the stone is transferred to kinetic energy in the water. The water *vibrates up and down* and a *wave moves across* the pond. Waves like this, where *the vibrations are at right angles to the direction of the wave*, are called **transverse waves** (Fig. 22.15).

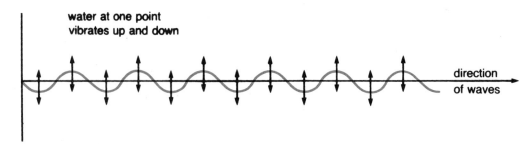

Fig. 22.15 Water waves are **transverse** waves

Light waves, microwaves and radiowaves are three more examples of transverse waves. Light waves, microwaves and radiowaves are produced when electrons in materials vibrate and release energy. As the electrons vibrate, they set up vibrating *electric and magnetic fields*. These vibrating electric and magnetic fields travel through space as waves – light waves, microwaves, radiowaves, etc. Because of their electric and magnetic character, these waves are described as **electromagnetic waves** (see 22.11). In electromagnetic waves, the magnetic and electric fields vibrate at right angles to each other and to the direction in which the wave is travelling (Fig. 22.16). They are therefore transverse waves.

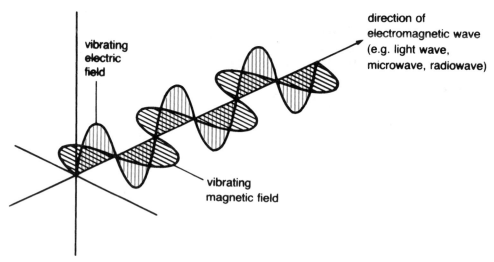

Fig. 22.16 In an electromagnetic wave, the energy is carried by vibrating electric and magnetic fields. These vibrate at right angles to each other and to the direction of the wave

Waves can also be studied using a rope or a stretched spring ('slinky') (Fig. 22.17). One end of the rope or 'slinky' is fixed. Then a wave is produced by holding the free end and moving your hand quickly to the side and then back to its original position. The *wave travels along* the slinky, but the *turns of the slinky move from side to side*. If you tie a piece of string to the 'slinky' and make more waves, the string moves from side to side exactly as your hand did to start the wave. These are examples of **transverse waves** – *the turns in the slinky move at right angles to the direction of the waves.*

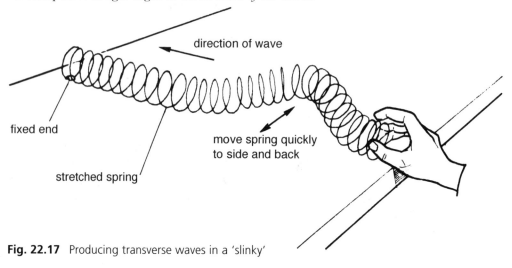

Fig. 22.17 Producing transverse waves in a 'slinky'

You can make a different kind of wave in a slinky by moving your hand quickly forwards and then back (see Fig. 22.18). This movement *compresses* and then *expands* the slinky.

This time a wave of closer coils moves along the spring. Tie a piece of string to the 'slinky' and make some more waves. The string moves forwards and backwards as each wave passes. This is similar to the way your hand moved to make the wave. The waves are made up of **compressions** and **expansions** which move along the slinky like the compressions and decompressions in a sound wave (Fig. 22.2). In the compressions, the turns of the spring are closer than normal. In the expansions, the turns of the spring are further apart than normal. In this case, the turns in the slinky move forwards and backwards in the *same direction* as the wave, like the molecules of air in a sound wave. These, of course, are called **longitudinal waves** (see 22.2).

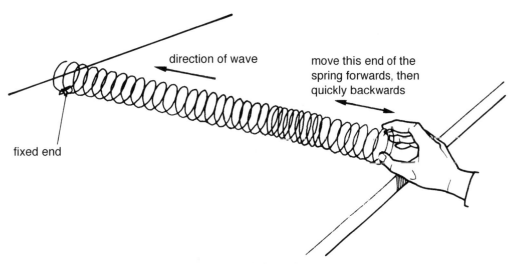

Fig. 22.18 Producing longitudinal waves in a 'slinky' coil

Common wave properties

There are many different kinds of waves. These waves have different properties and different uses, but they all have three important properties in common.

1. All wave motions obey the wave equation, $v = \lambda \times f$
2. All wave motions transfer energy from one place to another.
3. Wave motions do *not* transfer matter.

When a wave moves along a spring, across a pond or through the air, kinetic energy is transferred through the material, but the spring, the water and the air finish up where they started.

22.10 Evidence for the Earth's layered structure

The Earth is shaped like an orange and its structure is like a badly cracked egg (see 11.4). The Earth's crust is like the cracked shell of the egg, the mantle is like the egg 'white' and the core is like the yolk. Earthquakes provide good evidence for the layered structure of the Earth.

When an earthquake occurs, three kinds of shock waves (**seismic waves**) travel outwards from the centre of the quake (**epicentre**).

①**Surface waves** roll around the surface of the Earth like waves on a pond. Surface waves are *transverse* waves (see 22.9). They do most damage to buildings.

②**Primary waves** or **P waves** go through the Earth. P waves are *longitudinal* waves (see 22.2 and 22.9). P waves travel through the mantle and the core at 8 to 13 km/s.

③**Secondary waves (shear waves)** or **S waves** also go through the Earth. S waves are *transverse* waves. They travel through the mantle at 4 to 7 km/s, but are reflected when they hit the core.

Seismic waves can be detected using a **seismometer**. A large mass is suspended from a beam. Even a slight earth tremor will cause some movement to the suspended mass. This movement can be charted using a pen recorder. Scientists have obtained evidence for the Earth's internal structure from the records of P waves and S waves on seismometers (Fig. 22.19).

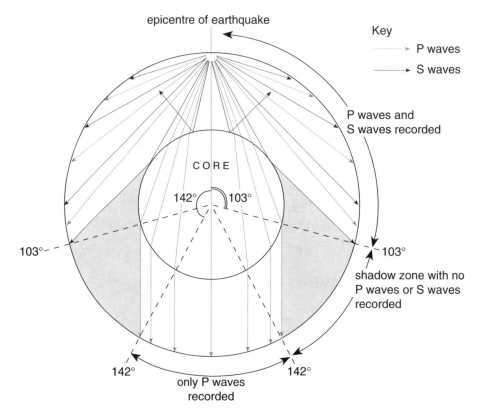

Fig. 22.19 Recording P waves and S waves after an earthquake

S waves are not detected by seismometers at an angle greater than 103° from the epicentre of the quake. P waves are also *not* detected after 103°, but they reappear again at 142°. This suggests that:

- S waves cannot pass through the Earth's dense, part liquid core. Some S waves travel straight from the epicentre through the mantle to other points on the Earth's surface where they are detected. Other S waves are reflected off the core to the point of detection.
- P waves are refracted at the core/mantle boundary.

22.11 Electromagnetic waves

Radiowaves, microwaves, infrared rays, visible light, ultraviolet rays, X-rays and gamma rays are all members of the large family of electromagnetic waves. These electromagnetic waves make up a continuous range of waves with different wavelengths and frequencies. The range of waves is called the **electromagnetic spectrum**. The range of wavelengths in the spectrum varies from 10^{-12} metres for gamma rays to ten kilometres (10 000 m) for the longest radiowaves. In spite of this variation in wavelengths, all electromagnetic waves have the following properties:

- They are produced when atoms or electrons lose energy.
- They are transverse waves.
- They transfer energy as vibrating electric and magnetic fields.
- They can travel through a vacuum.
- They all travel at a speed of 3×10^8 m/s in a vacuum. Their speed in air is virtually the same as this.

Examiner's tip

Table 22.1 is a very helpful summary of the properties and uses of different kinds of waves in the electromagnetic spectrum.

The properties and uses of the different waves in the electromagnetic spectrum are summarised in Table 22.1.

If you have had an X–ray picture taken, you may have wondered why it was alright for you to be exposed to the radiation, while the radiographer went behind a shield or left the room while the picture was being taken. Short exposure to radiation will not harm you, but radiographers take many X–ray pictures every day so they need to be shielded from the radiation.

22.12 Diffraction

When parallel water waves move towards a large gap, the middle parts of the waves go straight through the gap with a slight curving at the edges of the waves (Fig. 22.20(a)). If, however, the gap is smaller than the wavelength of the waves, the waves fan out in circles from the gap (Fig. 22.20(b)). The gap seems to act as a small vibrating source and waves spread out from the gap. This spreading out of the wave is called **diffraction**. Diffraction provides evidence for the wave nature of water waves, sound waves and light.

A good example of the diffraction of sound waves occurs when you hear people talking, out of sight, on the other side of a doorway. When the sound waves reach the doorway, they spread out and become diffracted *round* the doorway. This occurs because the wavelengths of some of the soundwaves are similar to the size of the gap in the doorway.

Although we can hear round corners, we cannot see round corners. Light waves have very small wavelengths. This means that when light waves reach a doorway they hardly diffract at all. Sound waves have much longer wavelengths so they diffract round the doorway.

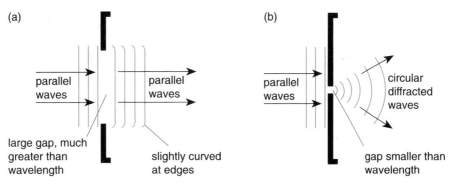

Fig. 22.20 Diffraction patterns

	Gamma rays	X-rays	Ultraviolet rays	Visible light	Infrared rays	Microwaves	Radiowaves
Wavelength/m	10^{-12}	10^{-8}	4×10^{-7}	7.5×10^{-7}	10^{-4}	1.0	UHF VHF short medium long — 10 — 10^4
Frequency/Hz	3×10^{20}	3×10^{16}	7.5×10^{14}	4×10^{14}	3×10^{12}	3×10^{8}	3×10^{4}
Properties	• emitted by radioactive materials • shortest wavelength of all e/m waves • most penetrating of all e/m waves • can destroy cells and cause mutations	• produced by accelerating electrons onto a metal target • penetration of matter depends on relative atomic mass of atoms • absorbed by bones and teeth, but pass through flesh • dangerous in high doses	• emitted by the Sun and other white hot objects • pass through the air, but *not* through solids • increase formation of vitamin D and melanin (the brown skin pigment that gives a suntan) • over-exposure can burn the skin and cause skin cancer	• light of different wavelengths appears as different colours to our eyes • violet light has the shortest wavelength; red light has the longest wavelength	• can be detected by special photographic film and heat-sensitive devices • emitted by all warm and hot surfaces – the hotter the surface, the more penetrating the radiation	• absorbed by some materials, e.g. water • reflected by metals • pass through glass, china, paper, cardboard and plastic	• radiowaves are e/m waves – they are different from sound waves • radiowaves with λ>10 m are transmitted around the Earth by reflection from the ionosphere (layers of ionised gas 100 to 400 km above the Earth) • radiowaves with λ<10 m pass through the ionosphere – used for communications with satellites
Uses	• treatment of cancer tumours • sterilisation of medical instruments and food	• examination of broken bones and of teeth • detecting diseased areas in the body	• sterilisation of materials • UV lamps and sun beds • marking goods with UV pens in crime prevention and detection	• electric light bulbs	• infrared detectors can be used to track and observe any warm objects e.g. rockets, nocturnal animals, people (e.g. burglars) • heaters, grills	• cooking in microwave ovens: water molecules in the food absorb the microwaves, become hot and cook • satellite transmissions	• carrying signals for radar, telephones, television and radio

Table 22.1 The properties and uses of different waves in the electromagnetic spectrum

Summary

1   **Waves** transfer energy and information without transferring matter.

2   **Sounds** are produced when something vibrates.

3   **Sound waves** can be reflected off materials, transmitted through materials or absorbed by materials, but they cannot travel through a vacuum.

4   The **wavelength** of a wave is the distance between one crest and the next. The **amplitude** of a wave is the height of a crest from the undisturbed position.

    The **frequency** of a wave is the number of waves which pass a point in one second.

5   The **pitch** of a note gets higher as the frequency increases. The **loudness** of a note (sound) increases as the amplitude increases.

6   **Speed** = wavelength × frequency, i.e. $v = \lambda \times f$. This is called the wave equation.

7   In **longitudinal waves**, vibrations are in the same direction as the direction of the wave. Sound waves are longitudinal waves.

8   In **transverse waves**, vibrations are at right angles to the direction of the wave. Light waves, water waves, microwaves and radiowaves are examples of transverse waves.

9   Radiowaves, microwaves, infrared, visible light, ultraviolet waves, X-rays and gamma rays are examples of **electromagnetic waves**. Electromagnetic waves all have the same speed. They make up a continuous range of waves with different wavelengths and different frequencies called the **electromagnetic spectrum**.

10   Electromagnetic waves can be reflected by, absorbed by and transmitted through materials. They can also travel through a vacuum.

11   **Diffraction** occurs when waves pass through a gap or round an object of roughly the same size or smaller than their wavelength, and then spread out.

12   As wave motions, both light and sound can be reflected, refracted and diffracted.

Quick test 22

Questions 1 to 5

The diagram below shows waves on the surface of the sea.

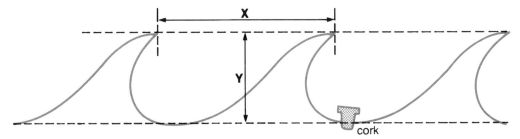

1   What is the distance X called?
2   What is the distance Y?
3   What happens to the cork floating on the surface as waves pass from left to right?
4   How could waves on the sea enable our supplies of fuel to last longer?
5   Suppose the distance between the waves is 10 metres and one wave arrives every 2 seconds. What is the speed of the waves?

Questions 6 and 7

6   What is the source of gamma rays?
7   Why are gamma rays used in the treatment of cancerous tissues?

Questions 8 to 11

As part of the planning for a large concert hall, experiments were carried out to determine how much sound energy was absorbed by brick, carpet and tiles at various frequencies. The results are given in the table.

Material	Percentage of sound energy absorbed at a certain frequency		
	125 Hz	500 Hz	2500 Hz
brick	0.05%	0.02%	0.05%
tiles	0.08%	0.5%	0.7%
carpet	0.17%	0.8%	0.9%

8   Which material is the best absorber at a frequency of 125 Hz?
9   Which material is a better absorber at frequencies of 125 Hz and 2500 Hz than at 500 Hz?
10 If 100 joules of sound energy of frequency 500 Hz hit the walls covered with tiles, how much sound energy is reflected?
11 In one particular theatre, the back wall is 33 m from the loudspeakers.
     (a) If the speed of sound is 330 m/s, calculate how long it will take the sound from the loudspeakers to reach the back wall.
     (b) Give *two* factors that must be considered when thinking about how long the sound will take to die down in the theatre.
     (c) Give *one* reason why, when the theatre is full of people, the time for the sound to die down might change.

(WJEC)

Questions 12 and 13

An electric guitar has strings stretched over a solid body. A Spanish guitar has a large, hollow body. Explain why:
12 the Spanish guitar sounds strong and lively and does not need an amplifier.
13 the electric guitar sounds weak and lifeless when it is not plugged into an amplifier.

(ULEAC)

Chapter 23
Light and colour

23.1 Laser beams and light rays

In Chapter 22, we learnt that light is a form of energy. It is a form of electromagnetic radiation (Table 22.1). Scientists believe that glowing (luminous) objects, such as the Sun, fires and candles, emit light when their atoms have large amounts of energy. In an electric lamp, this energy is provided by electricity.

Sometimes all the atoms in a material can be made to emit their excess energy at the same moment. In some cases, a narrow and extremely intense beam of light can be produced. This is the basis of **lasers**. Laser beams are a very concentrated energy source. Lasers can be used in a variety of ways from cutting through metal sheets to performing delicate surgical operations.

If you have used a torch in the dark you will know how it can be used as a searchlight. The torch can send out a beam of light in one particular direction. Beams of light are also produced by car headlights and when sunlight comes through a break in the clouds (a 'sunbeam'). The sharp edges of the beams from lasers, torches, car headlights and sunlight show that:

Light travels in straight lines.

The experiment shown in Fig. 23.1 can also be used to show that light travels in straight lines. In Fig. 23.1, the coloured line shows a **ray**. A ray is a very thin beam of light.

Light does, of course, travel much faster than sound. This explains why, when you are watching a cricket match from the boundary, you *see* a batsman hitting the ball before you *hear* the sound of ball on bat.

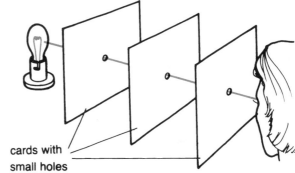

Fig. 23.1 Light from the lamp will only travel to the girl's eye if the holes in the cards are in a straight line.

cards with small holes

23.2 Reflecting light

When light rays hit a surface, three things can happen:
1. the light rays can be **transmitted** (e.g. through glass),
2. the light rays can be **absorbed** (e.g. by a black surface),
3. the light rays can be **reflected** (e.g. from a mirror).

Most surfaces will reflect some light. Shiny smooth surfaces reflect almost all the light which hits them. They produce clear images and are used for **mirrors**. Many mirrors are made by coating the back of a piece of glass with a thin layer of silver or aluminium. Other mirrors are just shiny pieces of metal.

Images in mirrors

We see objects because they reflect some of the light which falls on them. Rays of light reflected from the objects enter our eyes. Fig. 23.2 shows how you see an image in a mirror or in any shiny smooth surface. Rays from the penny travel in straight lines to the mirror where they are reflected. When the rays enter your eye, they *appear* to come from the image behind the mirror.

This sort of image is called a **virtual image**. Your brain thinks the penny is behind the mirror, but really there is nothing there. Virtual images cannot be projected on a screen or recorded on photographic film. Images that can be projected on a screen or recorded on film (as in a camera) are called **real images**.

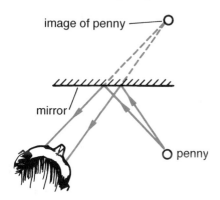

When you look at yourself in a mirror, the image you see is different from what your friends see when they look straight at you. If you move your left arm, your image moves its right arm. This effect is called **lateral inversion**. The lettering on ambulances is laterally inverted. The letters on the front of the ambulance are written as '**ƎƆИAⅬUᗺMA**'. Other drivers, looking in their rear-view mirrors, will see '**AMBULANCE**'. To see an effect of lateral inversion, just turn a piece of printed paper over and look at the writing from the reverse side.

Fig. 23.2 Seeing an image in a mirror. Notice that the image in the mirror is the same size as its object and appears to be as far behind the mirror as the object is in front.

Reflection by mirrors

Fig. 23.3 shows an arrangement to investigate the reflection of light by a mirror. Ray boxes are used to produce thin beams of light.

- Before the ray hits the mirror, it is called an **incident ray**.
- After the ray has been reflected, it is called a **reflected ray**.
- The line at right angles to the mirror where the incident ray hits the mirror is called the **normal**.
- The angle between the incident ray and the normal is called the **angle of incidence**, i.
- The angle between the reflected ray and the normal is called the **angle of reflection**, r.

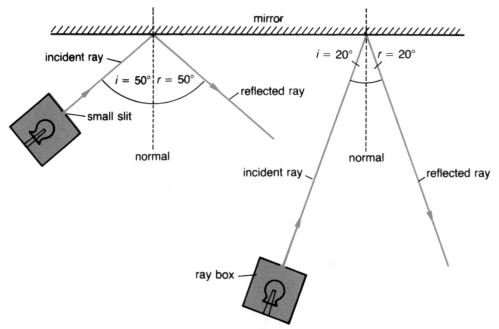

Fig. 23.3 Investigating the reflection of light by mirrors

From experiments like the one shown in Fig. 23.3, we know that:

The angle of incidence equals the angle of reflection, i.e. $i = r$.

Key points in the reflection of light by flat (plane) mirrors:
- the image is **virtual**
- the image is the **same size** as the object
- the image is **as far behind the mirror as the object is in front**
- the image is **laterally inverted**
- **angle of incidence = angle of reflection**

Mirrors are always smooth and shiny. This allows them to reflect light regularly and form clear images. On the other hand, rough and irregular surfaces reflect light in all directions. This diffuse reflection does not allow rough surfaces to form any clear images.

Using mirrors

Flat (plane) mirrors have many uses, e.g. in bathrooms, in shops, in restaurants and as hand mirrors. Large mirrors are often used in shops and restaurants to make the area seem lighter and more spacious.

Curved mirrors also reflect light rays and produce images. However, their curvature also enables them to concentrate light or spread it out. These properties make curved mirrors very useful. Some examples of the uses of curved mirrors are given in Fig. 23.4.

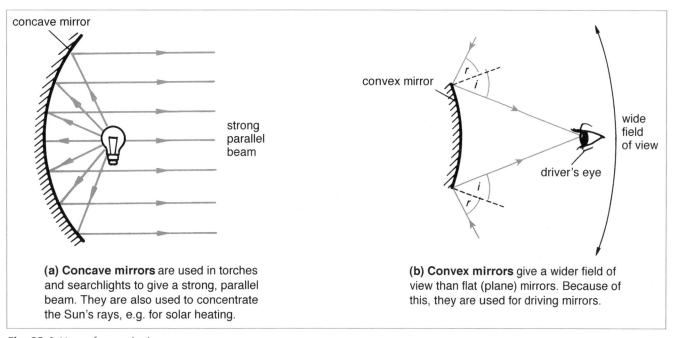

(a) Concave mirrors are used in torches and searchlights to give a strong, parallel beam. They are also used to concentrate the Sun's rays, e.g. for solar heating.

(b) Convex mirrors give a wider field of view than flat (plane) mirrors. Because of this, they are used for driving mirrors.

Fig. 23.4 Uses of curved mirrors

23.3 Refracting light

When a ray of light travels at an angle from air into a clear material such as glass or water, it *changes direction*. This is called **refraction**. Fig. 23.5 shows an experiment to study how light rays are refracted (bent) when they travel from air into a glass block.

- The angle between the incident ray and the normal is called the **angle of incidence**, *i*.
- The angle between the refracted ray and the normal is called the **angle of refraction**, *r*.

The results of this and similar experiments show that:

- A ray parallel to the normal goes straight through the glass.
- A ray passing into a denser material (e.g. from air into glass or water) is refracted (bent) towards the normal.
- A ray passing into a less dense material (e.g. from glass or water into air) is bent away from the normal.
- If the block has parallel sides, the ray comes out of the block at the same angle as it went in.

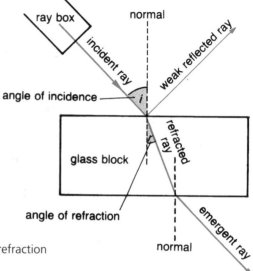

Fig. 23.5 Investigating the refraction of light rays

Unexpected effects of refraction

Refraction leads to some unexpected effects. For example, light rays from an object in water are bent away from the normal as they pass from the water into the air. This makes a pool appear shallower than it really is and it makes the fish seem nearer to the surface than they really are (Fig. 23.6).

The simple results of refraction can also lead to unexpected directions for light rays as they pass through different shapes of glass. Fig. 23.7 shows the direction of a light ray through a triangular glass prism. As the ray enters the glass, it is refracted towards the normal. As the ray leaves the glass, it is bent away from the normal.

Fig. 23.6 The boy fishing thinks that the rays of light come from the image at I, so the fish seems nearer the surface than it really is

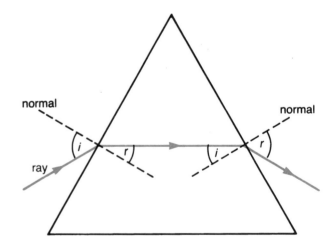

Fig. 23.7 The refraction of a ray of light through a triangular glass prism

Fig. 23.8 shows how the refraction of light can be explained by thinking in terms of waves. The frequency of the waves is the same in both air and glass, but the wavelength is greater in air than glass. This causes the wavefronts to slow down as they cross the air/glass boundary.

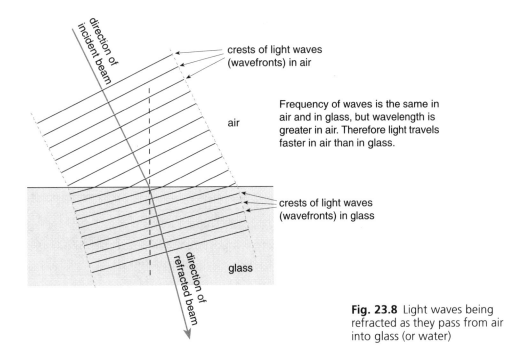

Frequency of waves is the same in air and in glass, but wavelength is greater in air. Therefore light travels faster in air than in glass.

Fig. 23.8 Light waves being refracted as they pass from air into glass (or water)

23.4 Total internal reflection

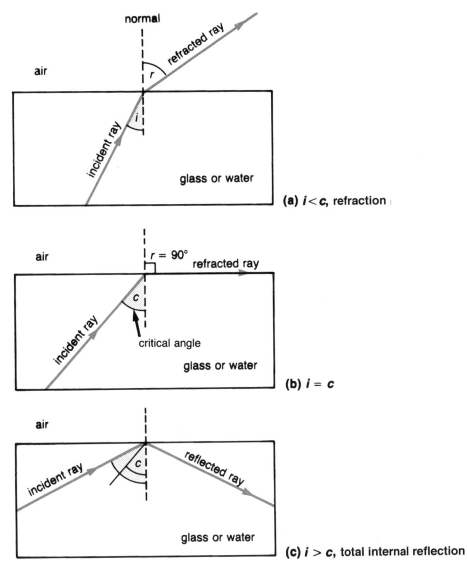

Fig. 23.9 Refraction and total internal reflection of a light ray as it passes from glass or water into air

When light travels at small angles of incidence from glass or water towards air, the light is refracted as it enters the air (Fig. 23.9(a)).

However, as the angle of incidence increases, the angle of refraction also increases. When the angle of incidence reaches 42° in glass or 49° in water, the refracted ray travels along the surface of the denser material (Fig. 23.9(b)). The angle of refraction is now 90°. When this position is reached, the angle of incidence is called the **critical angle**, *c*.

The critical angle for glass/air = 42°

The critical angle for water/air = 49°

If the angle of incidence is greater than the critical angle ($i > c$), there is *no refracted ray*. Instead, *all* the light is *reflected* back into the denser material (Fig. 23.9(c)). This is called **total internal reflection**.

Uses of total internal reflection

Total internal reflection is put to important use in periscopes, binoculars and cameras. In these instruments, prisms are used to change the direction of light rays (Fig. 23.10).

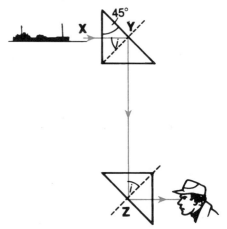

Fig. 23.10 Prisms which allow the total internal reflection of light are used in periscopes

Total internal reflection also enables glass fibres (optical fibres) to carry rays of light (Fig. 23.11). The fibres consist of two parts – an inner part (core) of glass fibre through which the light travels and an outer part of less dense material which protects the inner fibre. This use of optical fibres is sometimes called **fibre optics**.

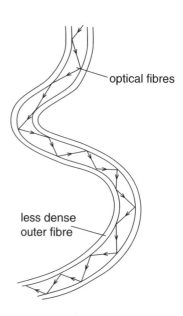

Fig. 23.11 Total internal reflection allows light to pass along the optical fibres in an endoscope

Surgeons use optical fibres in a device called an endoscope. This allows a surgeon to examine inside a patient's body without needing to operate. For example, it is possible to see right inside the stomach using a special endoscope which passes down the oesophagus.

An endoscope is made of two optical fibre bundles. One carries light down inside the patient, the other allows the surgeon to see what is there. Optical fibres are also used to carry and direct laser light in laser surgery.

Electronic messages can also be converted to light and other electromagnetic impulses and sent along optical fibres. This has enabled British Telecom to replace the copper cables in telephone systems with much thinner optical fibres which can carry hundreds of telephone calls at the same time.

Summary

1   Light travels in straight lines.

2   When light rays hit a surface, three things can happen:
  - the light rays can be **transmitted** (e.g. through glass),
  - the light rays can be **absorbed** (e.g. by a black surface),
  - the light rays can be **reflected** (e.g. from a mirror).

3   When light is reflected in a flat (plane) mirror,
  - the image is **virtual**,
  - the image is **laterally inverted**,
  - the **angle of incidence = the angle of reflection**.

4   When light is refracted,
  - a ray passing into a denser material is bent towards the normal,
  - waves passing into a denser material have a shorter wavelength and therefore a lower speed.

5   Light, like sound, can be reflected, refracted and diffracted. The diffraction of light is evidence for its wave nature.

6   When light travels from glass, perspex or water towards air at an angle of incidence less than the **critical angle**, the light is refracted.

7   When light travels from glass, perspex or water towards air at an angle of incidence greater than the critical angle, the light is reflected back into the denser medium. This is called **total internal reflection**.

8   Total internal reflection enables optical fibres to transmit light and other electromagnetic radiations.

9   Optical fibres are important in endoscopy and in the rapid transmission of data using digital signals.

Quick test 23

Questions 1 to 3

Are the following statements true or false?
Light waves
1   need no medium.
2   have the same speed as radiowaves.
3   travel through glass whereas sound waves do not.

Questions 4 to 6

The diagram below shows a ray of light travelling in material X, then being either reflected or refracted at material Y.

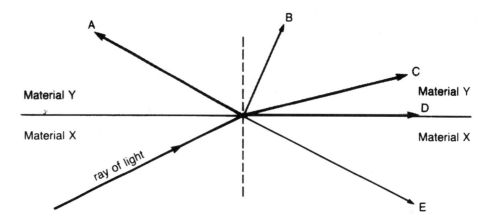

Choose from A to E, the final direction of the ray if

4   X is air and Y is glass.
5   X is glass and Y is air.
6   X is air and Y is a mirror.

Questions 7 to 9

7   Show how the word BACK would look when reflected in a mirror.
8   If you move towards a mirror at 2 m/s, at what speed does your image (a) approach the mirror, (b) approach you?
9   The image in a mirror is described as virtual. What does this mean?

Questions 10 to 12

The diagram shows two rays of light from a lamp at the bottom of a tank of water.

observer

lamp

10   On the diagram, draw lines to show the direction of the rays leaving the water surface.
11   Draw another line to find where the lamp appears to be to the observer looking directly into the water. Mark the apparent position of the lamp with the letter A.
12   Use measurements from the diagram to explain in what way the apparent depth of the tank differs from its real depth.   (*MEG*)

Chapter 24
Electricity and electric currents

24.1 Introduction

Most of the time we take electricity for granted. At the flick of a switch or the press of a button, we turn on electrical appliances which will cook our food, warm our homes, light our rooms and provide us with television pictures. Without electricity our lives would be very different. Most of the electrical devices in our homes use mains electricity. In addition to these, there are other appliances such as torches and radios which use electric currents from cells and batteries.

There are two main reasons why electricity is so useful in our modern society:

● It is a form of energy which is easily and conveniently transferred from one place to another.

● It is readily converted into other forms of energy such as heat and light.

24.2 Electric currents and circuits

Fig. 24.1 shows an **electrical circuit**. This type of diagram is sometimes called a **circuit diagram**. Notice the symbols used for the different pieces of equipment or **components**. Two bulbs are connected to an ammeter, a cell and a switch by connecting wires made of metal.

At present, the switch is open and this is called an **open circuit**. When the switch is closed (a **closed circuit**), there is a complete circuit (path) of conductors. Energy in the form of an electric current is now transferred from the cell to the other components in the circuit. An electric current flows and the bulbs light up. The electric current is measured by the **ammeter** in units called **amperes** (A). The electric current in the circuit is simply a flow of negatively charged electrons (see 15.1). The electrons flow from the negative terminal of the battery through the circuit to the positive terminal.

In electrical circuits, scientists have agreed to show the current flowing from positive to negative. This is usually called the **conventional current**. It is shown by an *arrow on the connecting wires* in circuit diagrams. This has been done in Fig. 24.1. We have used the arrow symbol for the conventional current in circuit diagrams in this book.

Be careful though – **electron flow** is from negative to positive. The electron flow in a circuit can be shown by *an arrow at the side of the circuit wires* as in Fig. 24.1.

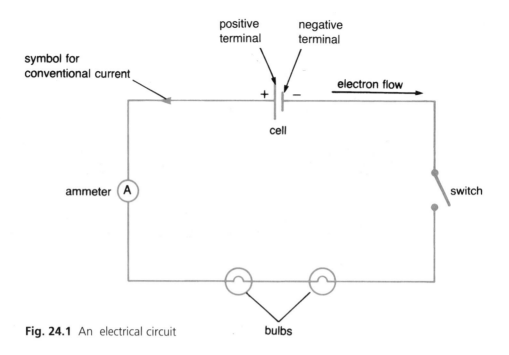

Fig. 24.1 An electrical circuit

Series circuits

In the circuit shown in Fig. 24.1, the bulbs, the cell and the ammeter are said to be **in series**. In a series circuit, there is **only one route** for the current. Another series circuit is shown in Fig. 24.2. In this circuit there are two identical bulbs, two ammeters and a battery in series. A **battery** is simply *two or more cells connected together.*

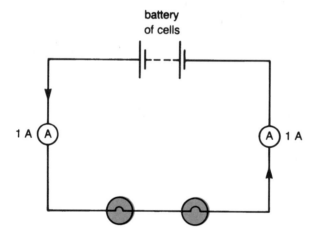

Fig. 24.2 Current in a series circuit

When the circuit in Fig. 24.2 is complete, both ammeters show the same current of one ampere (1 A). You cannot lose current as it goes round a circuit, so the current must be the same at all points in a series circuit.

If more bulbs are added to the circuit in Fig. 24.2, the current is smaller. For example, if two more identical bulbs are added to the circuit, the current falls to 0.5 A. The bulbs are said to cause a **resistance** to the current. The thin wire in the bulbs prevents the easy flow of electrons in the current.

Parallel circuits

Now look at Fig. 24.3, which contains three identical bulbs, A, B and C. This time there is a **branch** in the circuit. When the current gets to X, it has a choice of paths. It can either go through bulbs A and B or it can go through bulb C. In this circuit, bulbs A and B are in series with each other, but they are said to be **in parallel** with bulb C.

In parallel circuits, the current does not split equally if one route is easier than the other. In the circuit shown in Fig. 24.3, it is easier for the current to go through bulb C than to go through bulbs A and B. Bulb C, by itself, causes less resistance to the current than bulbs A and B together. So the current divides with two amperes going through bulb C and one ampere going through bulbs A and B.

A **short circuit** is an example of a parallel circuit. When we cause a short circuit, we provide an alternative, easier path for the current (see Fig. 24.4).

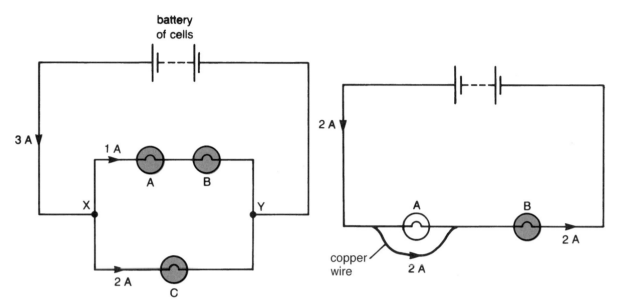

Fig. 24.3 Current in a parallel circuit

Fig. 24.4 The copper wire short circuits bulb A and provides an easier path for the current. Most current passes through the copper wire. Only a tiny amount of current flows through bulb A so the filament does not glow.

Important current rules

- The current is not 'used up' as it passes through bulbs and other components in circuits.

- In a series circuit, the current is the same at all points.

- In a parallel circuit, more current goes through the easier path.

- In a parallel circuit, the sum of currents approaching a junction equals the sum of currents leaving the junction.

- The current in a circuit depends on the number of cells and on the number of bulbs and other components.

- As the number of bulbs in a circuit increases, the resistance gets larger and the current gets smaller.

- As the number of cells in a circuit increases, the current gets larger.

24.3 Measuring current and charge

We could measure the amount of charge flowing in an electric current by counting the number of electrons which pass by. However, electrons have only a tiny charge. Instead our unit of charge is the **coulomb** (C). One coulomb is the charge on six million million million (6×10^{18}) electrons.

Electric currents are measured in **amperes** (amps for short). When the current is one ampere (1 amp or 1 A), the flow of charge is **one coulomb** (1 C) **per second**. When the current is two amps, the flow of charge is two coulombs per second (2 C/s).

$$\text{Current } (I) = \frac{\text{charge flowing } (Q)}{\text{time } (t)}$$

i.e. $I = \dfrac{Q}{t}$ and $\underset{\text{coulombs}}{Q} = \underset{\text{amps}}{I} \times \underset{\text{seconds}}{t}$

Example

During a flash of lightning, 20 coulombs of charge travel from the bottom of a thundercloud to the earth in 0.01 seconds. What is the size of the current?

$$\text{Current, } I = \frac{Q}{t} = \frac{20 \text{ C}}{0.01 \text{ s}}$$
$$= 2000 \text{ C/s}$$
$$= 2000 \text{ A}$$

24.4 Voltage and potential difference

In an electrical circuit, the cell or the battery provides the electrons with electrical potential energy. It turns chemical energy from the materials in the cell into electrical energy in the electrons. The electrons move through the circuit from the negative terminal where they have high electrical potential energy towards the positive terminal. When the electrons reach a bulb, they lose some of their electrical potential energy. This 'lost' energy is turned into heat and light (Fig. 24.5). Finally, the electrons return to the positive terminal of the battery with less energy. Therefore, there is a difference in electrical potential energy between the negative and positive terminals of the battery.

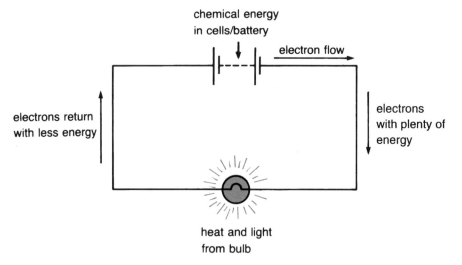

Fig. 24.5 Energy changes in an electrical circuit

This energy difference is measured by the **potential difference (p.d.)** or the **voltage** of the battery. The greater the voltage of a cell or battery, the more energy it can provide. For example, the voltage of a small cell used in a watch or a calculator is probably no more than two volts (2 V). The cells in a transistor radio or a torch provide between 6 V and 12 V. The voltage of the electricity supply to our homes is 240 V.

The potential difference (voltage) is measured in **volts (V)** using a **voltmeter**. The voltmeter is connected across (*in parallel* with) the parts of the circuit where we want to measure the voltage.

Fig. 24.6 demonstrates an important application of voltage. The two headlamps of a car should be arranged in parallel with the battery, *not* in series.

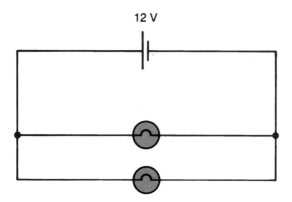

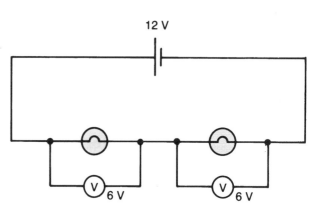

(a) Headlamps in parallel

Each bulb gets a voltage of 12 V from the battery, so the bulbs are very bright

(b) Headlamps in series

Each bulb gets only half the battery voltage (6 V), so the bulbs are dim

Fig. 24.6 The voltages across bulbs in parallel and in series

Important voltage rules

- Bulbs or appliances in parallel get the same voltage.
- Bulbs or appliances in series share the total voltage.
- Adding the voltages across the bulbs/appliances in a circuit gives the battery voltage.
- As the number of cells in a circuit increases, the voltage increases and the current gets larger.

24.5 Resistance and resistors

As the electrons in an electric current move around a circuit, they bump into the atoms in the wires through which they pass. Atoms of different elements impede (hold up) the electrons by different amounts. For example, electrons pass easily through copper wire, but much less easily through tungsten or nichrome wires. We say that copper has a lower **resistance** than nichrome or tungsten. This is why copper is used for the connecting wires and cables in electrical circuits.

When an electric current passes through thin nichrome or tungsten wire, the electrons cannot flow easily. They collide with atoms in the wire which vibrate more quickly. This causes the wire to warm up. If the resistance of the wire is high and the current is large, the wire may get red hot. Conductors like this which provide a high resistance are called **resistors**. The symbols used for resistors in circuit diagrams are shown in Fig. 24.7.

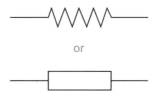

Fig. 24.7 Symbols for resistors

Important resistors

Figs. 24.8 and 24.9 show two important uses of resistors – as filaments in light bulbs and as heating elements in electrical appliances.

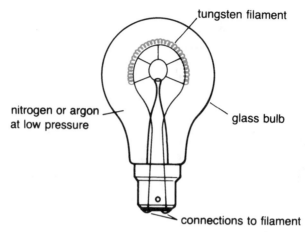

Fig. 24.8 Filaments in bulbs are made of thin tungsten wire. When a current flows through tungsten wire it becomes white hot at about 2500 °C. Fortunately, tungsten does not melt until 3380 °C.

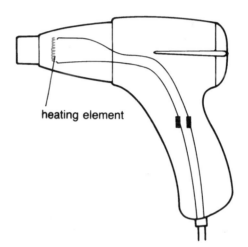

Fig. 24.9 Heating elements in hair dryers, irons, electric fires, electric kettles and hot plates are made from nichrome or other nickel alloys. These alloys stay red hot without melting or reacting with air.

Sometimes, it is necessary to vary the resistance in a circuit or in an electrical appliance. **Variable resistors** can be used to vary the brightness of bulbs and televisions and the volume on radios and TVs. The circuit symbols for variable resistors are shown in Fig. 24.10.

Fig. 24.10 Symbols for variable resistors

24.6 Measuring resistance – Ohm's law

During the 1820s, the German scientist, Georg Ohm, investigated the resistance of various metal conductors. The unit which we use for resistance is called the **ohm** in honour of Georg Ohm. The symbol for the ohm is Ω, so five ohms is written as 5 Ω.

Ohm used a circuit like the one shown in Fig. 24.11. He measured the voltage across a resistor for different values of current.

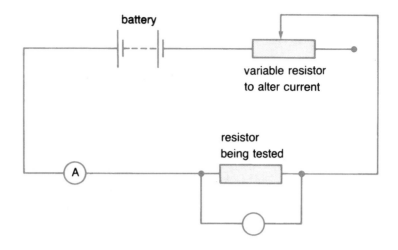

Fig. 24.11 The circuit used to investigate Ohm's law

Ohm used his results to plot a graph of voltage (V) against current (I) (Fig. 24.12). The results gave a straight line through the origin (O).

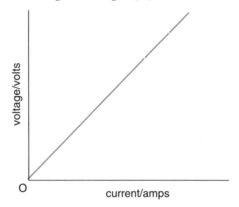

Fig. 24.12 A graph of voltage (*V*) against current (*I*)

This led to **Ohm's law**:

> The voltage across a metal conductor is proportional to the current through it, provided the temperature stays constant.

This can be written as

$$V \propto I$$

Because V is proportional to I, we can say that

$$\frac{V}{I} = a \ constant$$

Ohm's results show that doubling the voltage doubles the current. Treble the voltage will give treble the current, and so on. The larger the resistance, the greater the voltage needed to push each ampere of current through it. This led to the definition of one ohm:

> A resistor has a resistance of one ohm (1 Ω), if a voltage of one volt (1 V) will drive a current of one ampere (1 A) through it.

If a voltage of two volts (2 V) is needed to drive a current of one amp (1 A) through a resistor, its resistance is two ohms (2 Ω). If 3 V are needed to drive a current of 1 A through a resistor, its resistance is 3 Ω. Notice that the **resistance of a resistor** is the **voltage per unit of current**, i.e.

$$\text{Resistance (ohms)} = \frac{\text{Voltage (volts)}}{\text{Current (amps)}}$$

$$R = \frac{V}{I}$$

Example

A torch has a 6 V battery and a bulb with a resistance of 12 Ω. What is the current when the torch is working?

You are given voltage (V) = 6 V and resistance (R) = 12 Ω

The formula $R = \dfrac{V}{I}$ can be rearranged to $I = \dfrac{V}{R}$

So, current (I) $= \dfrac{V}{R} = \dfrac{6}{12} = 0.5$A

Some conductors do *not* obey Ohm's law. Conductors which do obey Ohm's law are called **ohmic conductors**. Metals and alloys at constant temperature are ohmic conductors. **Semiconductors**, such as silicon and germanium, do *not* obey Ohm's law. The differences between ohmic and non-ohmic conductors are summarised in Table 24.1.

Table 24.1 Comparing ohmic and non-ohmic conductors

Ohmic conductors	Non-ohmic conductors
Obey Ohm's law	Do not obey Ohm's law
Metals and alloys	Semiconductors
Resistance *increases* slowly with temperature	Resistance *decreases* with temperature
Number of electrons carrying the current stays constant as temperature rises. Atoms vibrate faster at higher temperatures and impede electrons more	Electrons are held strongly by atoms. At higher temperatures, more electrons can escape from their atoms so the current is larger
At very low temperatures, atoms hardly vibrate at all. Resistance is very low and some metals become **superconductors**	Some non-ohmic conductors have resistances which decrease rapidly with temperature. These are called **thermistors**

Examiner's tip

Most of the work in this chapter is related to the three important equations:
$V = I \times R$
E (energy) $= I \times V \times t$
P (power) $= I \times V$

Fig. 24.13 shows how current varies with voltage in a range of devices.

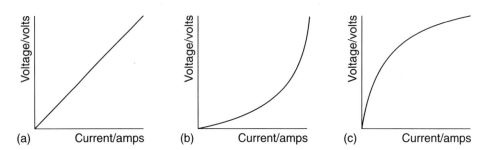

Fig. 24.13 The variation of current with voltage in a range of devices

Fig. 24.13(a) shows the graph of V against I for a resistor which obeys Ohm's Law and in which the temperature stays constant. Fig. 24.13(b) shows the relationship between voltage and current for a filament bulb. In this case, the temperature of the filament increases sharply as the current increases. This causes the resistance, R, to increase, so V/I increases as I increases. Fig. 24.13(c) shows the results for a thermistor or a light–dependent resistor (LDR). These devices are made of semiconductors in which the resistance decreases as the temperature rises with higher currents.

24.7 Voltage and energy

Ideas about voltage were introduced in 24.4.

A battery with a voltage of one volt (1 V) gives one joule (1 J) of energy to each coulomb of charge which passes round the circuit.

one volt = one joule per coulomb

A voltage of 2 V would give 2 joules per coulomb and so on. In other words,

Voltage (V) = Energy transferred per unit charge = $\dfrac{\text{Energy supplied } (E)}{\text{Charge flowing } (Q)}$

i.e. $V = \dfrac{E}{Q}$ and $E = V \times Q$

We know from 24.3 that

charge flowing = current × time

i.e. $Q = I \times t$

So, substituting for Q in the equation $E = V \times Q$, we get

$$
\begin{array}{ccccccc}
E & = & V & \times & I & \times & t \\
\textbf{energy} & = & \textbf{voltage} & \times & \textbf{current} & \times & \textbf{time} \\
\text{(joules)} & & \text{(volts)} & & \text{(amps)} & & \text{(seconds)}
\end{array}
$$

Example

A 6 V torch battery delivers a current of 0.5 A for one hour. How much electrical energy does it provide?

$$
\begin{array}{ccccccc}
E & = & V & \times & I & \times & t \\
\text{(joules)} & & \text{(volts)} & & \text{(amps)} & & \text{(seconds)}
\end{array}
$$

therefore, energy = 6 × 0.5 × (60 × 60) = 10 800 J

24.8 Electricity in the home

Electricity is transmitted from power stations to our homes and factories by the National Grid system. The current is carried from power stations to substations by thick cables supported by pylons. Thick cables have a lower resistance than thin cables, so a smaller proportion of the electrical energy is lost as heat.

Current from the National Grid

The current supplied to our homes by the National Grid is **alternating current (a.c.)**. In an alternating current, electrons flow forwards, then backwards. In the mains supply, the electrons change direction 50 times per second. We say it has a frequency of 50 Hz. In comparison, the current from a battery is **direct current (d.c.)**. In a direct current, the electrons flow in the same direction all the time.

There are two important reasons why power stations provide alternating current:

● It is easier to generate than d.c.
● Its voltage can be changed more easily (see 25.11).

Alternating currents and transmission by the National Grid are discussed further in 25.10 to 25.12.

Resistors provide a resistance to an alternating current in the same way as they resist a direct current. So, a.c. can be used for heating and lighting in our homes. However, unlike direct current from a cell, alternating current does *not* cause electrolysis (see 15.3). As the current goes first one way then the other way, each electrode is alternately positive then negative. This happens 50 times per second which is too fast for any reactions at the electrodes.

The mains supply to our homes

There are **two cables** from the mains supply to your home. One cable is **live**, the other is **neutral**. Electrical energy is supplied through the live wire and this is the dangerous

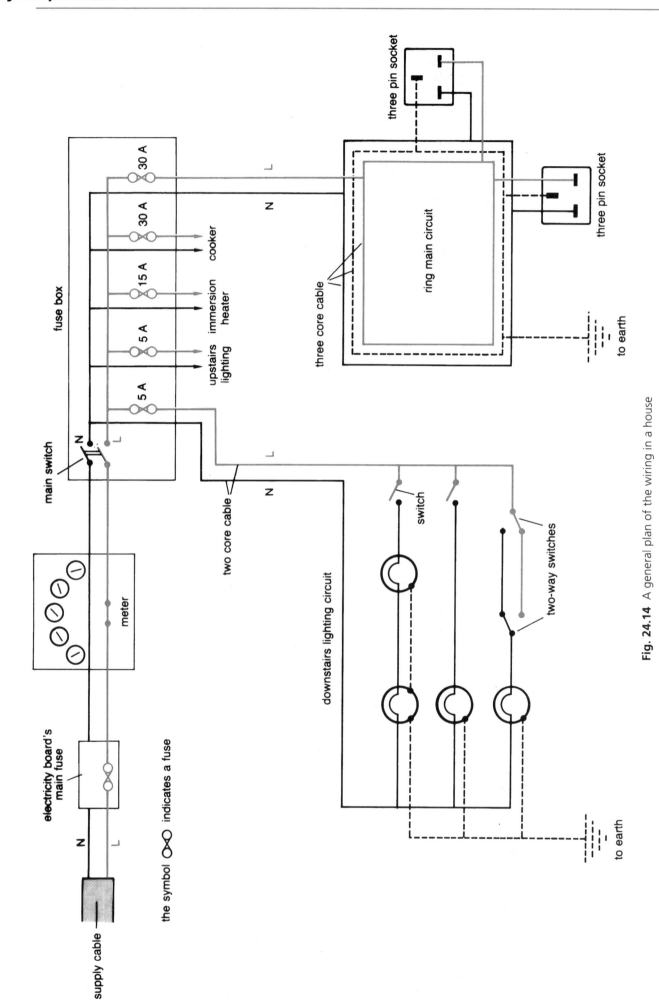

Fig. 24.14 A general plan of the wiring in a house

wire. It is alternately positive and then negative with a potential difference (voltage) of 240 V relative to the neutral wire. The voltage of the neutral wire stays close to zero. The neutral wire provides the return path for the electric current.

Fig. 24.14 shows a general plan of the wiring in a house. The supply from the mains cable passes through a main fuse and then through the electricity meter to a **fuse box**. The fuse box acts as a distribution point for the electricity supply to the house. In the fuse box, there are several fuses. Each fuse leads to a different circuit servicing different areas in the house.

Most houses have two or three **ring main circuits** for the three-pin wall sockets. Each ring main will have about ten sockets. Notice (in Fig. 24.14) that all the sockets are connected to the ring main circuit in parallel, so each one receives the full mains voltage. The long loop or 'ring' of cable which joins the sockets contains three wires – *the live wire*, *the neutral wire* and *an earth wire*. (Hence, it is called a three-core cable.) The ring main is protected by a 30 A fuse in the fuse box. This will melt ('blow') if the total current to the sockets is 30 A or greater.

In addition to the ring main circuits, there are usually two or three lighting circuits and separate circuits for appliances such as cookers and immersion (hot water) heaters which each use large currents.

24.9 Safety in electrical circuits

Faults in electrical circuits can cause fires and very painful, even fatal, electric shocks. There are two main safety components in electrical circuits – fuses (or circuit breakers) and earth wires.

Fuses

A fuse is simply a thin wire which melts if the current passing through it is too large. When a fault occurs, the fuse melts. This breaks the circuit and the current ceases.

The main purposes of a fuse are:

- to prevent fires which might easily occur if over-large currents caused part of the wiring to become red hot;
- to prevent harm to those using the electrical appliance;
- to prevent damage to electrical appliances.

Fuses are always placed in the live wire (Fig. 24.15). This means that if a fault occurs and the fuse 'blows', the live wire is disconnected. Switches are also placed in the live wire. If switches were placed in the neutral wire, you could get a shock from an electrical appliance even when it was switched off (Fig. 24.15(b)).

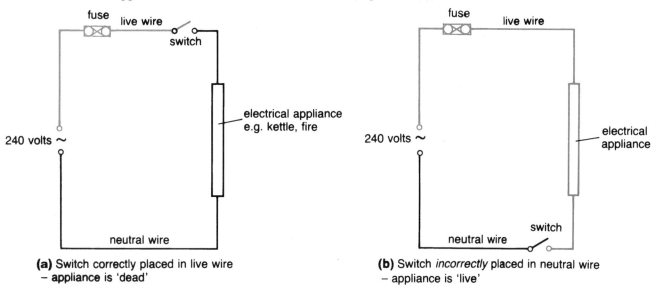

(a) Switch correctly placed in live wire
– appliance is 'dead'

(b) Switch *incorrectly* placed in neutral wire
– appliance is 'live'

Fig. 24.15 Fuses and switches must always be placed in the live wire

Earth wires

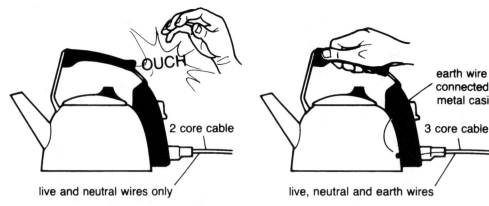

(a) No earth to kettle
If a fault develops and the live wire touches the metal casing, then anyone touching the metal parts will get a shock

(b) Earth wire connected to metal on kettle
If the live wire touches the metal casing now, any current will flow away along the earth wire

Fig. 24.16 Earth wires are important on electrical appliances with outer metal parts

Many modern electrical appliances have outer parts made of plastic. Plastic does not conduct electricity, so these appliances do not usually need an earth wire. This method of protection is called **double insulation** and is shown by the symbol ☐ .

Three-pin plugs are carefully designed with safety in mind. Fig. 24.17 shows a socket on the ring main circuit and a correctly wired three-pin plug.

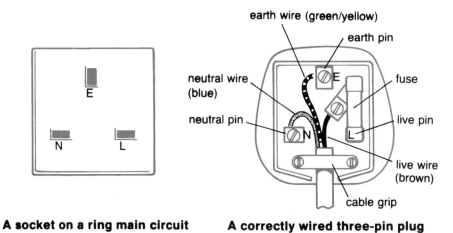

A socket on a ring main circuit   A correctly wired three-pin plug

Fig. 24.17 Correct wiring for a three-pin plug

Notice the following points:
1. The plug carries a fuse in the live circuit.
2. The plug has an earth pin.
3. The three wires in the cable must be connected to the correct pins in the plug:
   - the brown wire goes to the live pin, L;
   - the blue wire goes to the neutral pin, N;
   - the green/yellow wire goes to the earth pin, E.
4. The plug must have a fuse of the appropriate value:
   - appliances such as table lamps, radios and televisions take small currents (well below 3 amps). They should have plugs fitted with 3 A fuses.
   - kettles, irons and electric fires usually take currents of more than 3 amps, so they should have plugs with 5 or 13 A fuses.

Circuit breakers

Circuit breakers are now used in some appliances instead of fuses. There are two common types. The first contains an electromagnet which becomes strong enough to separate a pair of contacts and break the circuit when the current reaches a particular level. The second type, called a residual current circuit breaker, compares the currents in the live wire and the neutral wire. If these differ (indicating a leakage to earth), a switch is thrown open and the current in the live wire is cut off.

24.10 Power ratings

Most electrical appliances carry a **power rating** and an **operating voltage**. For example, an electric kettle may be labelled '2000 W, 240 V'. This means that its power rating is 2000 watts and its operating voltage is 240 volts.

In 24.7, we found that the electrical energy supplied by a current *I*, in time *t*, at a voltage of *V*, is given by the formula

$$E = V \times I \times t$$
(joules) (volts) (amps) (seconds)

In 21.4, power (wattage) was defined as follows:

$$\text{Power (watts)} = \frac{\text{Energy output (joules)}}{\text{Time taken (seconds)}}$$

i.e. Power $= \dfrac{E}{t}$

Substituting for *E*, we get

$$\text{Power} = \frac{V \times I \times t}{t} = V \times I$$

i.e. Power $=$ Voltage $\times$ Current
(watts) (volts) (amps)

Using the last equation we can find the current taken by the electric kettle with a power rating of 2000 watts.

power = voltage $\times$ current

So, in this case,

2000 watts = 240 volts $\times$ *I* amps

therefore, $I = \dfrac{2000}{240} = 8.3$ A

The current in the heating element of the kettle will be 8.3A. A 3 amp fuse would not be adequate. The kettle requires a 10 A or a 13 A fuse.

Table 24.2 shows the power ratings of some electrical appliances. The power of an appliance tells us its rate of working in watts or joules per second. For example, the television in Table 24.2 uses 60 joules of energy per second (i.e. 60 watts).

Table 24.2 Power ratings of common electrical appliances

Appliance	Power rating (W)
light bulb	100
television	60
electric iron	750
kettle	2000
electric fire	2500

24.11 Electricity bills

Electricity boards charge for the amount of electricity (energy) which you use. The amount of electricity which you use is recorded on a meter. The meter measures energy in units called **kilowatt hours (kWh)**. If you use a one kilowatt (1 kW) electric fire for one hour, you will use one kilowatt hour (1 kWh) of energy (i.e. 1 unit on the meter). The cost of electricity is about 7.5 pence per unit (i.e. 7.5p per kWh).

Electrical energy is measured by the Electricity Companies in kilowatt hours rather than joules, because one joule is a very small amount:

$$1 \text{ kWh} = 1 \text{ kW} \text{ for 1 hour}$$
$$= 1000 \text{ W for 3600 seconds}$$
$$\text{Energy} = \text{power} \times \text{time}$$
$$\text{so } 1 \text{ kWh} = 1000 \times 3600 = 3\ 600\ 000 \text{ joules}$$

Example
How much does it cost to use a 2500 W electric fire for 4 hours if electricity costs 7.5p per unit?

Power rating: 2500 W = 2.5 kW
$$\text{Energy used} = \text{power} \times \text{time}$$
$$= 2.5 \text{ kW} \times 4 \text{ hours}$$
$$= 10 \text{ kWh}$$
1 kWh (1 unit) costs 7.5p, therefore total cost will be 75p (10 × 7.5p)

24.12 Electric charges

We now know that an electric current consists of a flow of negatively charged electrons (see 15.1). In fact, electricity was first discovered when certain materials were rubbed against each other, making them electrically charged. The charges arose because electrons were transferred from one material to another. Here are some effects of electric charges that you may have experienced already.

- After you have combed your hair with a plastic comb, the comb will pick up tiny pieces of paper.
- When you remove a shirt or a pullover, you sometimes hear the crackle from tiny sparks.
- A balloon will stick to a wall after rubbing it against a woollen jersey.

All of these effects are produced by rubbing two objects together causing them to become charged. The rubbing (friction) causes the transfer of electrons from one object to the other.

If you comb your hair briskly with a plastic comb, electrons are removed by the comb from the outer parts of atoms in your hair. The comb will then be negative because it has more electrons than protons. Conversely, your hair will be positive because it has lost electrons and will now have more protons than electrons. Materials, like plastic, hair and wool, which hold their charges and do not allow electrons to pass through them are **insulators**. This is why plastics, like polythene and PVC, are used to insulate electrical wires and cables.

When you bring a negatively charged balloon close to the wall, it *repels* electrons from the area of the wall nearest to it (Fig. 24.18(a)). This part of the wall therefore becomes positive and the balloon is attracted to it because **opposite charges attract**. If the balloon is light enough, it may stick to the wall (Fig. 24.18(b)).

(a) Negatively charged   (b) Balloon sticks to wall due to
    balloon near wall   attraction of opposite charges

Fig. 24.18 Why does a charged balloon stick to the wall?

Have you noticed that your hair sometimes stands up when it is combed briskly? This will often happen when your hair is clean and dry because it holds charge better then. After brisk combing, each hair becomes positively charged and **like charges repel**.

Fig. 24.19 Each hair becomes positive after brisk combing

These various effects from *stationary* charges on materials are described as **electrostatic** phenomena. The effects show that there are:

● repulsive forces between objects with similar charge;
● attractive forces between objects with opposite charge.

24.13 The dangers and uses of electrostatic charges

When certain materials rub against each other, electrostatic charges can build up. If the materials conduct, or if they are in contact with conductors, then the charge is carried away. Sometimes, however, the charge cannot be carried away easily. As the charge on the object increases, electrons may jump across the gap between the object and any conductor which comes near it, forming a spark.

Petrol and other liquid fuels are very good insulators. When an aircraft is being refuelled, so much liquid flows along the pipes and into the tanks that a charge could build up. To prevent this happening, an **earthing lead** is attached to the aircraft body allowing any charge to run safely to earth and preventing sparks.

There are a number of other occasions when the build up of static charge should be avoided. Methods for avoiding the build up of static charge include conducting away the negative charge from electrons which build up on the inner surface of television screens and fitting cars with conducting tails.

Electrostatic charges can sometimes be useful. For example, they are used to reduce the amount of soot and ash released in the waste gases from coal-burning power stations. The waste gas, carrying dust and fine ash, passes through an **electrostatic precipitator** (Fig. 24.20). Inside the precipitator, a wire grid is maintained at a high negative voltage. The negative charge on the grid ionises the air and the negative ions in the air attach themselves to soot and ash particles. These particles are now repelled by the grid and attracted to positively charged plates in the precipitator. The soot and ash sticks to these plates and is later removed. The electrostatic precipitators in large power stations remove more than 20 tonnes of soot per hour.

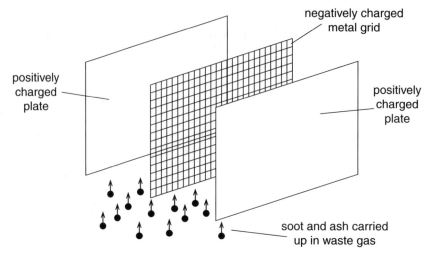

positively charged plate

negatively charged metal grid

positively charged plate

soot and ash carried up in waste gas

Fig. 24.20   Removing dust from waste gases by electrostatic precipitation

Summary

1   An electric current in a circuit is a **flow of electrons**. The electron flow is from negative to positive. However, in electrical circuits, the **conventional current** is shown by an arrow on the connecting wires from positive to negative. As the current flows round a circuit, energy is transferred from the battery to other components in the circuit such as bulbs.

2   The current in a circuit depends on the number of cells and on the number, nature and arrangement of other components.
   ● In a **series circuit**, the current is the same at all points.
   ● In a **parallel circuit**, more current takes the easier path with lower resistance.
   ● In a **parallel circuit**, the sum of currents into a junction equals the sum of currents out of the junction.

3   $\dfrac{\text{Current}}{\text{(amps)}} = \dfrac{\text{Charge flowing (coulombs)}}{\text{Time (seconds)}}$, i.e. $I = \dfrac{Q}{t}$

4   The **potential difference (p.d.)** or **voltage (V)** between two points is a measure of the difference in electrical potential energy between those points.

5   ● Bulbs and appliances (resistors) in parallel have the same voltage across them.
   ● Bulbs and appliances (resistors) in series share the total voltage in proportion to their resistance.

6   **Electrical energy** (J) =   Voltage   × Charge flowing
   =   Voltage   ×   Current   ×   Time
   (volts)   (amps)   (seconds)
   E = V × I × t

7   Electrical energy transferred   = Voltage × Charge flowing

   $\Rightarrow$ $\text{Voltage} = \dfrac{\text{Energy transferred}}{\text{Charge flowing}}$

   So, voltage is the energy transferred per unit charge.

8 **Resistance** is the voltage per unit current,

i.e. Resistance = $\dfrac{\text{Voltage}}{\text{Current}}$, $R = \dfrac{V}{I}$
(ohms)

For **ohmic conductors** (metals and alloys), $V \propto I$ at constant temperature.

9 The current supplied to our homes by the National Grid is **alternating current** with a frequency of 50 Hz.
- There are two cables to our homes from the mains supply – one **live** and one **neutral**.
- In our homes, lighting circuits and ring main circuits (for three-pin wall sockets) have connections to the live and neutral supplies and to **earth**.

10 There are two main **safety components** in electrical circuits.
- **Fuses** – thin wires which melt if the current through them is too large. Fuses prevent damage to electrical appliances and prevent fires.
- **Earth wires** which prevent metal components from becoming live if a fault develops.

11 $\dfrac{\textbf{Power}}{\text{(watts)}} = \dfrac{\text{Energy output (J)}}{\text{Time taken (seconds)}} = \dfrac{V \times I \times \cancel{t}}{\cancel{t}}$

$\rightarrow$ **Power = $V \times I$** = voltage × current

12 The electricity supplied to our homes is measured in **kilowatt hours** (kWh),

e.g. a 500 W iron used for 30 minutes uses $\dfrac{500}{1000} \times \dfrac{30}{60} = \dfrac{1}{4}$ kWh of electricity.

Quick test 24

Questions 1 to 3

The diagram shows a circuit which has two resistors in series with a 10 volt supply.
1 What is the total resistance of the two resistors?
2 What is the current flowing in the circuit?
3 What is the voltage across the 2 ohms resistor?

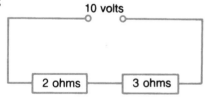

Questions 4 to 6

Many cars have a heated rear window. This is made of wires which are attached to the glass and which get hot when an electric current passes through them. The car's battery provides the electrical energy. Here is the electrical circuit.

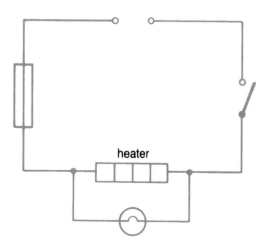

4 On the circuit, label these parts: switch, bulb (filament lamp), fuse, 12 V supply.
5 What happens if too much current flows in the circuit?
6 On a cold, damp morning the driver cannot see through the rear window because of water droplets (condensation). She turns on the window heater. After a few minutes, the window begins to clear.
   Describe in detail what happens to the water molecules as they gain energy from the heater.

(NEAB)

Questions 7 to 10

An electric kettle carries a label as shown here. It brings a kettle full of water to the boil in three minutes.

> 3 pints/1.7 litres
> 3 kW
> 230/240 volts

7   How long can the kettle be used on just one unit of electricity?
8   If the mains voltage is 240 V, what current will flow through the kettle after it is switched on?
9   What difference would there be in the current if the mains voltage was only 120 V?
10 What else would you need to know to find the cost of boiling a kettle full of water?

Questions 11 to 15

The drawing shows a fuse wire card. At points X, Y and Z, the wording has been removed.

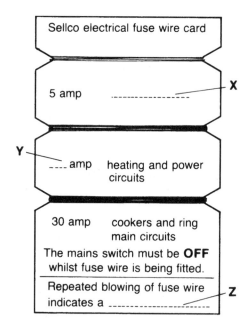

At point X several words are missing.

At point Y a number is missing.

At point Z one word is missing.
11 Suggest what should be written at (a) X, (b) Y, (c) Z.
12 What is the physical difference between 5 amp and 30 amp fuse wires?
13 Why do you think that fuse wire is always made of a metal or alloy?
14 (a) What could happen if the mains switch were not off when fuse wire is fitted?
    (b) What actually happens to fuse wire when a fuse blows?
    (c) How would you deal with a fire caused by an electrical fault?
15 How do you know that the lamps in your classroom are wired in parallel and not in series?

(WJEC)

Questions 16 and 17

16   The figure below shows the inside of a 13 A mains plug.

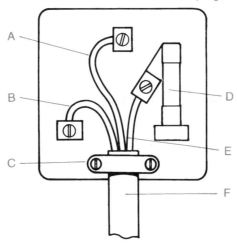

Name the parts labelled A to F.

17   Each year many people are killed in accidents at home involving electricity. Give *four* sensible safety rules for people using electrical appliances.

(ULEAC)

Chapter 25
Motors and generators

25.1 Magnets and magnetic poles

A few metals, including iron, are **magnetic**. They are attracted by magnets. When a magnet is dipped into a pile of iron filings the filings cling around the ends of the magnet. These ends of the magnet are called **poles**. The magnetic forces seem to come from these poles.

The magnet will also attract steel pins and nichrome wire, but nothing happens with brass tacks or plastic buttons. The only common materials which magnets attract are *iron*, *cobalt*, *nickel* and *their alloys* such as steel, nichrome and Alnico.

25.2 North and south poles

Fig. 25.1 shows what happens when a bar magnet is suspended from a fine thread. When the magnet comes to rest, one end always points north. This end of the magnet is called the **north-seeking pole** or **north pole** for short. The other end of the magnet is called the **south-seeking pole** or **south pole**. Because they behave in this way, magnets are used as compasses.

Every magnet has a north pole and a south pole. When the poles of two magnets are brought together:

- Like poles (two N-poles or two S-poles) repel each other.
- Unlike poles (a N-pole and a S-pole) attract.

Compare this with positive and negative charges (see 15.1, 15.4 and 24.12).

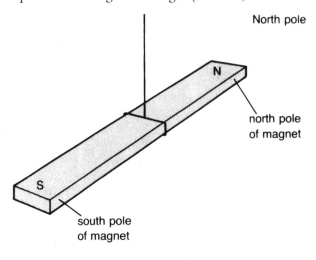

North pole

north pole
of magnet

south pole
of magnet

Fig. 25.1

25.3 Permanent and temporary magnets

When pieces of iron or steel are placed near a magnet, they become magnets themselves. The bar magnet **induces** an opposite pole in the iron or steel nearest itself. This **induced pole** is then attracted to the magnet (Fig. 25.2).

Experiments show that:

- Iron is easy to magnetise, but it loses its magnetism when the bar magnet is removed. Iron is said to form **temporary magnets**. Because of this property, iron is used in electromagnets, where the magnetism is 'switched' on and off very easily. Iron is often described as *soft iron* when it is used in electromagnets. This is because it is so easy to magnetise and demagnetise.
- Steel retains its magnetism much better than iron. If the bar magnet in Fig. 25.2 is removed, the steel will remain magnetised. Steel is used to make **permanent magnets**.

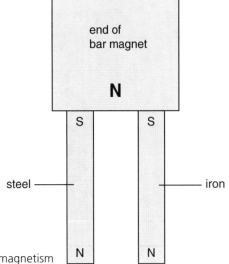

Fig. 25.2 Induced magnetism

25.4 Magnetic fields

Strong magnets can attract other magnetic materials:

- from a distance away;
- through non-magnetic materials, such as paper and wood;
- through a vacuum.

The regions of space where magnetic materials experience forces are called **magnetic fields**. Magnetic fields can be investigated by using **iron filings** or a **plotting compass**.

Using iron filings

Sprinkle iron filings onto a sheet of paper on top of the magnet. Tap the paper gently. The iron filings are quickly magnetised and line up in the direction of the magnetic field (Fig. 25.3).

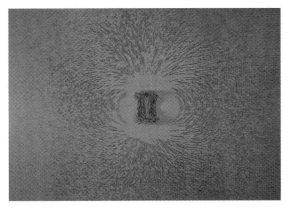

Fig. 25.3 Investigating the magnetic field around a bar magnet using iron filings

Using a plotting compass

This is a more accurate method of defining the magnetic field around a magnet. A plotting compass is a small compass with a magnetic needle. Using the plotting compass it is possible to draw a series of lines running from the north pole to the south pole (Fig. 25.4). These lines are called **lines of magnetic force**.

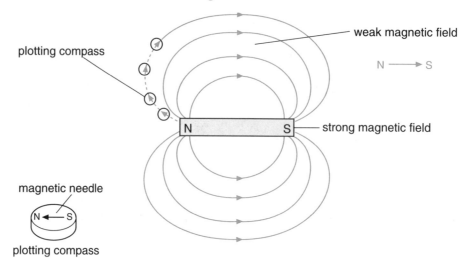

Fig. 25.4 Investigating the magnetic field around a bar magnet using a plotting compass

Notice that the **lines of force**:

- always point away from a N-pole and towards a S-pole.
- never cross.
- are close together where the field is strong and further apart where the field is weak.

25.5 The Earth's own magnetic field

The Earth has its own magnetic field. It behaves as if there is a huge bar magnet along its north–south axis (Fig. 25.5).

Notice two important points shown in Fig. 25.5:

- The Earth's magnetic north pole is not at the same point as the geographical north pole.
- The Earth's magnetic north pole *attracts* the north poles of magnets. Therefore, the Earth's magnetic north is really a *south-seeking pole*.

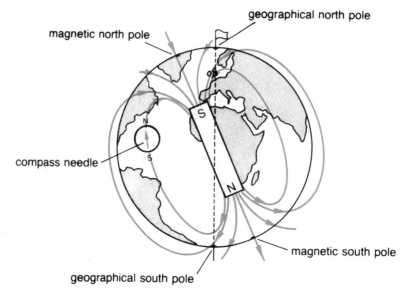

Fig. 25.5 The Earth's magnetic field

25.6 The magnetic effects of electric currents

Magnetism can be turned on and off at the flick of a switch. This is possible because:

> Every electric current produces a magnetic field.

The magnetism produced by electricity is called **electromagnetism**.

The magnetic field around a straight wire

The magnetic field around a straight wire can be investigated using the apparatus in Fig. 25.6.

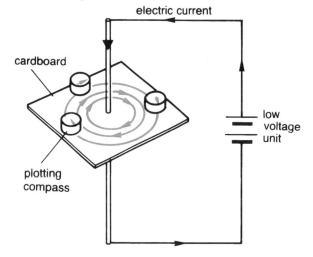

Fig. 25.6 Investigating the field around a straight wire carrying a current

If the current in the circuit is reversed, the compass will point in the opposite direction. If the direction of the current is known, the direction of the field can be predicted by the **right–hand grip rule**:

> *Imagine gripping the wire with your right hand so that your thumb points in the direction of the current. Your fingers will then be pointing around the wire in the direction of the magnetic field.*

The magnetic field around a solenoid

A solenoid is a long coil of wire. Fig. 25.7 shows what happens when an electric current is passed through a solenoid. The solenoid acts like a magnet. The lower part of the diagram shows a good way to work out whether the end of a solenoid is a north pole or a south pole. Remember that the arrows on the wires show the direction of the current (conventional current), *not* the direction of electron flow. The arrows come out of the letters N and S in the same direction as the current in the wire.

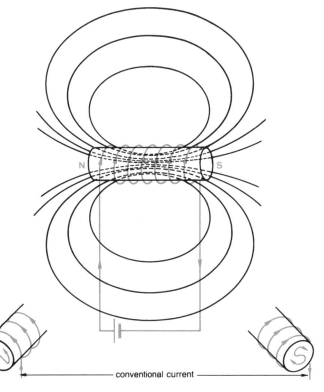

Fig. 25.7 The magnetic field around a solenoid. What is the direction of the magnetic field?

The strength of the magnetic field around a solenoid can be increased by:
- using a larger current;
- having more coils in the solenoid;
- having a soft iron core through the solenoid.

The solenoid in Fig. 25.7 will act as an electromagnet. When the current is switched off, the magnetism disappears. Electromagnets like this, based on solenoids, are used in electric bells, telephones, loudspeakers, relays and electric motors.

25.7 Uses of electromagnets

Electromagnetic relays

Relays are used to operate various appliances, including automatic doors, burglar alarms and car ignition systems. An electromagnetic relay is a switch controlled by an electromagnet. It works like a relay race. In a relay race, a baton is passed from one runner to the next. In an electromagnetic relay, signals are passed from one circuit to the next by electric currents.

Fig. 25.8 shows the electromagnetic relay in a car ignition system. The starter motor requires a very large current (about 100 A). This would normally require a heavy-duty switch. Such a switch might easily produce sparks which would be dangerous to the user. These problems are overcome by using a relay system.

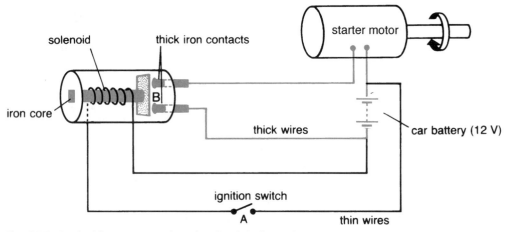

Fig. 25.8 Car ignition system – the relay circuit is shown in green

The relay circuit in Fig. 25.8 (in green) includes an iron core inside a solenoid. When the ignition is switched on at A, a small current flows in the solenoid. The iron core is magnetised and attracted towards the thick iron contacts at B. Contact is made at B and a large current flows to the starter motor.

Moving-coil loudspeakers

Fig. 25.9 shows a loudspeaker of the type used in a radio or a television. Notice the solenoid (coil) between the poles of the magnet. Electrical signals from the radio cause the current in the solenoid to change. As this current changes, the force on the solenoid (coil) from the permanent magnet changes and the coil moves. These changes happen very rapidly, making the paper cone vibrate in and out so rapidly that it produces audible sounds.

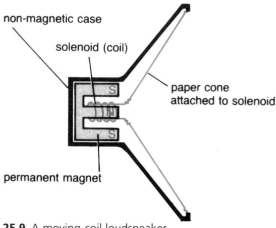

Fig. 25.9 A moving-coil loudspeaker

25.8 Electric motors

An electric motor uses electricity and magnetism to produce movement. This is called
the **motor effect**. It can be demonstrated using the apparatus shown in Fig. 25.10.

- The magnet provides magnetism.
- The current provides electricity.
- When the switch is closed, the wire jumps up.
- If the current is reversed *or* the field is reversed, the wire moves downwards.
- If both the current *and* the field are reversed, the wire jumps up again.

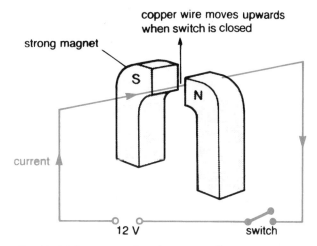

Fig. 25.10 Demonstrating the motor effect

Notice two important points from these results:

- The wire always moves at right angles to the direction of the field and the direction
  of the current.
- The direction of the wire's movement depends on the direction of the field and the
  direction of the current.

You can predict the direction in which the wire will move using the **left-hand motor
rule** (which is sometimes called **Fleming's left-hand rule**):

> *Hold the first finger, second finger and thumb of your left hand at right angles
> to each other (Fig. 25.11). If you place your hand so that the first finger points
> in the direction of the field from N to S and the second finger points in the
> direction of the current, then your thumb will point in the direction
> in which the wire will move.*

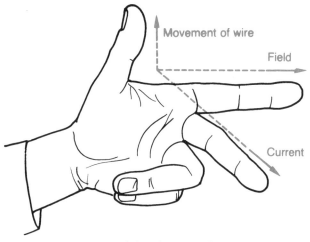

Fig. 25.11 Using the left-hand motor rule

The motor effect is put to use in electric motors (Fig. 25.12). A simple d.c. motor has a coil which can rotate between the poles of a magnet. The ends of the coil are connected to the two halves of a split metal ring called a **commutator**. The commutator rotates with the coil. Two carbon contacts (carbon brushes) press lightly on the commutator.

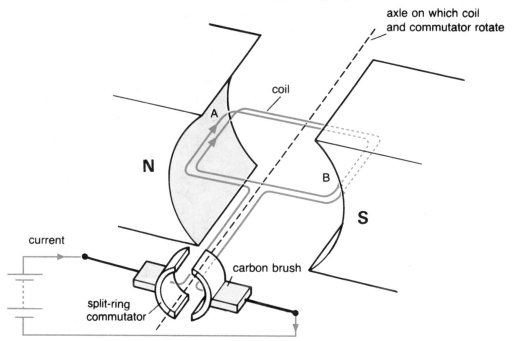

Fig. 25.12 A simple direct current (d.c.) motor

Applying the left–hand rule to Fig. 25.12: side A of the coil will try to move down, and side B of the coil will try to move up. So the forces acting on the coil will rotate it anticlockwise until it is vertical.

When the coil is vertical, the gaps in the commutator are opposite the brushes. So there is no current in the coil. This causes the coil to slow down, but as it overshoots the vertical position, the contacts at the commutator change over. Side B of the coil is now on the left where side A was before. In this position side B is forced downwards and side A is forced upwards. So, the coil continues to rotate anticlockwise.

In commercial motors:
- *electromagnets* are used rather than permanent magnets because permanent magnets slowly lose their magnetism.
- the coils have *dozens, or even hundreds, of turns* to increase the turning force.
- the coils are wound on a *soft iron core* to increase the strength of the magnetic field.

25.9 Electromagnetic induction

In an electric motor, an electric current passes through a coil in a magnetic field. This causes the coil to move.

i.e. electricity + magnetism → movement

The motor converts electrical energy into kinetic energy. This process can also be reversed. If a coil is moved in a magnetic field, an electric current is produced.

i.e. movement + magnetism → electricity

In this case, kinetic energy is converted to electrical energy.

Electric currents produced by this method are called *induced* currents and the effect is called **electromagnetic induction**. This effect is used in dynamos for bicycle lights, alternators in cars and generators in power stations. All these machines use movement and magnetism to generate electricity.

Investigating electromagnetic induction

Fig. 25.13 shows an experiment to investigate electromagnetic induction.

- There is no current when the wire is stationary.
- **To produce a current, the wire must move across the lines of magnetic force** between the poles of the magnet. Therefore, a current flows when the wire is moved up (direction 5) or down (direction 6). There is no current when the wire is moved in directions 1, 2, 3 and 4 – in these directions, the wire is moving *along* the line of force, not across them.
- The current only flows while the wire is moving.
- Reversing the movement reverses the current.
- An induced current also flows if the wire is stationary and the magnet is moved up and down.
- The induced current is larger when
  - the wire is moved faster;
  - a stronger magnet is used;
  - more turns of wire are used.

These results are summarised by **Faraday's law of electromagnetic induction**:

The size of the induced current is proportional to the rate at which the wire/coil moves across the magnetic lines of force.

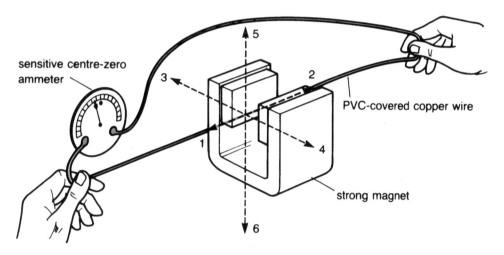

Fig. 25.13 Investigating electromagnetic induction

25.10 The a.c. generator (alternator)

Fig. 25.14 shows a simple alternating current (a.c.) generator. The rings on the axle are fixed to the coil and rotate with it. As the axle rotates, the coil moves through a magnetic field and an induced current is generated. This generator effect is the reverse or mirror image of the motor effect. So in this case, we use the **right–hand generator rule** (**Fleming's right–hand rule**) to predict the direction of the induced current:

Hold the first finger, second finger and thumb of your right hand at right angles to each other. If you place your hand so that the first finger points in the direction of the magnetic field from N to S and your thumb points in the direction of movement of the wire, then your second finger will point in the direction of the induced current.

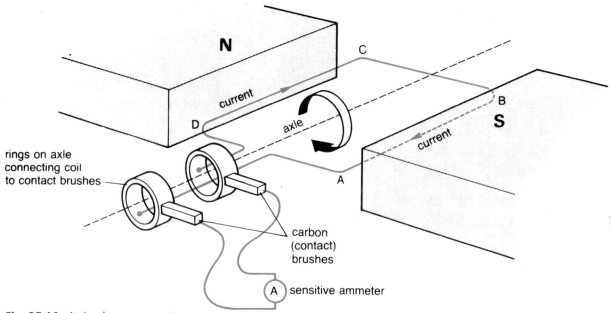

Fig. 25.14 A simple a.c. generator

Fig. 25.15 shows how the induced current varies during one turn of the coil:

Position (i)   coil horizontal
– cutting lines of force at fastest rate, therefore current is at a maximum. As coil moves towards the vertical position, current falls.

Position (ii)   coil vertical
– no lines of force being crossed, therefore current is zero. As coil moves towards the horizontal position, current increases but in *opposite* direction.

Position (iii)   coil horizontal
– current in opposite direction reaches a maximum. As coil moves towards the vertical again, current falls.

Position (iv)   coil vertical
– current zero again.

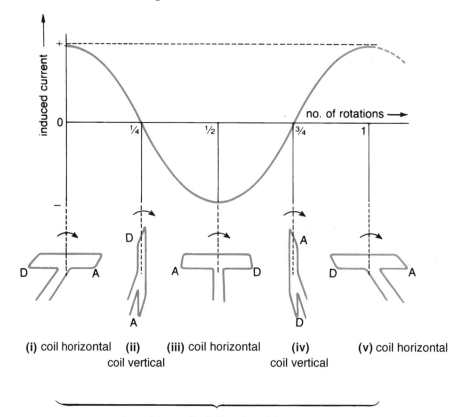

(i) coil horizontal   **(ii)**   **(iii)** coil horizontal   **(iv)**   **(v)** coil horizontal
coil vertical   coil vertical

1 turn of coil (i.e. 1 cycle)

Fig. 25.15 Variation in the induced current during one turn of the coil

Notice, from Fig. 25.15, that the current flowing from the generator is an alternating current. This is why an a.c. generator is sometimes called an **alternator**.

Power stations have huge a.c. generators. These have a rotating magnet rather than a rotating coil. The advantage of this is that rings and contact brushes are not needed. This cuts out the wear and tear from sparks and friction.

This arrangement is also used in car alternators. The engine causes an electromagnet to rotate inside several stationary coils. The alternating current is then changed into direct current so that it can recharge the car's battery.

The alternator (a.c. generator) is easily modified to give direct current. This can be done by using *split* rings (commutators). The commutators and contact brushes are arranged in the same way as in a d.c. motor (Fig. 25.12) so that the current always flows in the same direction (Fig. 25.16). Generators which produce direct current are sometimes called **dynamos**.

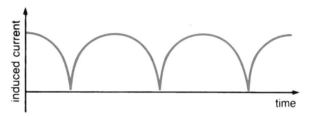

Fig. 25.16 The current from a d.c. generator (dynamo)

25.11 Transformers

In 25.9, we saw that an induced current is generated in a coil as long as it is cutting *across* the lines of force from a magnet.

An induced current can also be obtained in a (secondary) coil if the magnet is replaced by a coil (**primary coil**) carrying an alternating current. As the alternating current in the primary coil changes direction, the magnetic field continually increases and decreases. The lines of force cutting across the secondary coil continually change and this produces a continuous alternating voltage in the secondary coil.

This is the principle behind **transformers** (Fig. 25.17).

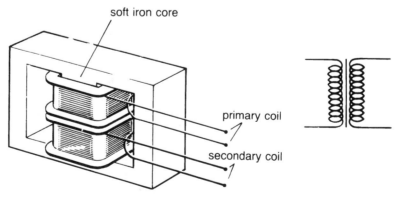

A transformer in which the coils are wound side by side
(in some transformers, one coil is wound over the other)

a circuit symbol
for a transformer

Fig. 25.17 Transformers

- A transformer is made by putting two coils of wire (a primary coil and a secondary coil) on a soft iron core.
- The primary coil is connected to an alternating current and an alternating voltage is induced in the secondary coil.
- The induced voltage in the secondary coil depends on the number of turns in the two coils. This makes transformers useful because they allow us to change the voltage of a supply.

The voltage, V, induced in a coil is proportional to the number of turns, n, i.e. $V \propto n$.

This means that:

$$\frac{\text{Voltage across secondary coil } (V_s)}{\text{Voltage across primary coil } (V_p)} = \frac{\text{Number of turns on secondary } (n_s)}{\text{Number of turns on primary } (n_p)}$$

Example

A transformer is being used to reduce the mains supply from 240 V to 12 V for use with a model railway. There are 500 turns on the primary coil in the transformer. How many turns are there on the secondary coil?

$$\frac{(V_s)}{(V_p)} = \frac{(n_s)}{(n_p)}, \text{ so } \frac{12}{240} = \frac{n_s}{500}$$

therefore, $n_s = 500 \times \dfrac{12}{240} = 25$ turns

In this example, the transformer is a **step-down transformer**. Step-down transformers give a *decrease in voltage*. They have fewer turns on the secondary coil than on the primary coil. **Step-up transformers** give an increase in voltage. They have more turns on the secondary coil than on the primary coil.

25.12 Transmitting electricity

Transformers are important in the transmission of electricity from power stations via the National Grid. Large power stations generate electricity at 25 000 volts. This is 'stepped up' to 275 000 or 400 000 volts using a transformer before being transmitted through the Grid.

Most transformers can transfer electrical power very efficiently from the primary circuit to the secondary circuit. If the transformer is 100% efficient:

power input from primary = power output from secondary

therefore $V_p \times I_p = V_s \times I_s$

From this equation, it is clear that if the voltage is stepped up from 25 000 to 400 000 volts for the Grid system, then the current must be stepped down proportionally. This is a big advantage. A small current has a much smaller heating effect in the cables. Less energy is therefore lost as heat. The lower current can also use thinner cables with pylons further apart. However, transmission at higher voltages requires greater insulation.

The Grid voltage is reduced by step-down transformers at substations before it is used in homes and factories. Some industrial plants take electrical energy from the Grid system at 33 000 or 11 000 V. Transformers reduce this further to 240 V for use in our homes.

Some people complain about the way in which electricity pylons and overhead cables spoil the environment. There is a lot of support for this view, particularly when pylons pass through beautiful countryside. However, laying cables underground would be more expensive and this would increase the cost of our electricity.

Summary

1   When a suspended magnet comes to rest, the **north-seeking pole** or **north pole** always points north.

2   **Like magnetic poles repel** each other, **unlike magnetic poles attract**.

3   The only common magnetic materials are iron, cobalt, nickel and their alloys.

4   Iron is easy to magnetise, but it loses its magnetism easily. It forms temporary **magnets**. Steel retains its magnetism much better than iron. It is used for **permanent magnets**.

5   Magnetic lines of force:
   * always point from a N-pole to a S-pole,
   * never cross,
   * become closer as the magnetic field gets stronger.

6   The **Earth's magnetic north pole** attracts the north poles of magnets. Therefore the Earth's magnetic north pole is really a south-seeking pole.

7   Every electric current produces a magnetic field. This magnetism produced by electricity is called **electromagnetism**.

8   The direction of the field around a wire carrying an electric current can be predicted by the **right-hand grip rule**. Grip the wire with your right hand, so that your thumb points in the direction of the current. Your fingers will then be pointing around the wire in the direction of the magnetic field.

9   **Electromagnets** are used in electric bells, telephones, loudspeakers, relays and electric motors.

10   A force is exerted on a current-carrying wire in a magnetic field. This effect finds an application in electric motors.

   In an electric motor,
   electricity + magnetism → force causing movement.
   This is called the **motor effect**. The direction of movement can be predicted using the **left-hand motor rule**.

11   When a conductor cuts through magnetic lines of force and when the magnetic field through a coil changes, a voltage is induced. If the conductor or coil is part of a complete circuit, an electric current flows. This effect finds an application in generators.

   In a generator (dynamo or alternator),
   movement + magnetism → electricity.
   This is called the **generator (dynamo) effect** or **electromagnetic induction**. The direction of the induced current can be predicted using the **right-hand generator rule**.

12   In a **transformer**, the voltage induced across a coil is proportional to the number of turns in it.

   So, $\dfrac{\text{Voltage across secondary coil}}{\text{Voltage across primary coil}} = \dfrac{\text{Number of turns on secondary}}{\text{Number of turns on primary}}$

13   If a transformer is 100% efficient,

   power input from primary = power output from secondary

   $$\therefore V_p \times I_p = V_s \times I_s$$

Quick test 25

Questions 1 to 6

The diagram shows a compass placed near one end of a coil in position 1. When a current is passed through the coil, the compass needle points in the direction shown.

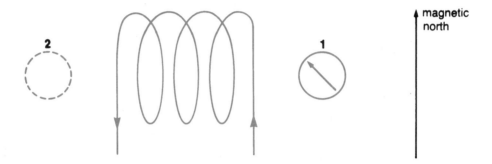

Other possible positions of the compass needle are:
A   closer to magnetic north,
B   further from magnetic north,
C   exactly as in position 1,
D   the same angle to magnetic north, but on the opposite side to that in position 1,
E   directly to magnetic north.

Which of the positions A to E will the compass needle take up if the:
1   current through the coil is decreased?
2   current flows in the opposite direction?
3   compass is moved to position 2?
4   coil has more turns?
5   coil is turned through 90°?
6   compass is moved to position 2 and the current is reversed?

Questions 7 to 9

Questions 7 to 9 concern the following pieces of equipment:
A   commutator
B   diode
C   relay
D   fuse
E   transformer

Which piece of equipment
7   is an essential part of a motor which uses direct current (d.c.)?
8   allows current to flow in one direction only?
9   is essential in the operation of a small 2 volt motor from the mains supply?

Questions 10 to 15

The apparatus shown in the diagram was used to study the magnetic field produced when an electric current flows through a solenoid. The magnet was placed on the force meter and the force meter was set to zero. For each current used, readings were taken with and without the iron core present. The results are shown in the table.

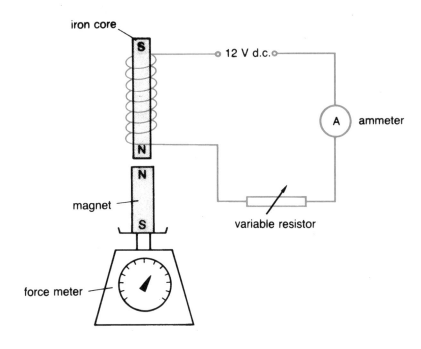

Current/amps	Force meter reading/N	
	without iron core	with iron core
0.2	4	6
0.4	8	11
0.8	15	20
1.0	20	25

10 Why does the force meter not register zero when the apparatus is set up?

11 Why is the force meter set to zero?

12 Why is a variable resistor included in the circuit?

13 Explain why the force meter shows a reading when there is a current in the solenoid.

14 How does the force from the magnetic field depend on the size of the current?

15 How does the iron core affect the force from the magnetic field?

16 The following article recently appeared in a local newspaper.

Overhead versus underground

Protestors at yesterday's meeting voted against the proposal that electricity pylons should be built to carry power to remote farms on the island. They wanted the power cables to be buried underground. Some local residents, however, were not in favour of underground cables as some trees would have to be destroyed, and it takes longer to repair underground cables than overhead cables. The Central Electricity Generating Board pointed out that overhead cables capable of carrying 400 kV through the National Grid cost £506 000 per km, whereas underground cable costs £6 509 000 per km.

(a) From this article and your own knowledge, suggest *two* disadvantages of overhead cables and *two* disadvantages of underground cables.

(b) Most domestic appliances in Britain are rated at 220–240 V. Why is it necessary to carry electricity through the National Grid at 400 kV (400 000 V)?

(*MEG*)

Chapter 26
Radioactivity and nuclear energy

26.1 Radioactivity

In 1896, **Henri Becquerel** (1852–1908) was investigating the reactions of uranium compounds. After one set of experiments, he left one of his uranium compounds in a drawer near a photographic plate wrapped in black paper. When Becquerel developed the photographic plate, he was surprised to find that it had been darkened in the part nearest the uranium compounds.

This prompted Becquerel to carry out further tests. He found that the uranium compound was emitting **radiation** which could pass through the black paper and affect the photographic plate. Becquerel called the phenomenon **radioactivity** and he described the uranium compound as **radioactive**.

Radioactivity (radioactive decay) is the spontaneous
break up (decay) of atoms.

Marie Curie (1867–1934), one of Becquerel's assistants, decided to examine the radioactivity of uranium compounds in more detail. She discovered that:

- all uranium compounds are radioactive,
- pitchblende (impure uranium sulphide) contains two other elements which are more radioactive than uranium. Marie named these elements **radium** and **polonium**. Radium is about two million times more radioactive than uranium.

26.2 Alpha, beta and gamma radiation

Radioactivity arises from the spontaneous breakdown of unstable nuclei.

When radioactive atoms break up, they release energy and lose three kinds of radiation (radioactive emissions). These radiations are called **alpha rays** (α-rays), **beta rays** (β-rays) and **gamma rays** (γ-rays).

α-rays and β-rays are made up of *particles*, so they are often described as α-particles and β-particles. Gamma rays are *electromagnetic waves* with the greatest penetrating power (see 22.11). The nature and properties of the three kinds of radiation are summarised in Table 26.1 and Fig. 26.1.

Table 26.1 The nature and properties of α-rays, β-rays and γ-rays

Radiation	Nature	Distance travelled in air	Effect of electric and magnetic fields
α-rays	α-particles = positive helium nuclei	a few centimetres	very small deflection
β-rays	β-particles = negative electrons	a few metres	large deflection
γ-rays	electromagnetic waves	several kilometres	no deflection

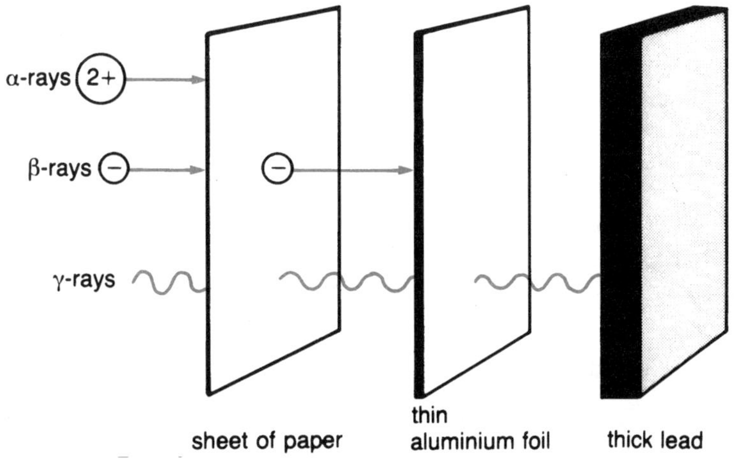

Fig. 26.1 The relative penetrating powers of α-rays, β-rays and γ-rays

Notice in Table 26.1 and Fig. 26.1 that γ-rays travel much further in air and have much greater penetrating power than α-rays and β-rays. γ-rays can penetrate paper and aluminium foil very easily. In fact, γ-rays will penetrate bricks and metal sheets. They carry enough energy to damage cells and kill organisms. Because of this, radioactive materials which emit γ-rays are often stored in thick lead containers. As radioactive materials give off γ-rays, they lose energy and become stable.

The other important point to notice from Table 26.1 is the effect of electric and magnetic fields. γ-rays have no charge. Therefore, they are unaffected by electric and magnetic fields. α- and β-particles are charged so they are affected. β-particles are much smaller and lighter than α-particles so they are affected the most.

Examiner's tip

Carefully note the properties of α-, β- and γ-rays.

26.3 Nuclear reactions

When radioactive atoms break up, they may lose α-particles or β-particles. The changes in mass number and atomic number during α-decay and β-decay are summarised in Table 26.2. The symbol for an electron can be written as $_{-1}^{0}$e because its relative mass is effectively zero and its charge is −1.

Examiner's tip

Note the changes in mass and charge when radioactive atoms lose α- and β-particles.

Table 26.2 Changes in mass number and atomic number during α-decay and β-decay

Type of radioactivity	Particle lost	Change in mass number	Change in atomic number
α-decay	helium nucleus $_{2}^{4}$He	−4	−2
β-decay	electron $_{-1}^{0}$e	0	+1

Uranium-238, an example of α-decay

We can illustrate α-decay with uranium-238. When an atom of $_{92}^{238}$U loses an α-particle, the part left behind will have a mass number which is four less than $_{92}^{238}$U and an atomic number which is two less than $_{92}^{238}$U. So, the atom left behind will have a *mass number of 234* and an *atomic number of 90*. Atoms with an atomic number of 90 are those of *thorium, Th*. Thus, the products of the decay of $_{92}^{238}$U are $_{90}^{234}$Th and $_{2}^{4}$He.

This can be summarised in a nuclear equation as follows:

$$_{92}^{238}\text{U} \longrightarrow \ _{90}^{234}\text{Th} + \ _{2}^{4}\text{He} + \text{Energy}$$

Carbon-14, an example of β-decay

We can illustrate β-decay with $_{6}^{14}$C. This time, the products are $_{-1}^{0}$e and $_{7}^{14}$N. The nuclear equation is:

$$_{6}^{14}\text{C} \longrightarrow \ _{7}^{14}\text{N} + \ _{-1}^{0}\text{e} + \text{Energy}$$

Notice in both these nuclear equations that the *total* mass in the superscripts and the *total* charge in the subscripts are the same before and after decay.

During β-decay, a neutron in the radioactive atom splits up into a proton and an electron.

$$\underset{\text{neutron}}{{}^{1}_{0}\text{n}} \longrightarrow \underset{\text{proton}}{{}^{1}_{1}\text{p}} + \underset{\text{electron}}{{}^{0}_{-1}\text{e}}$$

The electron is emitted in the β-rays, but the proton stays in the nucleus. In this way the mass number of the remaining fragment (number of protons plus neutrons) is the same as the original radioactive atom, but its atomic number (number of protons) goes up by one.

γ-decay

During γ-decay, the nucleus of an atom becomes much more stable by losing energy in the form of γ-rays.

26.4 Detecting radioactivity

Various rocks in the Earth, including granite, contain radioactive uranium, thorium and potassium compounds. In addition to this, we are also exposed to radiation from the Sun and to radiation from traces of radon in the air.

These *natural sources* of radiation are usually called **background radioactivity** or **background radiation**. Normal background radiation is very low. It causes no risk to our health. However, background radioactivity must be taken into account in performing accurate experiments.

Background radiation and other radioactivity can be detected using a **Geiger–Müller (GM) tube** (Geiger counter). Fig. 26.2 shows a diagram of a GM tube.

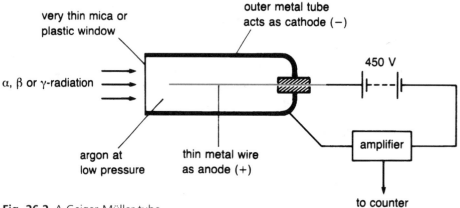

Fig. 26.2 A Geiger-Müller tube

When α-, β- or γ-rays enter the tube, they ionise the argon atoms inside.

$$\text{Ar} \longrightarrow \text{Ar}^{+} + \text{e}^{-}$$

The Ar^{+} ions and the electrons are attracted to the electrodes in the tube and a tiny current flows in the circuit. This current is then amplified and a counter can be used to show the amount of radiation entering the tube.

26.5 Half-life

The *rate of decay* of a radioactive isotope is shown by its **half-life**. This is the time it takes for half of any given amount of the isotope to decay.

Half-lives can vary from less than a second to millions of years. The half-life tells you how stable an isotope is. The longer the half-life, the slower the decay process and the more stable the isotope (Table 26.3).

Table 26.3 The half-lives of some radioactive isotopes

Isotope	Half-life	Stability
Carbon-14	5730 years	
Uranium-238	4500 years	
Cobalt-60	5.3 years	
Iodine-131	8 days	
Technetium-99	6 hours	
Polonium-234	0.15 milliseconds	

decreasing stability

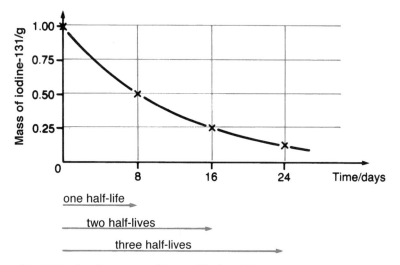

Fig. 26.3 The decay curve for 1g of iodine-131

Fig. 26.3 shows how a sample of iodine-131 will decay. If you start with one gram of iodine-131, only half a gram is left after eight days (one half-life). After another eight days, the half gram will have decayed to a quarter of a gram. Eight days later (i.e. 24 days from the start), only one-eighth of a gram will remain.

Radioactive iodine 131 is used by doctors to measure the activity of the thyroid gland. The thyroid gland plays an important part in our metabolism of iodine. First of all, the patient drinks some liquid containing a tiny amount of iodine-131. Then, by measuring the amount of radioactivity in the thyroid gland using a scanner, doctors can tell how fast iodine is being taken up by the gland.

26.6 Uses of radioactive materials

Radioactive materials have a large number of uses in industry, in medicine and in archaeology.

Industrial uses

Two important industrial uses of radioactive materials are illustrated in Fig. 26.4.

Detection of leaks in pipes without digging

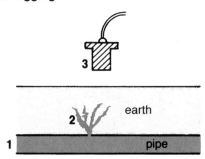

Thickness gauges
e.g. during production of polythene or paper

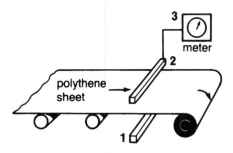

1 Radioactive tracer emitting penetrating γ-rays fed into pipe, then discontinued

2 Radioactive tracer leaks into soil

3 Geiger-Müller tube used to detect radiation and therefore the position of the leak

1 Long radioactive source emits less penetrating β-rays

2 Long Geiger-Müller tube used to detect radiation

3 Meter measures radiation level – the thicker the polythene or paper, the lower the reading

Fig. 26.4 Two industrial uses of radioactive materials: detection of leaks in underground pipes without having to dig, and thickness gauges

Medical uses

Treatment of cancer   Penetrating γ-rays from cobalt-60 are used to kill cancer cells and treat growths inside the body. Skin cancer can be treated with less penetrating β-rays. This is done by strapping a sheet containing phosphorus-32 or strontium-90 on the affected area.

Sterilisation of medical items   Medical items such as dressings and syringes are sealed in plastic bags and sterilised by intense γ-rays from cobalt-60. The γ-rays kill any microorganisms on the articles.

Archaeological uses

The common isotope of carbon is carbon-12. Therefore, carbon in living things and in carbon dioxide is mainly carbon-12 with a small fraction of radioactive **carbon-14**. The fraction of carbon as carbon-14 in living things always stays at the same level. Although the carbon-14 in the organism is continually decaying, it is also being replaced from food or by photosynthesis. When an animal or plant dies, its level of carbon-14 starts to fall.

Carbon-14 has a half-life of 5730 years. So after 5730 years, the fraction of carbon-14 in the remains of a dead organism will be half that in living specimens. By measuring the fraction of carbon-14 in ancient remains of animals and plants, scientists can calculate the age of the specimens.

Using a technique similar to carbon dating, geologists can work out the age of rocks. Most rocks contain traces of radioactive U-238. This decays in a series of reactions to form lead-206. The half-life for this decay is 4000 million years. If we assume that a rock contains no lead-206 when it is first formed, then the present ratio of U-238 to Pb-206 in the rock can be used to calculate the time since the rock was formed.

26.7 Dangers from radiation

People who work with radioactive materials must be aware of the dangers from radiation. With very penetrating radiation, these dangers include skin burns, loss of hair, sickness, cancers, sterility and even death from a very high dose.

Because of these dangers, people who work with radioactive materials must wear special **radiation badges**. These badges contain film sensitive to radiation. The film is developed at regular intervals to show how much radiation the wearer has been exposed to.

Scientists and technicians whose work involves dangerous isotopes emitting γ-rays must take **extra safety precautions**. These include:

- manipulating the isotopes by remote control from a safe distance;
- ensuring that any exposure to radiation is for the shortest possible time;
- protecting themselves by lead or concrete shielding.

Special precautions must also be taken in the **disposal of radioactive waste**. Some isotopes in radioactive waste have half-lives of hundreds of years. These waste materials must be sealed in concrete or steel containers and then buried deep underground or dropped to the bottom of the sea.

26.8 Nuclear energy

Nuclear fission

Large heavy atoms, like those of uranium and radium, can become more stable by losing an α-particle or a β-particle (see 26.3). Some of these heavy atoms such as uranium-235 can also become stable by **nuclear fission**. Fig. 26.5 shows how nuclear fission works.

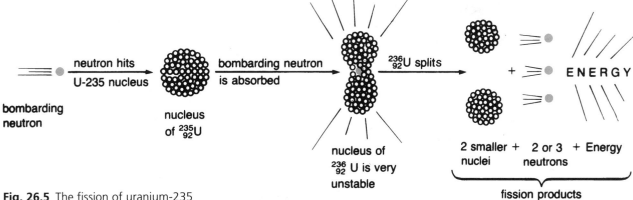

Fig. 26.5 The fission of uranium-235

Unlike radioactive decay which is quite random, nuclear fission is caused by bombardment of a nucleus with a neutron. The final products of fission are two smaller nuclei, two or three separate neutrons and enormous amounts of **energy**. The fission of a nucleus provides about 40 times more energy than the loss of an α-particle.

Controlling fission

Natural uranium consists of 0.7% uranium–235 and 99.3% uranium–238, but only the uranium–235 atoms will undergo nuclear fission. However, scientists realised that if a uranium sample contained a larger percentage of uranium–235, the neutrons released during fission of one uranium–235 nucleus would split another uranium–235 nucleus and so on. This could cause a **chain reaction**.

Fig. 26.6 shows an exploding chain reaction with uranium–235. One reaction releases 3 neutrons. These 3 neutrons release 9 more neutrons, then 27, 81 and so on. Each time, more and more energy is produced.

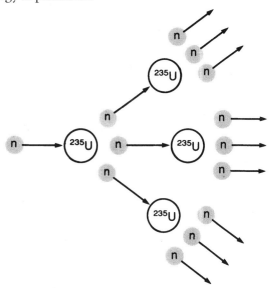

Fig. 26.6 An exploding chain reaction with uranium-235

If we can manipulate this chain reaction, we can use it in different ways. For example:

- **In an atomic bomb**, the fission of *pure* uranium–235 happens in an *uncontrolled* exploding chain reaction. All the neutrons released by fission cause further fissions. Enormous amounts of energy and radiation are released.
- **In an atomic (nuclear) reactor**, a *mixture* of 3% uranium–235 and 97% uranium–238 is used. This gives a *controlled* chain reaction. In this case, an average of only one neutron from each fission causes further fission. The heat produced is then used to generate electricity.

Nuclear reactors

Fig. 26.7 is a simplified diagram of a **gas-cooled nuclear reactor**. The function of each part of the reactor is shown in the diagram.

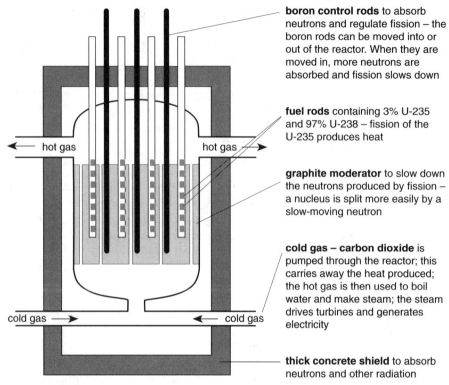

boron control rods to absorb neutrons and regulate fission – the boron rods can be moved into or out of the reactor. When they are moved in, more neutrons are absorbed and fission slows down

fuel rods containing 3% U-235 and 97% U-238 – fission of the U-235 produces heat

graphite moderator to slow down the neutrons produced by fission – a nucleus is split more easily by a slow-moving neutron

cold gas – carbon dioxide is pumped through the reactor; this carries away the heat produced; the hot gas is then used to boil water and make steam; the steam drives turbines and generates electricity

thick concrete shield to absorb neutrons and other radiation

hot gas   hot gas

cold gas   cold gas

Fig. 26.7 A gas-cooled nuclear reactor

The future

At present, about 18% of our electricity is generated from nuclear energy. The reason for our increased use of nuclear fuel is that fossil fuels are running out. However, there is also concern about the supplies of uranium-235. In order to reduce our reliance on uranium-235, scientists are trying to develop a new type of fission reactor called a **breeder reactor**. The first prototype breeder reactor was built at Dounreay in Scotland. This started working in 1976. The reactor uses **plutonium-239** as the fuel, not uranium-235. The plutonium-239 can be produced ('bred') from stable uranium-238 which makes up 99.7% of natural uranium. By using uranium-238 to 'breed' plutonium, our stocks of nuclear fuel will last for a few hundred years.

Fusion

In the distant future, scientists hope to harness energy from **fusion**. Fusion is the opposite to fission. It involves joining two nuclei together. The energy produced by the Sun comes from the fusion of heavy hydrogen (deuterium) nuclei (Fig. 26.8).

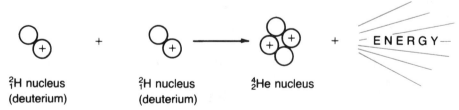

$^2_1$H nucleus (deuterium)   + $^2_1$H nucleus (deuterium)   → $^4_2$He nucleus   +   ENERGY

Fig. 26.8 The fusion of two deuterium nuclei

For many years, scientists have tried to fuse deuterium nuclei by producing very high temperatures, similar to those on the Sun. The energy liberated by the fusion of two nuclei is much greater than that liberated by fission. If we could harness the energy from fusion, we would have solved our energy problems for ever.

Summary

1   **Radioactivity** (radioactive decay) arises from the spontaneous break up (decay) of unstable nuclei.

2   When radioactive nuclei break up, they release energy and emit three kinds of radiation.
   - **alpha rays** which are the positive nuclei of helium atoms, $^4_2He^{2+}$
   - **beta rays** which are negative electrons,
   - **gamma rays** which are very penetrating electromagnetic waves.

3   During **alpha decay**, the mass number falls by 4 and the atomic number falls by 2. During **beta decay**, the mass number is unaffected, but the atomic number increases by 1. During **gamma decay**, energy is lost, but the mass number and atomic number are unchanged.

4   **Background radioactivity** (radiation) comes from the natural sources of radiation in the environment.

5   Radiation and radioactivity can be detected using a **Geiger-Müller (GM) tube**.

6   The **half-life** of a radioactive isotope is the time it takes for half of any given amount of the isotope to decay.

7   **Radioactive isotopes** have important uses in industry, in medicine and in dating rocks and archaeological remains.

8   The radiation from radioactive materials can have harmful effects. Very penetrating radiation can cause skin burns, loss of hair, cancers, sterility and even death from very high doses. However, β- and γ-radiation can also be used in medicine to kill cancer cells and treat the disease effectively.

9   **Nuclear fission** involves the break up of atoms under bombardment by neutrons which cause a **chain reaction**. In an atomic bomb, the chain reaction is uncontrolled. In an atomic (nuclear) reactor, the chain reaction is controlled by boron rods.

Quick test 26

Questions 1 to 4

These concern the five isotopes labelled A, B, C, D and E below.

	Mass number	Atomic number
A	1	1
B	3	2
C	4	2
D	4	3
E	7	4

1   Which is an isotope of hydrogen?
2   Which two are isotopes of the same element?
3   Which isotopes contain only one neutron?
4   Which isotope contains the most electrons?

Questions 5 to 10

A   neutron   D   beta particle
B   hydrogen atom   E   hydrogen ion
C   alpha particle

Which particle labelled A to E above
5   would be attracted by a positive plate?

6   is the heaviest?
7   could be used in a thickness gauge for polythene or paper?
8   causes fission of uranium-235?
9   is a proton?
10 contains the same number of protons and electrons?

11 The diagram shows alpha and beta particles passing between two charged plates.
    (a) Explain why alpha particles are deflected upwards in the electric field, but beta particles are deflected downwards.
    (b) Explain why a radioactive source which gives out only alpha and beta particles can be safely stored in an aluminium container.

charged plate (−)

alpha

radiation

beta

charged plate (+)

12 Radioactivity is used in hospitals to investigate the inside of a person's body without having to cut them open. Technetium-99 (^{99}Tc) which gives out gamma rays can be used for this.
    (a) Why is gamma radiation used rather than alpha rays or beta rays?
    (b) Why is lead used to shield hospital workers while they are using ^{99}Tc?
    (c) Medical equipment such as disposable syringes can be sterilised using gamma rays. Gamma rays kill bacteria and other microorganisms. Before being sterilised by the gamma rays the plastic syringes are sealed in aluminium foil packets. Discuss why this is a better method of sterilising the syringes than heating them at high temperatures using steam and then packing them.

13 (a) Radiation is always present in the environment. What is the general name given to this radiation?
    (b) Give *two* causes of this radiation.
    (c) Name the instrument used to measure the radiation level.

The diagram shows a gamma ray unit used in a hospital. A is a container of radioactive material. The unit is made 'safe' by moving the container to position B. Lead absorbs gamma rays.

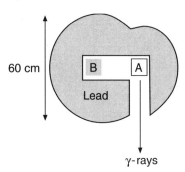

60 cm

B   A

Lead

γ-rays

Isotope	Proton number (atomic number)	Nucleon number (mass number)	Half-life
Cobalt-60	27	60	5.3 years
Caesium-137	55	137	35 years

The radioactive material is either cobalt-60 (^{60}Co) or caesium-137 (^{137}Cs). Cobalt-60 decays after a few years and must be replaced, but a container of caesium-137 usually lasts for the working life of the unit, which is about 20 years. The table shows some information about these isotopes.

In 1987, an old gamma ray unit was broken open by people who did not know how dangerous it could be. Some of them were killed by radiation after they touched caesium-137 from the unit.

14 Name the *two* types of particle in the nucleus of the isotope cobalt-60.
15 What is the proton number of the isotope cobalt-59?
16 What is the number of electrons in a neutral atom of caesium-137?
17 Explain the meanings of *decay* and *half-life*.
18 Why does a container of caesium-137 last longer than a container of cobalt-60?
19 Explain why the gamma ray unit is 'safe' when the container is in position B.
20 Suggest *three* safety precautions which a person should take when removing a container of cobalt-60.
                                                                    (ULEAC)

Chapter 27

The Earth's place in the universe

27.1 Introduction

Astronomy, the study of the heavens, has always fascinated men and women. Early star watchers used their eyes. Later, binoculars and telescopes gave a clearer picture. Nowadays, telescopes that detect invisible radiowaves from outer space are providing us with even more information. Since Ed Aldrin and Neil Armstrong landed on the Moon on 21st July 1969, our horizons have widened still further. Our colonisation of other planets is becoming a possibility.

27.2 What are stars?

Looking up into the sky on a clear night you will see thousands of stars. Stars were formed and continue to be formed by the compression of gas and dust scattered throughout space. Stars emit light as a result of reactions like those in nuclear reactors.

The **Sun** is a star. It is the nearest star to Earth and is at the centre of our **solar system**. The Sun and other stars are light sources. We see the planets, and other bodies in the sky, by light reflected from the Sun and stars.

Clusters of stars group together to form **galaxies** and billions of galaxies make up the whole **universe**. The Sun and the solar system are part of the **Milky Way** galaxy (Fig. 27.1). There are approximately 100 000 million stars in the Milky Way and the Sun is just

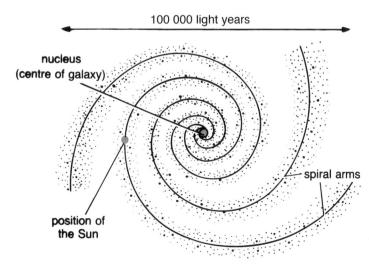

Fig. 27.1 The Milky Way galaxy

one of them. It would take 100 000 light years to cross the Milky Way (i.e. 100 000 years travelling at the speed of light). Light can travel about 10^{16} metres in one year alone. Just imagine how small the Earth really is compared to the size of the universe.

27.3 The Sun

Without the Sun there would be no life on Earth. The Sun provides light and warmth for photosynthesis, enabling plants to grow. Fig. 27.2 shows the structure of the Sun.

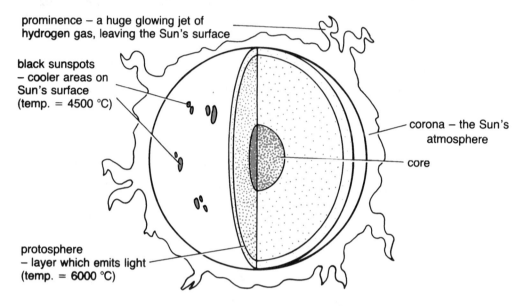

Fig. 27.2 The structure of the Sun

The high temperatures on the Sun are caused by nuclear fusion processes which occur in its core. During these nuclear processes two ordinary hydrogen nuclei fuse to form one heavy hydrogen (deuterium, $^2_1$H) nucleus and a positron. A positron is like a positively charged electron.

$$^1_1\text{H} + {}^1_1\text{H} \rightarrow {}^2_1\text{H} + {}^0_1\text{e} + \text{heat} + \text{light}$$

Two heavy hydrogen ($^2_1$H) nuclei then fuse to form helium ($^4_2$He) nuclei.

$$^2_1\text{H} + {}^2_1\text{H} \rightarrow {}^4_2\text{He} + \text{heat} + \text{light}$$

At the same time, enormous amounts of heat and light are emitted and the temperature in the core of the Sun reaches 15 000 000 °C.

Theories about the universe

Early Greek philosophers watched the Sun, the Moon and other planets carefully. They recorded their movements across the sky. In AD 150, Ptolemy suggested that the Earth was at the centre of the universe and the Sun and stars revolved around it.

A heliocentric theory, in which the Earth and planets revolve around the Sun, was first proposed by Aristarchus in the 3rd century BC. Copernicus provided further solid evidence for this theory in the 15th century. As more and more evidence was obtained, it became clear that:

- the Earth and other planets move around the Sun,
- the Earth rotates on a tilted axis once every 24 hours.

The apparent daily and annual movements of the Sun and other stars are caused by these movements of the Earth.

27.4 Planets and the solar system

Our solar system consists of the Sun and nine planets (Fig. 27.3). Notice that there are four planets (Mercury, Venus, Earth and Mars) relatively close to the Sun, and five planets (Jupiter, Saturn, Uranus, Neptune and Pluto) further away. All of the planets move in elliptical orbits in the same direction around the Sun. With the exception of Pluto, all the planets lie in much the same plane. Pluto's orbit is at an angle to this plane.

The time that a planet takes to orbit the Sun (its orbit time) depends on its distance from the Sun. As the distance from the Sun increases, so also does the orbit time. For example, Mercury takes only 88 days to orbit the Sun, Jupiter takes 12 years, whilst Pluto takes 248 years. The movements of planets in their orbits can be observed against a relatively 'fixed' background of star patterns (constellations). These observations are possible because stars (although they are moving) are very much further from the Earth than the planets.

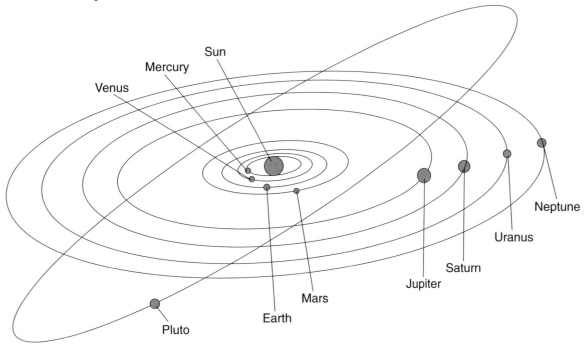

Fig. 27.3 The planets in our solar system

27.5 Gravity and gravitational forces

Experiments have shown that gravitational forces act between all masses. So, there is a gravitational force between you and everything else in the universe. However, **gravitational forces get stronger if the objects involved have larger masses or if they get**

closer. The largest object, close to you, is the Earth. Because of this, the gravitational force between you and the Earth may be 500 N or more. This, of course, is your **weight** (see 20.2). Even if you sit close to one of your friends, the gravitational force between the pair of you will only be about one millionth of a newton.

The Sun contains 99.8% of the mass of our solar system. Because of this, it exerts very strong gravitational forces. These gravitational forces are strong enough to hold the planets in orbit and to determine their movements around the Sun.

27.6 The origin of the solar system

xaminer's tip

Study sections 27.4 to 27.6 carefully. They are key sections in this chapter.

It is difficult to imagine how our solar system came about. Astronomers now agree that our Sun began to evolve from a cloud of dust about 10 000 million years ago. The planets in our solar system had formed, as we know them today, about 4600 million years ago. Fig. 27.4 shows the main stages in the process which lasted millions of years.

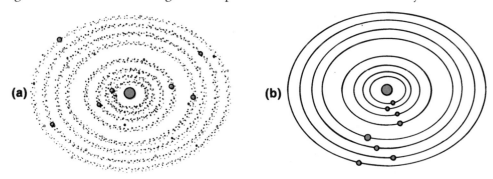

Fig. 27.4 Stages in the formation of our solar system

At first, a cloud of gas and dust rotated around a central heavy core like a flat disc. Dust particles attracted each other by gravity, building up the core and other large spheres within the disc (Fig. 27.4(a)).

Eventually, a small number of dense spheres resulted (Fig. 27.4(b)). The central sphere with the greatest concentration of mass was the Sun and the remainder gave rise to the planets. Gases formed in the atmospheres surrounding these planets.

On planets close to the Sun, where it is hotter, most of the gases have evaporated. This has left small rocky planets (Mercury, Venus, Earth and Mars) with iron cores (Table 27.1).

Further from the Sun, where it is colder, the gases have not evaporated fully leaving crystals of methane, ammonia and ice with the gases helium and hydrogen. Because of this, Jupiter, Saturn, Uranus and Neptune are much larger planets with small rocky cores surrounded by vast quantities of gas (Table 27.1).

Table 27.1 Data concerning the planets in our solar system

Planet	Average distance of planet from the Sun/millions of km	Diameter of planet relative to diameter of the Earth	Average surface temp/°C
Mercury	58	0.4	450
Venus	108	1	500
Earth	150	1	20
Mars	228	0.5	−40
Jupiter	778	11	−150
Saturn	1427	9.4	−160
Uranus	2870	4	−220
Neptune	4497	3.9	−230
Pluto	5900	0.5	−230

Pluto, furthest from the Sun, is thought to be a satellite of Neptune which has escaped and moved into its own orbit. It is very small and rocky.

Notice that the conditions on a planet depend on two key factors:

1. **its nearness to the Sun**, which determines the surface temperature and the evaporation of volatile substances,
2. **its relative size**, which determines the gravitational pull on any atmosphere it might have. In general, the small planets have little or only thin atmospheres due to their small gravitational attraction.

27.7 The Earth and its Moon

The Moon orbits the Earth once a month. It is therefore a satellite or planet of the Earth. Gravitational forces from the Earth hold the Moon in orbit and determine its movement around the Earth. Experiments during the American Apollo missions to the Moon in the 1960s have shown that there are no living organisms on the Moon.

At any moment, half of the Moon is lit up by the Sun, and the other half is in shadow. From the Earth we can see only the illuminated side. That is why we see the Moon in various phases or shapes (Fig. 27.5).

Along the line dividing the illuminated and dark sides of the Moon, the Sun's rays cast long shadows. These shadows highlight details of the lunar landscape such as craters and mountain ranges. The craters were caused by meteors (rocks in space) colliding with the Moon whilst it was still molten.

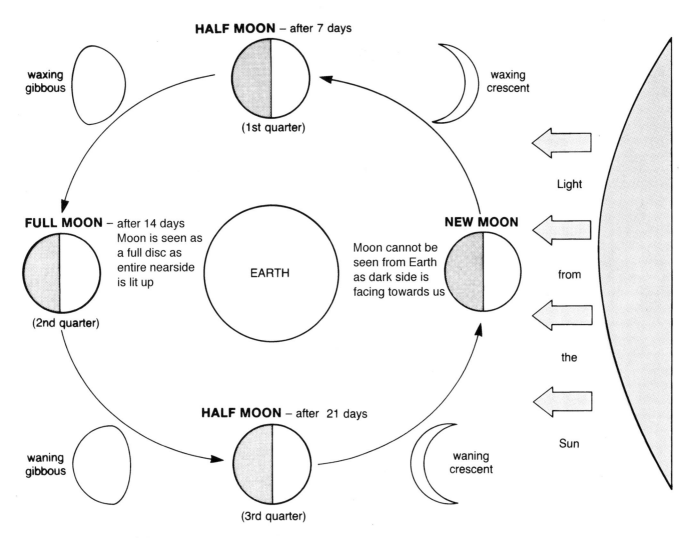

Fig. 27.5 The phases of the Moon

Tides

Tides occur due to the gravitational pull of the Moon on the oceans (and to a lesser extent the pull of the Sun). As the Moon orbits the Earth, its gravitational pull draws the oceans towards it (Fig. 27.6). This causes the sea to rise giving high tides at points A and B and low tides at points X and Y. As the Earth rotates once each day, this means that there are two high tides and two low tides each day at any one place on the Earth.

At certain times, the Sun and Moon are both in line with the Earth (see Fig. 27.5). When this happens, there are extra high tides called **spring tides**. At other times, the Sun and Moon are at right angles to the Earth (see Fig. 27.5). When this happens, their gravitational pulls tend to cancel each other out. This produces lower high tides called **neap tides**.

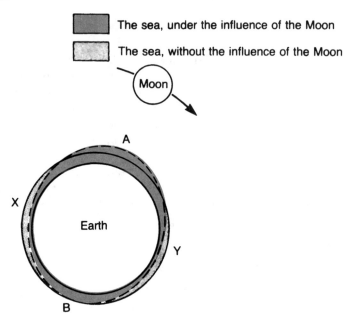

Fig. 27.6 The effect of the Moon on our tides

Comets

The movements of comets are determined largely by gravitational forces from the Sun. Comets travel around the Sun in very long, elliptical orbits and reappear every few years. Their orbits can be plotted and their arrival in our night sky can be predicted by astronomers. They are often spectacular to look at with bright heads and long sparkly tails, thousands of kilometres long (Fig. 27.7).

Fig. 27.7 The appearance of a comet

The comet's nucleus is thought to be rocky material covered with vast amounts of frozen gases. The coma is produced when the comet gets close to the Sun, causing some of the frozen gases to vaporise.

Each comet is named after the person who discovered it. The most famous comet is probably Halley's Comet, named after Edmond Halley in 1720. Halley used the idea of gravity and the movement of planets to predict when his comet would be visible again from the Earth. He was widely acclaimed when the comet reappeared almost exactly on the date he had predicted.

27.8 Our exploration of space

Over the centuries, astronomers have obtained much information about planets and stars by observing them from the Earth. More detailed information is now obtained by launching rockets into space. The launch and the orbit of any spacecraft are governed by the laws of gravity. Fig. 27.8 explains how a rocket can be launched to orbit the Moon.

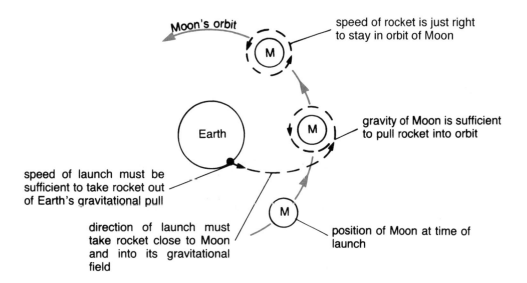

Fig. 27.8 Launching a rocket to orbit the Moon

Notice that the rocket must be launched very precisely so that its speed and direction allow it to be pulled into the Moon's gravitational field so that it circles the Moon.

Rockets have enabled scientists to study 'near space' very successfully. However, astronomers soon realised that artificial satellites would be a more thorough and economical way of studying space. These satellites could be carried into space by rockets and then set in stable orbits around the Earth or other planets. Satellites have already provided detailed photographs of the planets and they are also used to relay television pictures across the world.

More recently space stations have been built and launched. Scientists can live in these for several months, carrying out experiments which could not be done on Earth. The American Space Shuttle has reduced the cost of sending crews to space stations. It flies back to Earth like an aeroplane and can be used again and again.

Scientists in space stations have studied the Sun and stars in detail. They have also used the weightless conditions in space to purify vaccines and to make ultralightweight foamed steels from metals and glass.

Although colonisation of the Moon is possible, there are many problems to overcome.

① There is no air and no water on the Moon.
② The expense of travelling to the Moon would be considerable. Colonists would need to spend significant lengths of time there before returning to Earth.
③ Food supplies could not be carried to the Moon from the Earth. It would be necessary to grow plants and produce food there.

Ideally a lunar station would be self-supporting, recycling air, water and food.

At present, it is unlikely that anyone, other than scientists, could colonise the Moon. But, who knows! One day long holidays to the Moon could become a reality!

27.9 The life cycle of stars

Stars are not permanent. They go through 'birth', 'life' and 'death'. Our Sun is a middle-aged star which is about ten thousand million years old. In another ten thousand million years, it will stop emitting light and die.

A piece of coal is normally black. When it is heated it gradually changes colour to dull red and then bright yellow. In the same way, stars indicate their temperature and age by their brightness and colour. The stages in the life cycle of a star are shown in Fig. 27.9.

27.10 The evolution of the universe

In the 1920s, astronomers realised that our Sun is just a small part of an enormous galaxy of stars which they called the **Milky Way**. They also realised that there are millions of other galaxies in the universe.

The first scientist to look in detail at other galaxies was the American astronomer, Edwin Hubble. When Hubble looked at stars in different galaxies, he discovered two very important facts.

1. Spectra of light from other galaxies are shifted to longer wavelengths (i.e. towards the red end of the spectrum) compared to light from the Sun, Hubble called this the **red shift.**
2. The further a galaxy is from the Earth, the greater is its red shift. This is known as **Hubble's Law.**

Hubble explained his first observation by suggesting that the red shift was caused by the galaxies moving away from our own galaxy. This caused the light from them to appear to have a greater wavelength. But all the galaxies have a red shift, so they are all moving *away* from our galaxy. This means that the whole universe is expanding and that it may have started billions of years ago from one place with a huge explosion. This is usually called the **Big Bang Theory**.

Hubble's second observation also led to interesting conclusions. For galaxies further away, the red shift is greater so they must be moving away faster. Hubble's data showed, in fact, that the speed of a galaxy was proportional to its distance from us (Table 27.2). Thus, objects with an extra large red shift must be very far away indeed. This enabled astronomers to estimate the distances to stars which are millions of light years away. For example, the estimated speed of galaxies in the constellation of Bootes is 40 000 km/s (Table 27.2), so it must be approximately 2400 million light years away.

Table 27.2 Speed of galaxies and distance from Earth

Constellation	Distance of galaxy from Earth /millions of light years	Speed of galaxy /km/s
Ursa Minor	900	15 000
Corona Borealis	1200	20 000
Bootes	?	40 000
Hydra	3600	60 000

Furthermore, by measuring the rate of increase in speed of those galaxies that are furthest away, we can estimate when their speed was zero. Assuming that their speed was zero just before the Big Bang, we can get some idea of the age of the universe. Astronomers now believe that the Big Bang occurred about 15 000 million years ago.

Minutes after this, the universe contained only elementary particles (protons, neutrons and electrons) plus lots of radiation. After millions of years, gravity began to pull matter together into larger particles and lumps. After 1000 million years, galaxies of stars were forming. About 10 000 million years after the Big Bang, our Sun and solar system had

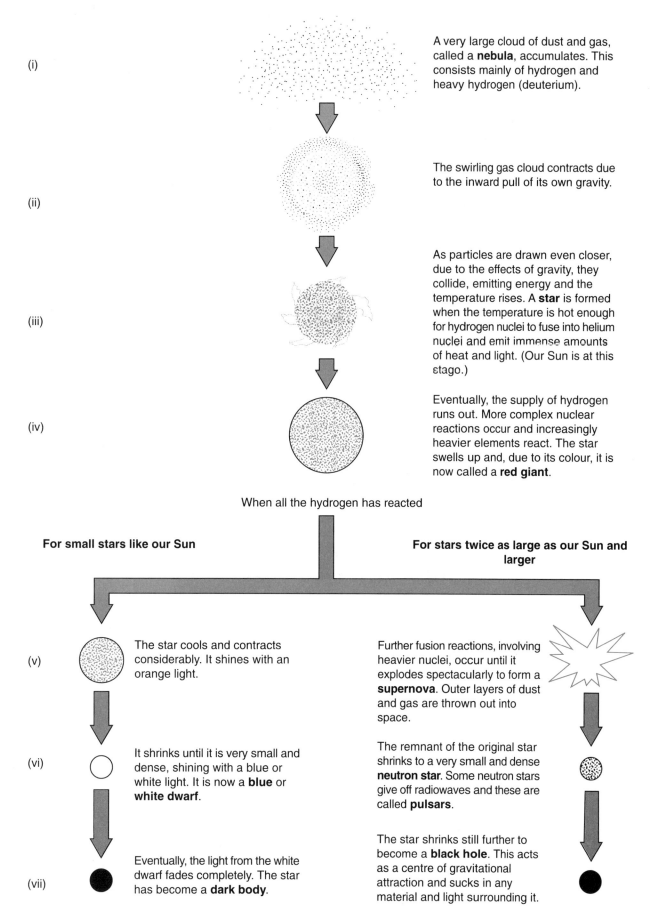

(i) A very large cloud of dust and gas, called a **nebula**, accumulates. This consists mainly of hydrogen and heavy hydrogen (deuterium).

(ii) The swirling gas cloud contracts due to the inward pull of its own gravity.

(iii) As particles are drawn even closer, due to the effects of gravity, they collide, emitting energy and the temperature rises. A **star** is formed when the temperature is hot enough for hydrogen nuclei to fuse into helium nuclei and emit immense amounts of heat and light. (Our Sun is at this stage.)

(iv) Eventually, the supply of hydrogen runs out. More complex nuclear reactions occur and increasingly heavier elements react. The star swells up and, due to its colour, it is now called a **red giant**.

When all the hydrogen has reacted

For small stars like our Sun

For stars twice as large as our Sun and larger

(v) The star cools and contracts considerably. It shines with an orange light.

Further fusion reactions, involving heavier nuclei, occur until it explodes spectacularly to form a **supernova**. Outer layers of dust and gas are thrown out into space.

(vi) It shrinks until it is very small and dense, shining with a blue or white light. It is now a **blue** or **white dwarf**.

The remnant of the original star shrinks to a very small and dense **neutron star**. Some neutron stars give off radiowaves and these are called **pulsars**.

(vii) Eventually, the light from the white dwarf fades completely. The star has become a **dark body**.

The star shrinks still further to become a **black hole**. This acts as a centre of gravitational attraction and sucks in any material and light surrounding it.

Fig. 27.9 The stages in the life cycle of a star

formed from the remains of a supernova. After 14 500 million years, the simplest life forms had evolved on the Earth.

Astronomy can suggest how the universe has evolved, but the ultimate questions still remain. Why was there a Big Bang and where did all the matter and energy in the universe come from?

Summary

1   **Day and night** result from the Earth's rotation on its axis.

2   **Seasons** and the varying lengths of days result from the tilt of the Earth's axis and the Earth's movement around the Sun.

3   **The phases** (shapes) **of the Moon** result from the Moon's movement around the Earth.

4   Our **solar system** consists of the Sun and nine planets. In order from the Sun these planets are Mercury, Venus, Earth, Mars, Jupiter, Saturn, Uranus, Neptune and Pluto.

5   **Gravitational forces** determine the movements of planets, moons, comets and satellites.

6   The Sun is a **star**. Stars are immense volumes of hot reacting gas and dust.

7   Clusters of stars make up **galaxies** and billions of galaxies make up the whole **universe**.

8   The **conditions on a planet** depend on two key factors:
    ● its nearness to the Sun and
    ● its relative size.

9   Tides occur due to the gravitational pull of the Moon (and to a lesser extent the Sun) on the oceans.

10 Stars have a life cycle. They begin as a cloud of dust (**nebula**) which contracts, causing thermonuclear reactions, to form a **star**. Eventually the supply of hydrogen runs out and the star cools and contracts.

Quick test 27

1   Which one of the following is the odd one out? Give one reason for your choice.
    Earth   Jupiter   Mars   Mercury   Neptune
    Pluto   Saturn   Sun   Uranus   Venus

2   Choose from the list below **seven** correct words to complete the sentences which follow.
    day, Earth, hour, Jupiter, planet, Mercury, month, Moon, Pluto, Saturn, satellite, orbit, Sun, year

    The Earth goes around the Sun once each .... The ....
    goes round the .... once each month. The Earth spins on
    its axis once each ....
    Every .... goes around the Sun. .... is nearest the
    Sun, and .... is furthest away from it.   (*SEG*, modified)

3   Rewrite the following list in order of their sizes, from the smallest to the largest.
    galaxy, Moon, planet, solar system, universe

4   Every object attracts every other object with a force.

Earth   Moon

(i)   What type of force is acting between the Earth and the Moon?
(ii) What two factors does this force depend on?
(iii) What evidence is there on Earth to show the force of the Moon?   (SEG)

5   The asteroids can be considered as bits of a planet that fell apart. They orbit between Mars and Jupiter. Use the following data to suggest similar data for these asteroids. Give a brief explanation for your suggestions.

Planet	Relative mass (Earth = 1)	Surface gravity field/N/kg	Distance from Sun/ millions of km	Surface temp./°C
Mercury	0.05	3.6	58.0	350
Venus	0.81	0.87	107.5	460
Earth	1.0	9.8	149.6	20
Mars	0.11	3.7	228	-23
Jupiter	318.0	25.9	778	-120
Saturn	95.0	11.3	1427	-180
Uranus	14.0	10.4	2870	-210
Neptune	17.5	14.0	4497	-220
Pluto	0.003	-	5900	-230

Questions 6 to 13

The table below gives information about our solar system.

Planet	Average distance from Sun/km	Relative mass value	Number of known satellites	Period of rotation	Relative volume	Average surface temp./°C
Mercury	58×10^6	0.056	0	88 days	0.055	350
Venus	108×10^6	0.817	0	225 days	0.876	460
Earth	150×10^6	1.000	1	23 h 56 m	1.000	20
Mars	228×10^6	0.108	2	24 h 37 m	0.151	-23
Jupiter	778×10^6	318.354	12	9 h 50 m	1313.0	-120
Saturn	1427×10^6	95.0	9	10 h 15 m	761.0	-180
Uranus	2870×10^6	14.580	5	10 h 48 m	59.4	-210
Neptune	4497×10^6	17.264	2	15 h 40 m	42.6	-220
Pluto	5900×10^6	0.003	0	?	0.10	-230

6   The solar system is part of a galaxy. What is a galaxy part of?
7   Which planet has the most satellites?
8   Which planet has the longest day?
9   Why has Mercury little or no atmosphere?
10 Suggest two reasons why the average surface temperature on Mercury is so high.
11 Why does the temperature fall rapidly at night on Mercury?
12 There are valleys on Mars. What does this suggest?
13 Why are living things unlikely to exist on Pluto?
14 Explain why it is warm enough to eat your turkey on the beach and sunbathe in Australia on Christmas Day.

Longer exam questions

Before attempting these exam questions, you should read the section headed 'The examination' on pages 18 and 19 at the start of the book. Most of the questions in the 'Quick tests' at the end of each chapter are objective questions requiring short answers. They are also confined to the topics in their chapter. In general, they are similar to the questions used in module tests and to the shorter structured questions in terminal exams. If you are aiming for a CC grading (double award)/grade C (single award) or better in the GCSE, you will need to gain at least 50% of the marks in the relevant questions in the 'Quick tests'. If you are aiming for an AA grading (double award)/grade A (single award), you will need to score at least 80% in the 'Quick tests'.

The questions in this section are longer structured questions. They require extended prose (three or four sentences) for the answers to some parts. Some of the questions test ideas covered in more than one chapter of this book. You should be able to tackle each question successfully when you have covered the chapter with the same number (i.e. question 1 after Chapter 1, question 2 after Chapter 2, etc.).

Almost all of these longer questions are taken from the specimen materials provided by the examining groups for the higher tier. Most of the questions are aimed at grade C and above with about 25% of marks at each of grades A★, A, B and C. To obtain a BB grading (double award)/grade B (single award) you should aim to score at least 50% of the possible marks on the relevant longer questions.

Even if you are not aiming for a high grade, remember that there is an overlap of levels between higher tier papers (grades D to A★) and the foundation tier papers (grades G to C).

Therefore it is important to attempt the longer exam questions in this section, as well as the 'Quick tests', whatever level you are working at.

The marks allocated to different parts of the questions appear in brackets after the question.

Answers to the longer exam questions are given on pages 351–357.

1 (a) In certain parts of Africa special areas of grassland have been set aside as game farms. These game farms contain large numbers of primary consumers, such as nilgai and zebras, which still roam wild. The large secondary consumers are kept out of the game farms. Each year a sizeable number of primary consumers is 'cropped' for food.
   (i) Why are the large secondary consumers kept out of the farm? (1)
   (ii) What advice would you give to the manager of the game farm about the age and sex of the primary consumers to be culled? (2)
   (iii)What might happen to the grassland if the primary consumers were not 'cropped'? (1)
   (b) Some people have suggested that the nilgai could be kept on small farms as a source of meat. The meat tastes like the meat from a deer. Cattle, deer and nilgai all live in herds. The table below compares some features of the nilgai with deer and cattle.

	Nilgai	Deer	Cattle
Average mass of adult (kg)	200–250	250–300	500–700
Fat content of meat (%)	1	2	10–20
Energy content of meat (kJ/g)	4	6	16
Usual number of young born at the same time	2	1	1
Time for young to grow in womb (months)	$7\frac{1}{2}$	8	9

Use the information in the table to answer the following:
(i) Suggest why the energy content of beef from the cattle is much higher than the energy content of nilgai. (2)
(ii) Suggest *one* way in which nilgai would be more economical for farming than deer. (1)
(iii)Suggest *one other* piece of information that would be important to a farmer who was deciding to farm nilgai instead of deer. (1)
(c) One disadvantage of nilgai is that they are often very nervous. If a herd is disturbed they may injure one another with their horns.

Nervousness is inherited. Explain how animal breeders could develop nilgai that are less nervous. (4)

WJEC, NEAB and ULEAC

2 (a) Choose words from the following list to fill the gaps in the sentences below. Each word may be used once or not at all.

cells	chloroplasts	chromosomes	genes
organs	organisms	nucleus	tissues

Each body cell contains a _____(i)_____ which controls the cell's activities and characteristics. This contains pairs of _____(ii)_____ which are made up of a number of small units of inheritance called _____(iii)_____.
Collections of similar cells working together are called _____(iv)_____.
These make up _____(v)_____ which work together as systems allowing _____(vi)_____ to survive. (6)

(b) Cells are surrounded by a cell membrane. Give *two* jobs carried out by a cell membrane. (2)
(c) This part is about photosynthesis in green plants.
(i) Use chemical symbols to write the balanced equation for photosynthesis. (4)
(ii) Give *two* factors other than temperature that would limit the rate of photosynthesis. (2)
(iii)Photosynthesis is a process that involves enzymes. On axes similar to those below, sketch a graph to show how the rate of reaction of photosynthesis is likely to change with temperature. Explain, in writing or by using labels, the shape of your graph. (5)

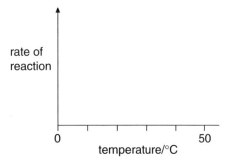

SEG

3 Use the table below to answer the questions which follow.

	Amount per 100 g				
Dairy product	Protein/g	Fat/g	Energy content/kJ	Calcium/mg	Iron/mg
Cow's milk, whole	3.4	3.7	276	120	0.1
Cow's milk, skimmed	3.5	0.2	146	124	0.1
Butter	0.4	85.1	3318	15	0.2
Margarine	0.2	85.3	3326	4	0.3
Cheese	25.4	34.5	1778	810	0.6

(a) (i) Which product gives the greatest amount of energy per 100 g?
(ii) Which class of food is the main source of energy in butter? (2)
(b) Explain why cheese contains more minerals than milk. (1)

(c) (i) Which of the foods in the table would be best for someone with heart disease?
   (ii) Give a reason for your answer. (2)

(d) The fat that we eat is sometimes stored for future use. Write down *two* uses of this stored fat. (2)

(e) Why should babies and young children be given whole milk and not skimmed milk? (1)

(f) Why is calcium an essential mineral in our diet? (1)

WJEC

4 Particles from the carbohydrates in the chips which John eats pass through the walls of his small intestine and enter his bloodstream. This process is called digestion. Describe what happens in this process. A start has been made for you. (8)

As soon as John starts to chew a chip, an enzyme called......

SEG

5 (a) Red blood cells transport the body's oxygen and some of its carbon dioxide. The cells are flattened discs with depressed (concave) surfaces. They contain the large molecules of haemoglobin which are responsible for the transport of oxygen and some of the carbon dioxide.

(i) What sort of molecule is haemoglobin? (1)

(ii) Name the metal that is needed to make a haemoglobin molecule. (1)

(iii) Explain how the shape of red cells helps in the transport of the two gases. (2)

(b) The reactions of haemoglobin with oxygen and carbon dioxide are shown by the equations below.

    oxygen + haemoglobin $\rightleftharpoons$ oxyhaemoglobin
    carbon dioxide + haemoglobin $\rightleftharpoons$ carbaminohaemoglobin

(i) In which part of the body is oxygen added to haemoglobin? (1)

(ii) Explain why it is necessary for the reaction of haemoglobin with both oxygen and carbon dioxide to be *reversible*. (4)

(iii) State *one* way that carbon dioxide can be transported by the blood other than as carbaminohaemoglobin. (1)

(c) Some people suffer from an inherited disorder called sickle-cell anaemia. This means that when the concentration of oxygen is low, the red cells change and become sickle-shaped, as shown below. In this form they carry less oxygen.

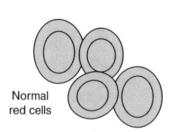
Normal red cells

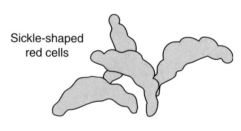
Sickle-shaped red cells

Explain what might happen at high altitudes to a person who suffers from sickle-cell anaemia. (3)

SEG

6 As part of a fitness check a number of tests can be done on volunteers.

(a) Test 1 **Heart rate**

Heart rate is the number of heart beats there are per minute. Fit people usually have:

    low heart rates

    heart rates which quickly return to normal after exercise.

Sally and Jane decide to go for a jog together. They take their heart rates before, and for 3 minutes after jogging. Their results are shown in the table below.

| | Heart rate (beats per minute) | |
	Sally	Jane
Before jogging	70	60
0 seconds afterwards	160	150
30 seconds afterwards	140	120
60 seconds afterwards	120	100
90 seconds afterwards	100	80
120 seconds afterwards	90	70
150 seconds afterwards	85	65
180 seconds afterwards	80	60

(i) The instructor tells Jane that she is fitter than Sally.
　Give *two* reasons for this conclusion. (2)
(ii) Explain why the heart beats more quickly during exercise. (2)
(b) Test 2 **Breathing rate**
Jane has her breathing rate taken while doing certain activities. This chart shows the results.

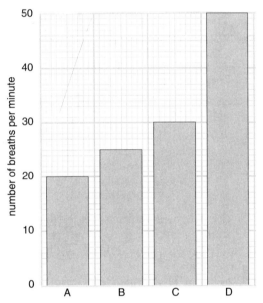

(i) Which section of the bar chart (A, B, C or D) represents:
running; sleeping; walking; sitting? (2)
(ii) This table shows the difference between air breathed in and air breathed out.

Gas	Breathed in	Breathed out
oxygen	21%	16%
carbon dioxide	trace	4%
nitrogen	78%	78%
noble gases	1%	1%
water vapour	trace	1%

Compare the figures in the two columns. List and explain *two* differences and *one* similarity that you can find. (3)
(c) Test 3 **Work rate**
Sally and Jane decide to compare their work rates. They lift as many 10 newton sandbags as they can on to a table in 1 minute. Here are their results.

	Sally	Jane
Weight of sandbag	10 N	10 N
Distance lifted	1 m	1 m
Number of sandbags lifted	30	36
Time of exercise	1 minute	1 minute

In the calculations below remember to show your working and also the unit in each case.

(i) What total weight does Sally lift in 1 minute? (2)

(ii) Jane lifts a total of 360 N. Calculate how much work she does. (3)

(iii)Jane actually used 1440 J of energy when she lifted the bags. With the help of your answer to (ii) work out her efficiency. (3)

NEAB and ULEAC

7 (a) The diagram shows a section through a human eye with rays of light from a nearby object.

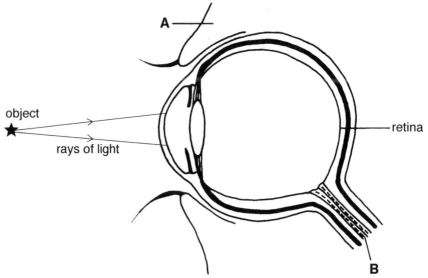

(i) On the diagram, draw arrows to label (1) the iris, (2) the cornea. (2)

(ii) What are the functions of the parts labelled A and B. (2)

(iii)On the diagram, extend the rays of light to show how they would be focused on the retina. (4)

(iv)Describe the change in the shape of the lens when the eye focuses on distant objects. (1)

(b) The diagram shows an experiment using oat seedlings placed in a box with a hole cut in one side.

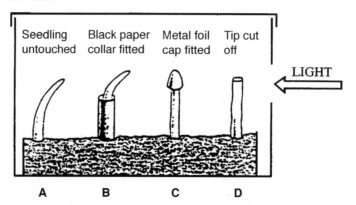

(i) Name the growth movement of plants in response to light. (1)

(ii) Which seedlings, in the diagram, show this response? (1)

(iii)Explain how these results show that it is the tip of an oat seedling which responds to light. (3)

NICCEA

8   A strawberry grower found some small strawberries with a particularly nice flavour growing on a strawberry plant.
   (a) How could the grower develop plants with strawberries which were larger but had the same flavour? Carefully describe each step. (4)
   (b) Once the grower had developed his new plants, he could use runners to produce more plants which had the new, large and tasty strawberries.
       (i) What type of reproduction is this called? (1)
       (ii) Suggest *three* reasons why he uses this type of reproduction to produce more new plants. (3)

NEAB

9   In mice, the allele for black fur is dominant over the allele for brown fur. The allele for black fur can be represented by 'B' whilst 'b' represents the allele for brown fur.
   (a) (i) What is the genotype of a brown mouse? (1)
       (ii) What are the possible genotypes of a black mouse? (2)
   (b) A pure breeding (homozygous) black female mouse mated with a pure breeding brown male.
       (i) What is the genotype of all the offspring? (1)
       (ii) What is the phenotype of all the offspring? (1)
   (c) A male mouse and a female mouse, both with the genotype Bb, mate. The female produces a litter of twelve. Use a genetic diagram to show the genotypes of the offspring and to predict the numbers of brown and black offspring. (4)

SEG

10 The following table shows the concentration of 'greenhouse gases' in 1850 and 1985 and their estimated concentration in 2050.

| 'Greenhouse gas' | Concentration in parts per million in each year | | |
	1850	1985	2050
carbon dioxide	275	345	400–600
methane	0.7	1.7	2.1–4.0
nitrous oxide	0.29	0.30	0.35–0.45
CFC 11	0	0.22	0.7–3.0

   (a) Give *one* reason why the concentration of carbon dioxide has increased since 1850. (1)
   (b) Which gas is estimated to have the greatest percentage increase between 1985 and 2050? (Work this out approximately, you do not need to do an accurate calculation.) (1)
   (c) Suggest why there was no CFC 11 in 1850. (1)
   (d) One source of methane is the burying of garbage (household rubbish) in huge landfill sites. Suggest *two* ways in which garbage disposal could help conserve scarce resources. (2)
   (e) The projections to the year 2050 were made in 1988. Which projection do you think may now be much too high? Give a reason for your answer. (2)
   (f) 'Deforestation and farming have endangered water resources'. What is the truth of this statement? (8)

ULEAC

11 (a) The diagram below shows a simplified part of the rock cycle.

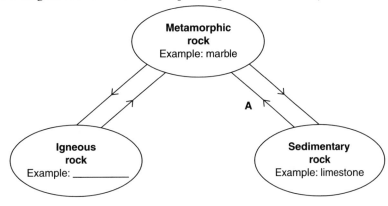

(i) Name an example of an igneous rock. (1)

(ii) What conditions would be necessary for the process 'A' to take place? (1)

(iii) In which type of rock are fossils found? (1)

(iv) Which of the following is a metamorphic rock?
    clay, sandstone, shale, slate. (1)

(v) What process causes the water in the cracks of rocks to make the rocks splinter into smaller pieces? (1)

(b) A specimen of an igneous rock was examined to look at the crystal sizes. A separate specimen of the same igneous rock, from a region several hundred miles away, was also examined.
The crystal sizes in the two specimens were very different. Give *two* reasons for the differences in crystal size. (2)

(c) What happens when plates in the Earth's crust continuously move apart on the ocean bed? (2)

(d) Millions of years ago, the composition of the air was very different from its composition at the present time. Millions of years ago, it is thought that the atmosphere then contained large amounts of ammonia, carbon dioxide, methane and water vapour.

(i) Why has the amount of water vapour decreased considerably since that time? (1)

(ii) Name *two* processes which have resulted in a marked decrease in the amount of carbon dioxide in the air. (2)

(iii) Explain how the removal of ammonia from the early atmosphere is likely to have taken place. (2)

12 (a) Rock salt contains insoluble solids and the soluble salt, sodium chloride. The following processes are needed to separate sodium chloride from rock salt.
    addition of water, crystallisation, evaporation, filtration, stirring.
Put each of these five processes in the correct order, explaining the purpose of each process. (7)

SEG

(b) Golf club shafts need to be strong and reasonably stiff. They are made from wood, metal or composite materials such as carbon fibre-reinforced plastic.

(i) What do you understand by the term 'composite material'? (2)

Some properties of selected materials are given below.

Material	Density g/cm³	Relative strength	Relative stiffness
wood	0.6	1	20
steel	7.8	10	105
aluminium	2.7	2	35
glass fibre-reinforced plastic	1.9	15	10
carbon fibre-reinforced plastic	1.6	18	100
nylon	1.1	0.8	1.5

(ii) Which material from the list above would be the *least* suitable for the shafts of golf clubs? Give a reason for your choice. (2)

(iii) Cricket, hockey and hurling still use bats or sticks made from wood. Suggest *two* reasons why wood is still used. (2)

NICCEA

13 The chemical equation below describes what happens during a chemical reaction. (The equation is *not* balanced.)
$$Mg(s) + HCl(aq) \rightarrow MgCl_2(aq) + H_2(g)$$

(a) Describe in words, and as fully as you can, what happens during this reaction. (10)

(b) What does the formula $MgCl_2$ tell you about this substance? (3)

(c) Balance the chemical equation for this reaction:
$$Mg(s) + HCl(aq) \rightarrow MgCl_2(aq) + H_2(g)$$ (1)

(d) When calcium carbonate is heated, calcium oxide and carbon dioxide are produced:

$$CaCO_3(s) \rightarrow CaO(s) + CO_2(g)$$

Work out how much calcium carbonate is needed to produce 1.4 g of calcium oxide. (Ca = 40, C = 12, O = 16) (6)

NEAB

14 (a) The main ore of iron is haematite which is mainly iron(III) oxide. The ore is mixed with coke and limestone and added to a blast furnace to make iron.

(i) What is meant by the term 'ore'? (1)

(ii) Name the *four* raw materials added to a blast furnace to produce iron. (2)

(b) The *two* reactions taking place which produce iron are:

iron(III) oxide + carbon → iron + carbon dioxide

iron(III) oxide + carbon monoxide → iron + carbon dioxide

(i) What type of reaction is the conversion of iron(III) oxide to iron? (1)

(ii) Explain the reason for your choice of reaction type in (b)(i). (1)

(iii) Why is limestone added to the mixture in the blast furnace? (1)

(iv) Name the main impurity present in the iron produced in a blast furnace. (1)

(c) The rusting of six identical nails was investigated by treating each nail as shown in the table below. All six nails were left exposed to the air for a few months.

Treatment given	Cost of treatment	Mass of nail + coating before exposure to air/g	Mass of nail + coating after exposure to air/g
A waxed	cheap	5.0	5.3
B oiled	cheap	5.0	5.2
C painted	cheap	5.0	5.4
D galvanised	expensive	5.0	5.1
E dipped in salt	cheap	5.0	6.7
F untreated	nil	4.9	6.1

(i) Which treatment gives the best protection? (1)

(ii) Which treatment would be the most practicable to use to protect iron railings from rusting? (1)

(iii) Explain your choice of treatment in (c)(ii). (1)

(iv) Which treatment is worse than no treatment at all? (1)

(v) Give the name of the other substance which, with oxygen, causes iron to rust. (1)

(vi) Give the name of the process that takes place when a metal reacts with oxygen to form an oxide. (1)

15 Aluminium is the most abundant metal in the Earth's crust. Bauxite, the main ore of aluminium, is an impure form of aluminium oxide. To make aluminium, purified aluminium oxide (Al_2O_3) is dissolved in molten cryolite (Na_3AlF_6) at 900 °C and then electrolysed.

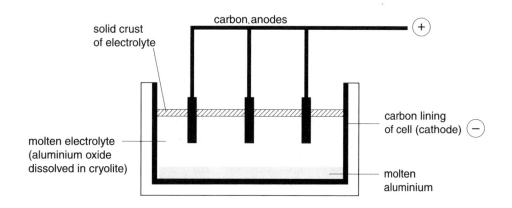

(a) (i) Explain why the cryolite and aluminium oxide must be kept molten for electrolysis. (2)

(ii) Write an electron-transfer equation to show the formation of aluminium at the negative electrode. (2)

(iii) During a 24 hour period a current of 30 000 A was passed through the cell. What mass of aluminium was produced?
(One coulomb of charge flows when a current of one amp flows for one second. The charge due to one mole of electrons is 96 000 C. The relative atomic mass of aluminium is 27.) (4)

(iv) Explain why the carbon anodes need to be replaced at regular intervals. (3)

(b) State *one* reason other than cost why

(i) aluminium is preferred to steel for the manufacture of soft drink cans;

(ii) steel is preferred to aluminium for the manufacture of car bodies. (2)

SEG

16 Indigestion is caused by having too much hydrochloric acid in the stomach. Indigestion tablets called **antacids** are taken to treat this.

(a) Darren wanted to find out why some antacids worked better than others. He carried out the following experiment. He timed how long it would take for one tablet of each brand to disappear in 250 cm³ of dilute hydrochloric acid. The table shows his results.

Brand of antacid tablets	Time taken for one tablet to disappear/s
Calmers	90
Fizzers	163
Tummies	90
Crispin's	145
Scouts	154

(i) Darren repeated the experiment again but diluted the acid each time with the same amount of water. Suggest what happened to the time it took for the tablets to disappear. (1)

(ii) Mark criticised Darren's experiment. He said that the tablets contained different mixtures of chemicals. The size and shape of tablets were also different. Explain how the following factors could affect Darren's experiment. Different chemicals; different sizes; different shapes. (3)

Mark did his own experiment to find the volume of hydrochloric acid needed to completely react with each tablet. The table shows his results.

Brand of antacid tablet	Volume of hydrochloric acid needed to completely react with one tablet/cm³
Calmers	52
Fizzers	68
Tummies	100
Crispin's	68
Scouts	100

Mark said that Calmers were the least effective brand of tablet for curing indigestion.

(b) Explain how the information in both tables supports this idea. (2)

(c) Mark found that the tablets in Scouts and Tummies both contained 0.5 g of calcium carbonate. When calcium carbonate ($CaCO_3$) reacts with hydrochloric acid it produces calcium chloride ($CaCl_2$), carbon dioxide and water.

(i) Write a balanced chemical equation for this reaction. (2)

(ii) How many moles of calcium carbonate are contained in each tablet? (2)
(Ca = 40, C = 12, O = 16)

(iii) Use your answers and the information given to work out the concentration of the hydrochloric acid used by Mark in his experiment. (3)

MEG

17 (a) The table below shows the amount of hydrogen formed in the reaction of magnesium with excess dilute hydrochloric acid at 20 °C.

Time in seconds	0	20	40	60	80	100	120	140	160
Volume of hydrogen in cm³	0	7	21	36	51	66	70	72	72

    (i) Plot a graph of the results showing the volume of hydrogen on the vertical axis and time along the horizontal axis. (5)

    (ii) Write a word equation for the reaction. (1)

    (iii) Write a balanced chemical equation for the reaction. (2)

    (iv) Explain *one* possible reason why the rate is slower near the end of the reaction. (2)

    (v) Suppose you have been told that copper powder will act as a catalyst in the reaction between magnesium and hydrochloric acid. How could you show whether or not this suggestion is true? (4)

    (vi) Other than by using a catalyst, give *two* ways by which the rate of reaction could be increased. (2)

  (b) In the Haber Process, ammonia is manufactured from nitrogen and hydrogen using the reaction

$$N_2(g) + 3H_2(g) \rightleftharpoons 2NH_3(g)$$

The reaction is <u>reversible</u> and the formation of ammonia is <u>exothermic</u>

    (i) What is meant by a reversible reaction? (1)

    (ii) What is meant by an exothermic reaction? (1)

    (iii) In this process, what *two* conditions are normally changed to increase the *rate* of reaction between nitrogen and hydrogen? (2)

    (iv) How should the manufacturing conditions be set to keep the *yield* of ammonia as high as possible? (2)

  (c) Ammonia can be used to manufacture ammonium salts which are used as nitrogenous fertilisers. When fertilisers are used on farmland, some are dissolved in the ground water and eventually drain into rivers causing <u>eutrophication</u>. Explain what is meant by eutrophication and why it is a problem. (4)

18 (a) 'Perspex' is a trade name for a polymer called poly(methyl methacrylate). A laminated windscreen of a car can consist of a sandwich of 'Perspex' between two layers of glass.
Suggest an advantage of a laminated windscreen over a windscreen made of glass and over a windscreen made of 'Perspex'. (2)

  (b) Chloroethene is a monomer used to produce poly(chloroethene). This polymer is also called poly(vinyl chloride) or pvc. Chloroethene can be produced by the reaction of ethyne and hydrogen chloride.

$$H-C \equiv C-H \ + \ HCl \ \rightarrow$$

H   Cl

C = C

H   H

        ethyne   hydrogen chloride   chloroethene

    (i) Suggest a reason why a factory producing pvc should not be built in a residential area. (1)

    (ii) Calculate the mass of chloroethene which can be produced from 26 tonnes of ethyne. (3)
(C = 12, H = 1, Cl = 35.5)

    (iii) A chloroethene molecule can react with a further molecule of hydrogen chloride. Draw the structural formula of the product and explain why it would be unsuitable for use as a monomer for polymer production. (3)

  (c) Combustion of poly(chloroethene) can produce hydrogen chloride gas. Hydrogen chloride gas is also produced when hydrogen and chlorine gas are reacted together. A mixture of hydrogen and chlorine explodes in sunlight at room temperature.

$$H_2(g) + Cl_2(g) \rightarrow 2HCl(g)$$

The reaction is very exothermic.

(i) For each of experiments 1 to 4, state whether the reaction between hydrogen and chlorine will be faster, slower or the same as the original experiment, and give a reason for your answer. (4)

Expt. number	Pressure of gas mixture	Light conditions	Temperature	Other conditions
original	1 atm	sunlight	room	–
1	2 atm	sunlight	room	–
2	1 atm	in the dark	room	–
3	1 atm	sunlight	room	–
4	1 atm	sunlight	room	hydrogen and chlorine mixed with argon gas in a larger reaction vessel

(ii) Explain, in terms of making and breaking bonds, the changes which take place when hydrogen chloride is formed from hydrogen and chlorine. From the energy of the reaction, what can you conclude about the energy taken in or given out when these bonds are made or broken? (4)

MEG

19 (a) The diagram below shows the electronic structure of a particular element. In a similar way, show the electronic structure of another element from the same group in the periodic table and name the element you select. (You may look at the periodic table on page 213 to answer any part of this question.) (4)

(b) The element lithium gives a moderate reaction with cold water, releasing hydrogen and forming a solution of lithium hydroxide.
  (i) Describe how sodium is similar to, and how it is different from, lithium in its chemical reaction with cold water. (2)
  (ii) Explain any similarity or difference in terms of their atomic structure. (3)
(c) Chlorine will combine with the non-metal element carbon to form the molecular compound below.

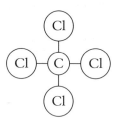

  (i) What type are the bonds in this molecule? (1)
  (ii) Explain how these bonds are formed. (You should draw a diagram as part of your answer.) (4)

NEAB

20 (a) An athlete runs 100 metres in 12.5 seconds. What is his average speed? (3)
(b) One of the nuts on a car wheel is very tight. The diagram below shows how this nut can be slackened.

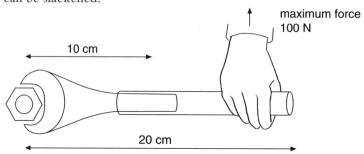

Explain, as fully as you can, why the spanner now works more effectively. (6)

(c) The diagram below shows a toy boat floating on water. The boat weighs 4 N.

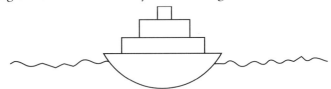

Redraw the diagram and show the size and direction of the forces acting on the boat. (4)

(d) The graph below shows the speed of a car in the first few seconds after it pulls away from some traffic lights.

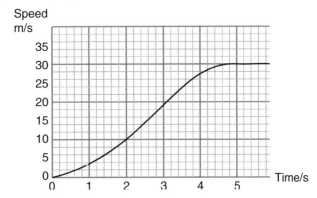

(i) Work out the acceleration of the car during the first 5 seconds. (4)

(ii) The mass of the car is 800 kg. What driving force do the car's wheels exert? (3)

(iii) Between 1 second and 5 seconds after starting off the car travels 50 m. Work out the power developed by the car's engine. (5)

NEAB

21 (a) In order to generate electricity, we must start with a source of energy. Four possible sources are coal, gas, oil and wind. The following bar chart shows estimates of how long some of these are expected to last.

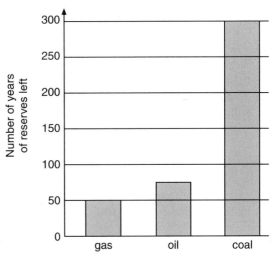

(i) How long is oil expected to last? (1)

(ii) Suggest *one* reason why coal will last longer than gas. (1)

(iii) Why is it not possible to show information for wind energy on the bar chart? (1)

(iv) A lot of effort has been put into developing the generation of electricity from wind energy. One reason why so much effort has been put into the use of wind energy is that we will eventually run out of coal, gas and oil. Explain *one* other reason. (2)

(b) Most of the energy available to us originated in the Sun. Explain how some of the Sun's energy has become the energy which is now stored in coal. You should name the process and the type of energy involved at each stage. (6)

(c) In the United Kingdom, about 20% of the electricity is generated in nuclear power stations.

(i) From which part of an atom does nuclear energy come? (1)

(ii) The following are all parts of a nuclear power station.

boiler   generator   reactor   turbine

Put them in the correct order to show how they are used to produce electricity. (2)

(iii) What useful energy transfer takes place in a generator?

_____ energy → _____ energy. (1)

(d) Harry is an elderly person who needs to keep warm. To do this Harry wears clothing and uses bedding which traps air.

(i) By what process is heat transferred by air which is free to move? (1)

(ii) Explain how the process in (d)(i) occurs. (2)

(iii) By which process is heat transferred through Harry's clothing and bedding? (1)

(iv) Why is the trapped air important? (1)

SEG

22 The diagram represents water waves approaching a coast. The parallel lines represent the wave crests and the arrow shows the direction of travel. At high tide the beach is just submerged and the waves are refracted as they enter the shallow water over the beach.

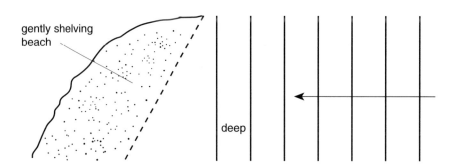

(a) (i) Complete the diagram by drawing in the wave crests over the beach. (2)

(ii) What causes the change which takes place when the waves go over the beach? (1)

(b) The energy from sea waves can be used for the generation of electricity.

Suggest *two* advantages of generating electricity using wave energy instead of using fossil fuels. (2)

(c) The diagram shows the pattern on an oscilloscope when a bar on the xylophone is hit.

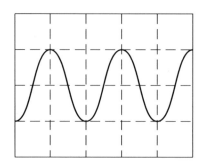

(i) Draw a grid the same size as the one above and show the pattern that is seen if the same bar is made to produce a louder note. (2)

(ii) Draw another grid the same size as the one above and show the pattern that is seen if a shorter bar is struck. (1)

23 (a) Mr. Westwood bought some green filter sunglasses.
   (i) Figure 1 shows the window area of a house. How will the colours shown appear to Mr. Westwood when he wears his new sunglasses? (3)

Figure 1

   (ii) Would the green sunglasses be suitable for Mr. Westwood when driving his car? Explain your answer. (2)
(b) Figure 2 shows part of the electromagnetic spectrum.

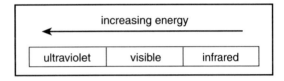

Figure 2

Tungsten is used for the filaments in light bulbs. When the filament gets hot, (1000 °C) it becomes red at first and then orange (1500 °C).
   (i) Explain why the black filament changes colour as its temperature rises. (2)
   (ii) Suggest what colour the filament might be at 2000 °C and explain your answer. (2)
(c) (i) Complete Figure 3 below to show the path of each light ray through the glass block and out the other side. (3)
   (ii) What term is given to this behaviour of light waves in glass? (1)

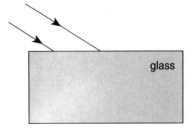

Figure 3

24 Washrooms often have hot-air hand driers which work in the same way as hair driers. Here is the label on one type of drier.

SWIZZDRY

**THE CLEAN HYGIENIC WAY
TO DRY YOUR HANDS**

**Voltage   240 Volts
Current   10 Amps**

DRIER OPERATES FOR 50 SECONDS

(a) Calculate the power of the hand drier. Include the unit of power. (4)

(b) How much electrical energy (joules) is used by the drier from when the person switches the drier on until it switches itself off? (3)

(c) Explain as fully as possible, using the kinetic model, why hot, moving air will dry your hands more quickly than if you held them in cool, still air. (5)

(d) A drier does not seem to be working properly. The electrical engineer sent out to fix it wants to check that the drier is working at the correct voltage and current, and that it is on for the correct time.

Explain, in as much detail as you can, how the engineer should make the measurements he needs. You should explain what instruments he needs to use and where in the circuit he should use them. You may draw on the circuit diagram if it will help you. (6)

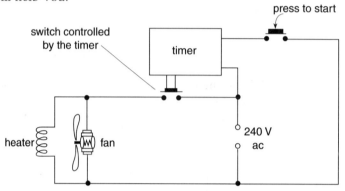

NEAB and ULEAC

25 (a) A transformer has 1000 turns on the primary coil and 30 000 turns on the secondary coil.

If the input voltage is 10 volts, what will be the output voltage? (Include in your answer the equation you are going to use. Show clearly how you get to your final answer and give the unit.) (3)

(b) Electricity is transmitted through the National Grid at a very high voltage and at a relatively low current. This is because it is cheaper than transmitting it at a lower voltage and higher current.

(i) Explain why it is cheaper. (2)

(ii) Apart from the risk of electric shocks and the cost and appearance of the transformers, cables and pylons, explain *one* other disadvantage of transmitting the electricity at very high voltages through cables supported by steel pylons. (2)

(c) The relay circuit shown is used to switch on a car starter motor.

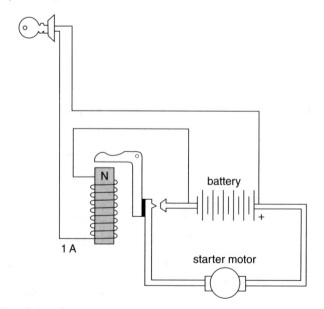

(i) Explain how this relay works when the key is turned. (3)

(ii) Name *one* other device that uses an electromagnet. (1)

(d) Explain what is meant by electromagnetic induction and state the factors that affect electromagnetic induction when moving a magnet into a coil.　　(6)

SEG

26　Americium-241 is a radioactive isotope. Its atomic number is 95.
　　(a) Work out the number of protons, neutrons and electrons in an atom of americium-241. State where these particles are found in the atom.　　(3)
　　(b) Other americium atoms have a mass number of 243. How do these atoms differ from atoms of americium-241?　　(1)
　　(c) What instrument could be used to measure the radiation produced by americium-241?　　(1)
　　(d) There are three different types of radiation which can be emitted by radioactive isotopes. The diagram below shows the penetrating properties of each type.

radiation	sheet of mica	few sheets of paper	aluminium 4 mm thick	lead 4 cm thick
alpha				
beta				
gamma				

Using a radioactive source and a detector, design a method to check that aluminium drinks cans have been filled to the correct level. Draw a diagram to illustrate your answer.　　(5)

SEG and ULEAC

27　Astronomers can take many measurements about the stars from their observatories on Earth.
　　(a) Suggest and explain why all the world's large astronomical telescopes are located as far away as possible from large cities and often on the tops of large mountains. (2)
　　(b) The Sun emits light with a wavelength of 5×10^{-7} m.
　　　 The speed of light is 3×10^8 m/s.
　　　 (i) What is the frequency of the light from the Sun?　　(2)
　　　 (ii) How long does it take for the Sun to emit one complete wave of light? (2)
　　(c) The diagram below represents a single wave of light emitted from the Sun.

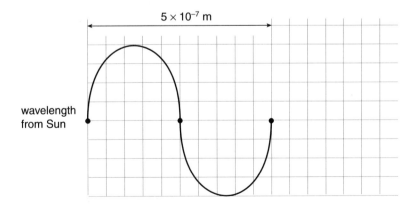

If a star is moving away from the Earth, as below, the light wave is 'stretched' so that its wavelength is longer. It still takes the same time for the star to emit the wave.

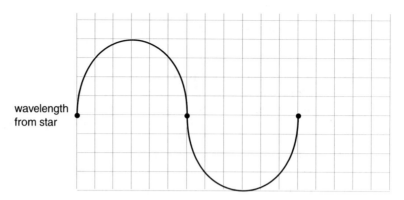

Both diagrams of the light waves are drawn to scale.

(i) What is the wavelength of light from the star which is moving away from the Earth? (1)

(ii) How far has the star moved while emitting this complete wave of light? (1)

(iii) Use your answers to (b)(i) and (c)(ii) to work out how fast the star is moving away from the Earth. (2)

(iv) Explain what would happen to the wavelength of light emitted from a star as its speed away from the Earth increases? (1)

(d) One theory about the Solar System suggests that the movements of the Moon produce a small drag on the Earth's rotation as it spins on its axis.

(i) What effect will this 'drag' have on the length of a day on Earth? Give a reason for your answer. (2)

(ii) In what way would this 'drag' affect the length of a year on Earth? Give a reason for your answer. (2)

MEG

Further invaluable question practice can be found in Letts *GCSE Questions and Answers Science.*

Answers to longer questions

1 (a) (i) they would disturb/eat the primary consumers **(1)**
        (ii) crop old/injured animals/young males **(1)**; maintain correct male/female balance **(1)**
        (iii) overgrazing – grassland depleted **(1)**
    (b) (i) more fat **(1)** fats yield more energy per g **(1)**
        (ii) produce two young each time **(1)**
        (iii) one sensible suggestion, e.g. time to grow to maturity **(1)**
    (c) select **(1)** least nervous animals **(1)**, breed **(1)**, reselect **(1)**

2 (a) (i) nucleus **(1)**, (ii) chromosomes **(1)**, (iii) genes **(1)**, (iv) tissues **(1)**, (v) organs **(1)**, (vi) organisms **(1)**
    (b) holds cells together/maintains shape **(1)**, protects cells **(1)**, allows movements of substances in/out of cell **(1)** (any 2)

Examiner's tip

The equation in 2(c)(i) provides a very helpful summary for photosynthesis. Make sure you know this equation and how it summarises photosynthesis.

    (c) (i) $6CO_2 + 6H_2O \xrightarrow[chlorophyll]{light} C_6H_{12}O_6 + 6O_2$

        formulas of reactants **(1)**, formulas of products **(1)**, number of moles of reactants **(1)**, number of moles of products **(1)**
        (ii) availability/concentration of CO_2 **(1)**, availability/supply of water **(1)**, light intensity/colour/wavelength **(1)** (any 2)
        (iii) Graph – exponential rise **(1)**, clear optimum and decrease **(1)**
        Explanation – enzymes denatured/breakdown **(1)** at high temperatures so there is an optimum at about 40 °C **(1)**; at higher temperatures, the rate decreases due to loss of enzyme activity **(1)**

3 (a) (i) margarine **(1)**
        (ii) fat **(1)**
    (b) 100 g of cheese is made from several 100 g of milk **(1)**
    (c) (i) skimmed cow's milk **(1)**
        (ii) it has a very low fat content **(1)**
    (d) provides energy **(1)**, provides insulation **(1)**, protects vital organs **(1)** (any 2)
    (e) they need large quantities of energy for growth **(1)**
    (f) it is required for strong bones/teeth **(1)**

Examiner's tip

The captions to Fig. 4.3 provide the details to answer this question.

4 As soon as John starts to chew a chip, an enzyme called amylase **(1)** catalyses **(1)** the breakdown of starch to maltose **(1)**. Chewing increases the surface area for reaction **(1)**, muscles in the gullet push food down to the stomach **(1)**, the pancreas produces enzymes **(1)**, which also hydrolyse **(1)** starch to maltose. The ileum produces enzymes **(1)**, which break down maltose to glucose **(1)**. Overall, large starch molecules are broken down to small glucose molecules **(1)**. These small molecules pass through the walls of the small intestine **(1)** and into the blood. Mention of solubility of glucose **(1)** and large surface area due to villi **(1)** (any 8)

5 (a) (i) protein (with haem group) **(1)**
        (ii) iron **(1)**
        (iii) flattened (biconcave) shape gives large surface area **(1)**, this allows more rapid absorption/bonding **(1)** of O_2/CO_2 with constituent haemoglobin **(1)** (any 2)
    (b) (i) lungs/alveoli **(1)**
        (ii) Oxygen must join up with haemoglobin in the lungs **(1)** and then be given up to cells in different tissues **(1)**. Carbon dioxide must be taken up by haemoglobin in tissues **(1)** and then released into lungs **(1)**
        (iii) as dissolved CO_2/carbonic acid/carbonate/hydrogencarbonate **(1)**

(c) At high altitude oxygen concentration is low **(1)**. This causes red cells to become sickle-shaped **(1)** and cells cannot carry as much oxygen **(1)**. Respiration rate falls **(1)** and the person has much less energy **(1)** (any 3)

6 (a) (i) Jane has a lower heart rate **(1)**, Jane's heart rate does not go as high during exercise **(1)**, Jane's heart rate returns to normal more quickly **(1)** (any 2)
   (ii) more energy is required **(1)**, so more nutrients and oxygen are required **(1)**
   (b) (i) D, A, C, B **(2)**
   (ii) Differences: oxygen used in body during respiration **(1)**, carbon dioxide produced during respiration **(1)**, water vapour produced during respiration **(1)** (any 2)
   Similarity: either nitrogen or noble gases play no part in body processes/ metabolism **(1)**
   (c) (i) 300 **(1)** N **(1)**
   (ii) work = force × distance **(1)**, 360 **(1)** J **(1)**
   (iii) efficiency = $\dfrac{\text{energy output}}{\text{energy input}}$ × 100 **(1)**, $\dfrac{360}{1440}$ × 100 **(1)**, 25% **(1)**

7 (a) (i)

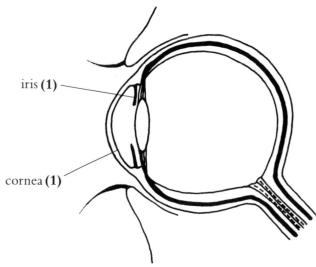

iris **(1)**

cornea **(1)**

   (ii) A – protects the eye **(1)**
       B – carries impulses/messages to the brain **(1)**
   (iii) rays bending at cornea **(1)**, rays bending at lens **(1)**, focused on retina **(1)**, at same horizontal height as object **(1)**
   (iv) lens becomes thinner **(1)**
   (b) (i) phototropism **(1)**
   (ii) A and B **(1)**
   (iii) when a black collar is fitted, the tip still responds to light **(1)**, when a metal cap covers the tip, no response to light **(1)**, when the tip is cut off, no response to light **(1)**

8 (a) select plants with large fruits **(1)**, cross with plants with small tasty fruit **(1)**, grow from their seeds **(1)**, select the best plants (large and tasty fruit) **(1)**, repeat the process **(1)** (any 4)
   (b) (i) asexual/vegetative/cloning **(1)**
   (ii) identical copies (genetic stock, clones) **(1)**, identical qualities **(1)**, large number produced **(1)**, quicker **(1)**, cheaper (more economical) **(1)** (any 3)

9 (a) (i) bb **(1)**
   (ii) BB **(1)** and Bb **(1)**
   (b) (i) Bb **(1)**
   (ii) black **(1)**

Examiner's tip

In answer to 9(c), the genetic diagram can be drawn as

	Male	Female
Phenotype	Black	Black
Genotype	Bb	Bb
Gametes	B b	B b

Possible offspring: BB Bb Bb bb

Phenotype: Black Black Black Brown

(c) gametes correct, i.e. B, b, B, b **(1)**
offspring correct, i.e. BB, Bb, Bb, bb **(1)**
genetic diagram clear and accurate **(1)**
ratio of black : brown = 3:1 **(1)**
so, 9 black and 3 brown offspring **(1)** (any 4)

10 (a) burning fossil fuels/deforestation has reduced uptake of CO_2 **(1)**
(b) CFC 11 **(1)**
(c) In 1850, CFCs were not being manufactured for use in aerosols, refrigerants, foams **(1)**
(d) recycle glass/metals/paper **(1)**, collect methane as alternative to fossil fuels **(1)**, form compost from organic waste **(1)**, incinerate waste and use for heating **(1)** (any 2)
(e) CFCs **(1)** – use to be controlled/alternatives developed **(1)**
(f) Deforestation: reduced uptake of water from soil **(1)**; reduced loss of water from transpiration **(1)**; reduction in humidity/cloud formation **(1)**; reduction in rainfall **(1)**; increased likelihood of soil erosion **(1)**; dust bowl effect/desertification **(1)**.
Farming: overuse of fertilisers **(1)**; use of pesticides **(1)**; run off in rain water contaminates ground, water, reservoirs, rivers **(1)**; water becomes toxic **(1)**; intensive animal husbandry **(1)** reduces vegetation **(1)** and hence transpiration; leakage of animal waste into rivers/water supplies **(1)**; irrigation diverts water supplies **(1)** (any 8)

11 (a) (i) granite, quartz or basalt **(1)**
(ii) heat and/or pressure **(1)**
(iii) sedimentary **(1)**
(iv) slate **(1)**
(v) freezing **(1)**
(b) rate of cooling **(1)**, depth below the Earth's surface **(1)**, temperature as the rock solidified **(1)**, impurities **(1)** (any 2)
(c) hot magma pours out of crust **(1)**, as a volcano **(1)**; this solidifies causing ocean ridges **(1)** (any 2)

Examiner's tip

Questions related to the three rock types, their differences and how the rocks were formed are very poplular.

(d) (i) water vapour has condensed to form rivers, lakes, seas or water vapour has been removed by plant photosynthesis **(1)**
(ii) some CO_2 has dissolved in the water of lakes, seas, etc. **(1)**, some CO_2 has been removed by photosynthesis **(1)**
(iii) some NH_3 has dissolved in the water of lakes, seas, etc. **(1)**, some NH_3 has been converted to amino acids/proteins **(1)**, some NH_3 has reacted with acidic substances **(1)** (any 2)

12 (a) 1st – addition of water – to dissolve salt/sodium chloride **(1)**
2nd – stirring – to ensure/speed up dissolving/formation of solution **(1)**
3rd – filtration – to remove insoluble solids **(1)**
4th – evaporation – to remove water/form a saturated (concentrated) solution **(1)**
5th – crystallisation – allow crystals (solid) salt/sodium chloride to form **(1)**
correct order **(2)** (allow **(1)** for one process out of order)
(b) (i) *Either* a material (which combines the properties) of more than one material **(1)**, to produce a more useful material **(1)**
Or a material composed of a matrix **(1)** with a filter/fibres/strands/rods **(1)**
(ii) nylon **(1)**, too weak/not stiff enough **(1)**
(iii) cost **(1)**, tradition **(1)**, relatively light **(1)**, strong enough **(1)**, stiff enough **(1)** (any 2)

13 (a) magnesium **(1)** a solid **(1)** made of atoms **(1)** and hydrogen chloride/hydrochloric acid **(1)** in aqueous solution/dissolved in water **(1)** react/are the reactants **(1)**. They produce/the products are **(1)** magnesium chloride **(1)** in aqueous solution/dissolved in water **(1)** and hydrogen **(1)** a gas made of molecules **(1)** (any 10)
(b) contains magnesium and chlorine **(1)** atoms/ions **(1)** in the ratio 1:2 **(1)**
(c) 2HCl(aq) **(1)**

(d) 1 RFM (mole) of $CaCO_3$ → 1 RFM (mole) of CaO **(2)**
∴ 100 g $CaCO_3$ **(1)** → 56 g CaO **(1)**
56 g CaO from 100 g $CaCO_3$
⇒ 1 g CaO from $\dfrac{100}{56}$ g $CaCO_3$
1.4 g CaO from $\dfrac{100}{56} \times 1.4$ g **(1)** = 2.5 g **(1)** $CaCO_3$

14 (a) (i) the rocks (minerals) from which metals are extracted **(1)**
(ii) iron ore, limestone, coke, air **(2)** for all 4 (**(1)** for 3)
(b) (i) reduction **(1)**
(ii) iron(III) oxide → iron is the loss of oxygen **(1)**
(iii) to remove impurities (sand) in the iron ore **(1)**
(iv) carbon **(1)**
(c) (i) galvanising **(1)**
(ii) painting **(1)**
(iii) gives protection and is fairly permanent and cheap **(1)**
(iv) dipping in salt **(1)**
(v) water **(1)**
(vi) oxidation **(1)**

15 (a) (i) ions must be able to move to the electrodes **(1)** for electrolysis (electron transfer) to occur **(1)**
(ii) $Al^{3+} + 3e^- \rightarrow Al$ **(2)**
(iii) $2O^{2-} \rightarrow O_2 + 4e^- (O^{2-})$ **(1)**

two O^{2-} ions **(1)**

release of four e^- **(1)**

(iv) oxygen is produced at the anode **(1)**, which reacts with the carbon **(1)** forming CO_2 which is lost to the air **(1)**
(b) (i) aluminium does not rust **(1)**
(ii) steel is stronger **(1)**

16 (a) (i) it would take longer for the tablets to disappear **(1)**
(ii) different chemicals will react at different rates with the acid **(1)**; different sizes will contain different masses (moles) of chemicals **(1)** which will react for different lengths of time; different shapes will have different surface areas **(1)** and therefore react at different rates
(b) each tablet reacts with the least volume of acid **(1)**
each tablet reacts at the (equal) fastest rate **(1)**
(c) (i) $CaCO_3 + 2HCl \rightarrow CaCl_2 + CO_2 + H_2O$ **(2)**
(ii) 1 mole (RFM) of calcium carbonate = 40 + 12 + (3 × 16) = 100 g **(1)**
∴ no. of moles in one tablet = $\dfrac{0.5}{100}$ = 0.005 **(1)**
(iii) 1 mole $CaCO_3$ reacts with 2 moles HCl **(1)**
∴ 0.005 moles $CaCO_3$ (in one tablet) reacts with 0.01 moles HCl
∴ 100 cm³ of HCl contains 0.01 moles **(1)**
So, concentration of HCl is 0.01 moles per 100 cm³
or 0.1 moles per 1000 cm³/litre/dm³ **(1)**

17 (a) (i) labels on axes **(1)**, units shown **(1)**, scales on axes **(1)**, points plotted correctly **(1)**, smooth continuous line drawn **(1)**
(ii) magnesium + hydrochloric acid → magnesium chloride + hydrogen **(1)**
(iii) $Mg + 2HCl \rightarrow MgCl_2 + H_2$
formulas correct **(1)**, balancing correct **(1)**
(iv) most of the Mg had reacted **(1)**, less surface area **(1)** *or* acid had reacted/less acid **(1)**, ∴ acid less concentrated **(1)**

(v) idea of noting rate **(1)** with and then without copper **(1)**, all other things being exactly the same **(1)**; idea of checking that copper is not used up **(1)**

(vi) heat/increase the temperature **(1)**, use more concentrated acid **(1)**, use powdered Mg **(1)** (any 2)

(b) (i) the reaction can go in both directions **(1)**

(ii) the reaction gives out heat **(1)**

(iii) increase in pressure **(1)**, increase in temperature **(1)**

(iv) high pressure **(1)**, only moderate temperature **(1)**, remove ammonia quickly **(1)** (any 2)

(c) algae/water plants grow rapidly **(1)**, this uses up oxygen in the water **(1)**, the algae/plants die **(1)** and are fed on by consumers/decay **(1)**; the river begins to stink/smell **(1)** (any 4)

18 (a) A laminated windscreen is harder than Perspex on its own and will not scratch because glass is harder than Perspex **(1)**
A laminated windscreen will bend and crack but will not shatter like glass does as Perspex does not shatter **(1)**

(b) (i) hydrogen chloride is a very acidic gas **(1)**

(ii) 1 RFM (mole) ethyne gives 1 RFM (mole) chloroethene **(1)**
⇒ 26 g ethyne gives 62.5 g chloroethyne **(1)**
mass produced = 62.5 tonnes **(1)**

(iii)

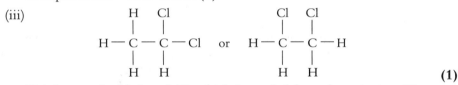

(1)

This has no double bond **(1)** which is needed for polymerisation **(1)**

(c) (i) Expt 1 – faster – pressure (concentration) of gases is greater **(1)**
Expt 2 – slower – sunlight provides energy for the reaction and expt 2 is in the dark **(1)**
Expt 3 – same – conditions are the same as the original expt **(1)**
Expt 4 – slower – pressures (concentrations) of H_2 and Cl_2 are lower due to presence of argon **(1)**

(ii) H—H bonds break, Cl—Cl bonds break **(1)**
H—Cl bonds form **(1)**
bond breaking requires energy, bond making gives out energy **(1)**
∴ the energy given out when the H—Cl bonds are made is greater than the energy taken in when the H—H and Cl—Cl bonds are broken **(1)**

19 (a) magnesium 2,8,2 or calcium 2,8,8,2
element named **(1)**, inner shell 2 electrons **(1)**, outer shell 2 electrons **(1)**, intermediate shell(s) correct **(1)**

(b) (i) similar – hydrogen and alkali/hydroxide produced **(1)**
difference – rate of reaction faster for sodium **(1)**

(ii) chemical reaction of metals involves a loss of an electron **(1)**; similarity is due to same number of electrons in outer shell **(1)**; difference is due to outer electron more easily lost from sodium atom **(1)**

(c) (i) covalent **(1)**

(ii)

shared electrons **(1)**, one shared pair between each Cl and the C atom **(1)**, four shared pairs around the C atom **(1)** and one shared pair plus six electrons of its own for each Cl **(1)**

20 (a) speed = $\dfrac{\text{distance}}{\text{time}}$ **(1)** = $\dfrac{100}{12.5}$ = 8 **(1)** metres per second or m/s **(1)**

(b) makes it easier to apply a force **(1)**, reduces (muscular) strain **(1)**, bigger distance **(1)** between applied force and pivot **(1)**, produces a bigger turning force (torque) **(1)**, which is twice (double) the size **(1)**

(c) upthrust of 4 N **(1)** acts upwards along central line of boat **(1)**; weight of 4 N **(1)** acts downwards along central line of boat **(1)**

(d) (i) acceleration = $\dfrac{\text{change in speed}}{\text{time}}$ **(1)** = $\dfrac{30}{5}$ **(1)** = 6 **(1)** m/s² **(1)**

(ii) force   = mass × acceleration **(1)**
          = 800 × 6 **(1)** = 4800 N **(1)**

(iii) power   = $\dfrac{\text{work done}}{\text{time taken}}$ **(1)**

work done = force × distance   **(1)**
            = 4800 N × 50 m   **(1)**
            = 240 000 J   **(1)**

∴ power   = $\dfrac{240\,000\text{ J}}{4\text{ s}}$ = 60 000 J/s or W **(1)**

21 (a) (i) 75 years (allow 70–80 years) **(1)**

(ii) more of it/being used at a lower rate **(1)**

(iii) it is renewable/will not run out **(1)**

(iv) *either* fossil fuels will become expensive **(1)**, will be more valuable as raw materials (for the chemical industry) **(1)** *or* no pollution **(1)** (with some explanation or amplification) **(1)**

(b) nuclear energy in Sun **(1)**, fusion (of hydrogen to helium) **(1)**, heat/light from the Sun (to Earth) **(1)**, by radiation **(1)**, used by green plants **(1)**, for photosynthesis **(1)**, chemical energy in plants **(1)**, (dead) plants converted over millions of years **(1)**, by heat **(1)**, by pressure **(1)**, to chemical energy in coal **(1)** (any 6)

(c) (i) nucleus **(1)**

(ii) reactor → boiler → turbine → generator **(2)**
(one out of place – **(1)**)

(iii) kinetic (movement) → electrical **(1)**

(d) (i) convection **(1)**

(ii) heat causes expansion **(1)**, density is less **(1)**, warmed air rises **(1)**, cold air falls **(1)** (any 2)

(iii) conduction **(1)**

(iv) it is a (very) poor conductor/good insulator **(1)**

Examiner's tip

Notice in 22(a)(i) that the wavelength gets shorter in shallow water. As a result, the wave is refracted (bent) at the boundary between deep and shallow water.

22 (a) (i)

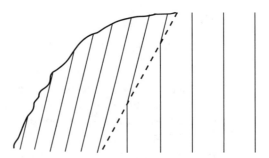

waves getting gradually closer together as water gets shallower **(1)**, waves parallel over beach **(1)** but at an angle to incoming wave as refraction has occurred **(1)** (any 2)

(ii) the wavelength is shorter in shallower water **(1)**

(b) cheap **(1)**, non-polluting **(1)**, renewable **(1)** (any 2)

(c) (i) greater amplitude **(1)** with same frequency – 2.5 waves on screen **(1)**

(ii) higher frequency (more waves on screen) **(1)**

23 (a) (i) curtains will look black **(1)**, flowers black **(1)**, leaves green **(1)**

(ii) no, the only colour which the sunglasses transmit is green **(1)**; green and white articles will look green, all other colours will look black **(1)**

(b) (i) as its temperature rises, it emits light (radiation) with increasing energy **(1)**, i.e. red at 1000 °C, orange at 1500 °C **(1)**

(ii) yellow at 2000 °C **(1)**, radiation emitted will have greater energy than at 1500 °C **(1)**

(c) (i) refracted towards normal in glass **(1)**, refracted away from normal emerging in air **(1)**, incident and emergent rays parallel **(1)**

(ii) refraction **(1)**

24 (a) power = current × voltage **(1)** = 10 × 240 **(1)** = 2400 **(1)** W **(1)**

(b) energy used = power × time **(1)** = 2400 × 50 **(1)** = 120 000 **(1)** J

(c) hot air transfers more energy to water on your hands **(1)** than cold air **(1)**, this energy provides energy for water molecules **(1)** which move around faster and evaporate **(1)**; moving air increases evaporation rate **(1)** by sweeping away water already evaporated **(1)** (any 5)

(d) voltmeter used to measure voltage **(1)** *across* input **(1)**; ammeter **(1)** used to measure current to heater and fan **(1)**, i.e. in the circuit before or after the parallel heater/fan portion **(1)**, stopwatch **(1)** used to time operation time

25 (a) $\frac{V_s}{V_p} = \frac{N_s}{N_p}$ **(1)**, $\frac{V_s}{10} = \frac{30\ 000}{1000}$ **(1)**, output voltage = 300 volts or 300 V **(1)**

(b) (i) current produces heat in wires **(1)**, low current causes less heat/power/energy loss **(1)**, thinner wire/small pylons can be used **(1)** (any 2)

(ii) difficult to insulate very high voltages **(1)**, needs ceramic insulation between cable and pylon **(1)**; if not well insulated, current will 'leak' to earth/will be conducted through metal (steel) pylon **(1)** (any 2)

(c) (i) when key is turned, circuit including coil is complete **(1)**, electromagnet is energised **(1)**, this attracts the angled bar **(1)**, and completes the starter motor circuit **(1)** (any 3)

(ii) electric bell, etc. **(1)**

(d) Electromagnetic induction occurs when a coil of wire **(1)** is moved in a magnetic field **(1)** and an induced current (or voltage) **(1)** is produced in the wire. Factors which affect electromagnetic induction all relate to the rate at which the coil/wire crosses magnetic lines of force **(1)**. The induced current is larger when: the wire/coil is moved faster **(1)**, a stronger magnet is used **(1)**, more turns of wire are used **(1)** (any 6)

26 (a) 95 protons in nucleus **(1)**, 146 neutrons in nucleus **(1)**, 95 electrons in orbit (shells) around nucleus **(1)**

(b) they have 148 neutrons **(1)**

(c) Geiger–Müller tube **(1)**

(d) gamma source **(1)** to penetrate right through can **(1)**, detector on opposite side of can to source **(1)**, drink will interfere with beam of gamma rays **(1)**, move source and detector simultaneously up (or down) can to detect level of liquid in can **(1)**, lead shield as protection **(1)** (any 5)

27 (a) high location gives good panorama for viewing sky **(1)**, location away from cities avoids smoke and exhaust gases from industry, vehicles, etc. **(1)**

(b) (i) speed = wavelength × frequency **(1)**
$3 \times 10^8 = 5 \times 10^{-7} \times f \Rightarrow$ frequency $= 6 \times 10^{14}$ Hz **(1)**

(ii) 6×10^{14} waves per second **(1)**

∴ 1 wave takes $\frac{1}{6 \times 10^{14}}$ s $= 1.7 \times 10^{-15}$ s **(1)**

Examiner's tip

Q27(c) and its answer should help you to understand how the wavelength of light from a distant galaxy increases and therefore shifts towards the red end of the spectrum.

(c) (i) 6×10^{-7} m **(1)**

(ii) 1×10^{-7} m **(1)**

(iii) star moves 1×10^{-7} m in $\frac{1}{6 \times 10^{14}}$ s **(1)**

∴ speed away from Earth $= \frac{1 \times 10^{-7}}{1/(6 \times 10^{14})} = 6 \times 10^7$ m/s **(1)**

(iv) the wavelength would increase **(1)**

(d) (i) the length of day increases **(1)**, because the Earth's spin is slower **(1)**

(ii) the length of year is unaffected **(1)**, because the length of year is *not* affected by the rotation of the Earth on its axis **(1)**

Answers to quick tests

Quick test 1

1 *auratus*
2 *Carassius*
3 fish
4 animals with backbones
5 animals
6 A and D
7 C and E
8 D
9 E
10 A
11 response to stimuli
12 movement
13 requirement for energy
14 E
15 C
16 B
17 food web
18 foxes
19 grasses and shrubs
20 grasses and shrubs
21 sunlight
22 There would be more grass for sheep.
   Foxes would be more likely to take sheep.
23 sunlight
24 It is the first organism in the food chain
   or it produces energy (foods) for other organisms
   in the food chain.
25 (a) 100 kJ   (b) 10 kJ   (c) 1 kJ
26 any two of:
   heat during respiration
   to maintain chemical processes in organisms
   in faeces
   in urine
27 Energy is lost at each stage of the food chain.
   Vegetable food is the first link in the chain,
   therefore less energy has been lost.

Quick test 2

1 C
2 A
3 D
4 B
5 C
6 B
7 A
8 C
9 D
10 C
11 E
12 C
13 D
14 B
15 B
16 B and D
17 Increased CO_2 concentration increases the
   rate of photosynthesis
18 Water the plants more, increase the light
   intensity, raise the temperature
19 glucose and oxygen
20 light energy to chemical energy

Quick test 3

1 protein
2 added sugar, added salt
3 fibre
4 salt
5 fibre and added sugar
6 25 g
7 water
8 water
9 roast beef
10 cheese
11 roast beef
12 carrots
13 170 kJ
14 6000 kJ
15 it increases
16 it decreases

Quick test 4

1 D
2 D
3 B
4 mouth and duodenum
5 stomach and duodenum
6 duodenum
7 ileum
8 it helps break down proteins
9 mouth and stomach
10 iodine
11 dark blue/black
12 concentration of amylase, concentration of
   starch, length of experiment
13 maltose
14 acidity
15 6.9
16 3 minutes
17 20–21 minutes
18 Every sweet can produce dental attack for 20–
   21 minutes. Not eating sweets between meals
   keeps the period of attack to a minimum.
19 bacteria
20 more than 7 (alkaline)
21 to neutralise acidity in the mouth
22 fluoride

Quick test 5

1 D
2 B
3 A
4 red blood cells
5 white blood cells
6 plasma
7 Japan
8 N. Ireland
9 Finland, England and Wales
10 C
11 Paula
12 Paula has a lower heart rate. Paula's heart rate returns to normal more quickly.
13 any four of: exercise, stress, disease, smoking, anger and excitement
14 a blood clot forming in a coronary blood vessel
15 lack of iron in the diet
16 any two of: arteries carry blood away from the heart, veins carry blood to the heart; arteries have thicker walls than veins; arteries are not as close to the surface of the body as veins; blood is at a greater pressure in arteries than in veins.
17 blood group test
18

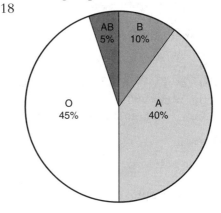

Quick test 6

1 35 000 cm³
2 25 000 cm³
3 ⅕
4 ⅕ × 25 000 = 5000 cm³
5 oxygen
6 carbon dioxide
7 cellular respiration ('respiration' would be accepted)
8 barley (malt)
9 ethanol (alcohol) and carbon dioxide
10 fermentation will take place more quickly
11 boiling kills the yeast
12 two
13 six
14 to make sure no water came from the incoming air
15 to give a larger surface area to absorb water
16 to prevent water coming directly from the soil in the plant pot
17 to prevent photosynthesis which would use up water
18 mass of tube B before and after the experiment
19 put another calcium chloride tube in the system (before the pump) and check its weight before and after the experiment

Quick test 7

1 B
2 C
3 D
4 F
5 B
6 E
7 A
8 F
9 eye
10 ear
11 tongue (strictly speaking tongue and nose)
12 nose
13 F
14 E
15 D
16 B
17 F D E A C B
18 the growing tip
19 test 3
20 to provide a control (comparison)
21 any three of:
    the starting size of cutting,
    the number of leaves on cutting,
    the type of soil used,
    the amount of soil used,
    the watering of the soil,
    the plant pots used (same size and shape),
    the position of the pots during the experiment (same temperature, lighting, etc., throughout the experiment)

Quick test 8

1 B
2 E
3 D
4 A
5 15 years
6 10 years
7 12 years
8 18 years
9 C
10 D
11 B
12 two of:
    maintains similar plants,
    maintains healthy plants,
    reproduction is more rapid

Quick test 9

1 D
2 A
3 A
4 C
5 D
6 B
7 female (mother)
8 only X
9 X or Y
10 The predator thinks that fly is a bee because of similar characteristics,
   learns that bee stings,
   so avoids bee and fly
11 change in a gene
12 Mutation in ancestor produced characteristics of bee. Both bee and fly continued to reproduce.
13 Bacteria become immune to antibiotics.
14 grey
15 Grey male has genotype **GG**, so all babies must have one dominant **G** gene.
16 Some grey babies will have the genotype **Gg**. If two **Gg** parents mate:

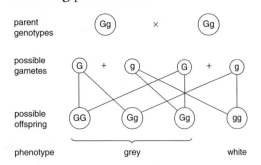

So, two **Gg** parents can mate to produce **gg** babies which will be white.
17 Mate two white rabbits: they will both have the genotype **gg** and all their babies will have the genotype **gg** and be white.
18 Very large ears are needed
   ● for cooling in hot desert;
   ● to hear prey at night.
19 Population B lives in open grassland, therefore they need larger ears
   ● to hear predators in poor light of early morning or late evening;
   ● to hear predators in open grassland areas.
20 thick coat

Quick test 10

1 A
2 C
3 C
4 B
5 D
6 D
7 B
8 C
9 A
10 E
11 Mass rises steadily from Jan. to Aug.
   Mass falls sharply to zero in Aug.
12 Increased temperature and sunlight causes wheat to grow from Jan. to Aug.
   Mass falls sharply when wheat is harvested in Aug.
13 any two of:
   migration, breeding, increasing food supply.
14 Wheat is food for mice, therefore population of mice fluctuates with wheat (food) supply.
15 any factor (other than food supply) that could give rise to fluctuations in the numbers of field mice, e.g. migration, death, litters, being prey to carnivorous birds.
16 30 tonnes in each 100 tonnes of scrap
17 Only ⅓ of what could be recycled, actually is recycled
18 to conserve our resources of aluminium

Quick test 11

1 Helios
2 Any three of the following points:
   ● It has a supply of oxygen.
   ● It has a supply of carbon dioxide so that plants can photosynthesise.
   ● It has a supply of water.
   ● It has a temperature range which suits life as we know it.
3 Carmel
4 Its surface is covered with water and swampland. Some of this water will evaporate but the low temperatures on Solos will cause this to condense.
5 Helios
6 It has the highest recorded surface temperature.
7 Carmel
8 There is no atmosphere for sound to travel through.
9 It contains carbon dioxide and water which plants need to photosynthesise and grow.
10 C
11 A
12 B
13 D
14 C
15 B
16 E
17 K
18 L
19 M
20 J

Quick test 12

1 D
2 2
3 C
4 B and D

5 B
6 C
7 A
8 E
9 D
10 C
11 E
12 A
13 D
14 B
15 C
16 A
17 E
18 A, B and D
19 B and D
20 food and oxygen
21 carbon dioxide and water

Quick test 13

1 B
2 A
3 D
4 C
5 B
6 80 litres
7 1 atmosphere
8 E
9 C
10 B
11 D
12 A
13 5
14 7
15 $C + O_2 \rightarrow CO_2$
16 $CH_4 + 2O_2 \rightarrow CO_2 + 2H_2O$
17 $CuO + H_2SO_4 \rightarrow CuSO_4 + H_2O$
18 $N_2 + 3H_2 \rightarrow 2NH_3$

Quick test 14

1 A
2 D
3 B
4 E
5 C
6 burns vigorously,
  barium + oxygen → barium oxide
7 reacts steadily, bubbles of gas form
  barium + water → barium oxide + hydrogen
8 violent reaction, gas produced
  barium + hydrochloric acid → barium chloride + hydrogen
9 Rb, Sr, V, Cu
10 hot water tanks/pipes/radiators/saucepans
11 they react violently with water
12 they react with oxygen and/or water
13 (a) not at all

(b) a little
(c) a little
(d) a lot
14 two of: oiling, painting, plastic coating, tin plating, chromium plating, galvanising
15 one of: haematite, magnetite, siderite
16 coke, limestone, air
17 carbon monoxide
18 dissolve them in water; melt them
19 it can be used to obtain the metal
20 coke will not reduce all ores to the metal
21 silver/gold/platinum
22 the metal is very unreactive

Quick test 15

1 R
2 to adjust the current/set an exact current
3 silver
4 C
5 Silver ions in the solution are attracted to the metal spoon which is the negative cathode. Silver is then deposited.
6 A
7 carbon
8 (a) covalent
  (b) ionic
9 ionic bonds are very strong so the melting point of salt is very high
10 ions
11 by electrolysis of molten aluminium oxide
12 *Cathode* (–) $Al^{3+} + 3e^- \rightarrow Al$
13 C
14 D
15 A
16 E
17 B
18 C

Quick test 16

1 C
2 D
3 B
4 A
5 B
6 D
7 E
8 C
9 (a) 1 m² polythene sheet
  (b) clean beaker
  (c) test tube
  (d) teat pipette
10 So as not to affect the acidity (pH) of the rain water collected
11 (a) carbon dioxide
  (b) pH rises
12 H^+

13 (a)

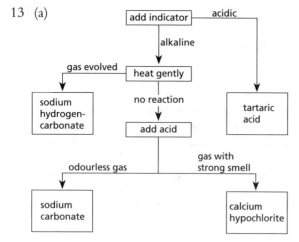

(b) (i) 44
  (ii) 106

(c) $106 \text{ g Na}_2\text{CO}_3 \rightarrow 44 \text{ g CO}_2$

$\therefore 1 \text{ g Na}_2\text{CO}_3 \rightarrow \dfrac{44}{106} \text{ g CO}_2$

$\therefore 212 \text{ g Na}_2\text{CO}_3 \rightarrow \dfrac{44}{106} \times 212 \text{ g CO}_2$

$= 88 \text{ g CO}_2$

Quick test 17

1 B
2 E
3 D
4 A
5 A and E
6 C
7 B and D
8 They cannot convert nitrogen gas to nitrogen compounds which they need to grow and metabolise.
9 Nitrogen compounds are produced by lightning, by decay of dead animals and plants, or by nitrogen-fixing bacteria on leguminous plants.
10 If crops are harvested and not left to decay on the land, the other natural sources of nitrogen cannot replenish the nitrogen compounds in the soil.
11 Hydrogen from steam and natural gas. Nitrogen from the air.
12 to increase the reaction rate
13 ammonia + nitric acid → ammonium nitrate
14 35% (see calculation, Table 17.2)
15 The percentage of ammonia increases
  ● as the pressure increases;
  ● as the temperature decreases.
16 low temperature; high pressure
17 N nitrogen; P phosphorus; K potassium
18 They convert nitrogen in the air into nitrogen compounds for plants.
19 Some of the nitrates are
  ● washed out of the soil;
  ● decomposed by bacteria to nitrogen;
  ● used by bacteria in the soil. (any two)

20 In deep soil, in waterlogged soil, in hard, compacted soil, etc. (any two suggestions which prevent air getting into the soil)

Quick test 18

1 methane
2 It produces no SO_2, which is poisonous and causes acid rain.
  It produces no CO, which is poisonous.
  It produces no ash. (any two)
3 tides, waves
4 'sea' power is well worth using because it
  ● does not cause smoke/ash pollution.
  ● has no radiation hazards.
  ● is renewable, unlike nuclear power and coal.
  ● is cheap; nuclear materials and coal are expensive. As nuclear and coal fuel costs increase, they will become more costly to run. (any three)
5 (a) fractional distillation
  (b) *higher* boiling points
    smaller molecules
6 (a) cracking
  (b) high temperatures
    or high temperatures and a catalyst
7 (a)

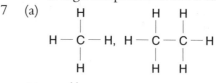

  (b)

8 The series of compounds have similar properties. There is a gradual change in property from one member in the series to the next.
9 Mass of water = 200 g = 0.2 kg
  Temperature rise = 57 − 21 = 36°C
  4200 J heats 1 kg by 1°C
  so 4200 × 0.2 × 36 heats 0.2 kg by 36°C
  i.e. 30 240 J was given out when the butane burnt
10 Mass of butane burnt = 0.6 g
  0.6 g butane gives 30 240 J
  $\therefore 1 \text{ g butane gives } \dfrac{30\,240}{0.6} \text{ J}$
  $\therefore 1 \text{ kg butane gives } \dfrac{30\,240}{0.6} \times 1000 \text{ J}$
  = 50 400 000 J = 50 400 kJ
11 1 kg butane produces approximately 50 000 kJ
  So, 2 kg butane produces 100 000 kJ
  Cost of 2 kg butane = £1.00
12 carbon dioxide and water
13 Ensure no heat from burning butane is lost to the air. Calculate heat from burning butane given to metal can. Ensure butane burns completely. (any two)

Quick test 19

1 D
2 E
3 C
4 B
5 A
6 C
7 D
8 14
9 7
10 8
11 3
12 (a) they increase
    (b) they get darker
    (c) they become slower
13 one atom of hydrogen combines with one atom of the halogen
14 m.p. between 204 and 244°C; colour black; HAt; very very slow (m.p. is best predicted by drawing a graph of m.p. against RAM)
15 (a) 127
    (b) 131
    (c) $\dfrac{127 + 127 + 127 + 127 + 131}{5} = 127.8$

    or $(\dfrac{80}{100} \times 127) + (\dfrac{20}{100} \times 131) = 127.8$

Quick test 20

1 newton
2 metre
3 kilogram
4 metres per second per second (m/s²)
5 newtons per square metre (or pascal)
6 4 km/h
7 3 km/h NE
8 10 km
9 15 km
10 $\dfrac{25}{¾} = 33\,⅓$ km/h
11 J
12 B, F, K
13 H
14 D, L
15 200 m
16 15 s
17 at the end of the race
18 $\dfrac{200 \text{ m}}{25 \text{ s}} = 8$ m/s
19 the runner
20 90 kg
21 135 N
22 10 m/s² (acceleration due to gravity)
23 100 m/s
24 50 m/s
25 500 m
26 B
27 D
28 C

Quick test 21

1 $\dfrac{1000}{10} = 100$ J/s (i.e. 100 W)
2 $\dfrac{600}{10} = 60$ J/s or 60 W
3 40 J
4 X kinetic energy; Y electrical energy (electricity)
5 30
6 The energy is lost as heat to the surroundings from burning the fuel and as friction between parts of the machines.
7 It wastes a smaller fraction (%) of the energy put into it.
8 80 N × 20 m = 1600 J
9 power $= \dfrac{\text{work done}}{\text{time taken}} = \dfrac{1600 \text{ J}}{5 \text{ s}}$
    $= 320$ J/s (320 W)

Quick test 22

1 wavelength
2 2 × amplitude
3 it moves up and down
4 Waves on the sea could be used to drive small turbines and generate electricity. This would reduce our use of fossil fuels.
5 $\lambda = 10$ m, $f = ½$ Hz
    speed $= \lambda \times f = 10 \times ½$
    $= 5$ m/s
6 Gamma rays are emitted by radioactive materials.
7 Gamma rays are the most penetrating electromagnetic waves. They can destroy cells. Cancer cells are very susceptible because they multiply rapidly.
8 carpet
9 brick
10 99.5 joules
11 (a) 330 metres in 1 second, so 33 metres in 0.1 (¹⁄₁₀) second
    (b) two of:
        the shape of the theatre
        the size of the theatre
        the number of people present
        the materials used for seating, walls, furnishings
    (c) people will absorb the sound
12 Air in the body of the Spanish guitar and its body vibrate as well as the strings when it is plucked.
13 The solid body of the electric guitar does not vibrate. Without the amplifier, sound only comes from the strings.

Quick test 23

1 true
2 true
3 false
4 B
5 E

6   E
7   BACK
8   (a) 2 m/s
     (b) 4 m/s
9   A virtual image is unreal. It cannot be projected onto a screen or recorded on film.
10   and 11

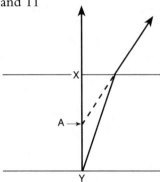

12   Apparent depth is XA; real depth is XY. Apparent depth is less than its real depth.

Quick test 24

1   5 ohms
2    $I = \dfrac{V}{R} = \dfrac{10}{5} = 2$ A
3    $V = I \times R = 2$ A $\times 2\,\Omega = 4$ volts
4   top, 12 V supply; right, switch; bottom, bulb; left, fuse
5   The fuse wire gets hot and eventually melts. The current ceases.
6   The water molecules move around each other faster.
     Eventually some water molecules near the surface of the water droplets have enough energy to escape from the droplet into the air. The molecules have evaporated.
     In time, all the water molecules have enough energy to evaporate.
7   1 unit = 1 kWh
     The kettle has a power of 3 kW
     energy   = power × time
     1 kWh   = 3 kW × time (hours, h)
     so time used = ⅓ h = 20 minutes
8   Power = $V \times I$
     3000   = $240 \times I$
     so current = $\dfrac{3000}{240}$ = 12.5 A
9   The current would be twice as large.
10   the cost per unit of electricity
11   (a) lighting circuits
     (b) 15
     (c) fault
12   5 amp fuse wire is thinner
13   it must conduct electricity
14   (a) you could get an electric shock
     (b) the wire melts
     (c) Switch off the supply at the mains, then use sand, foam or CO_2 to cut off the supply of air.

15   They can be switched on and off one at a time. If they were in series, they would all go on and off together.
16   A earth wire; B neutral wire; C cord grip; D fuse; E live wire; F cord
17   Always switch off at the mains before investigating circuit faults.
     Repair appliances/wiring as soon as faults occur.
     Disconnect appliances before doing repairs.
     Choose the right fuse for each appliance.
     Ensure that appliances with outer metal parts are earthed.
     Make sure the wires from an electrical appliance are connected to the correct terminals in the plug. (any four)

Quick test 25

1   A
2   D
3   D
4   B
5   E
6   C
7   A
8   B
9   E
10   because of the weight of the magnet
11   so that the forcemeter registers only the force from the magnetic field
12   to vary the current through the coil
13   The current in the solenoid creates a magnetic field with a N pole at the lower end of the solenoid.
     This repels the magnet and pushes on the forcemeter.
14   Current ∝ force from magnetic field
15   The iron core increases the force from the magnetic field.
16   (a) Disadvantages of overhead cables:
     ● unsightly pylons and cables
     ● installation damages environment
     ● may interfere with radio/TV reception
     ● danger from electrocution (any two)
     Disadvantages of underground cables:
     ● trees in the cable path are destroyed
     ● take longer to repair
     ● more expensive to lay (any two)
     (b) A higher voltage means that a small current can be used. This has a smaller heating effect in the wire so less energy is lost.

Quick test 26

1   A
2   B and C
3   B and D
4   E
5   D
6   C
7   D

8 A
9 E
10 B
11 (a) α-particles are positive, therefore they are attracted to upper plate which is negative. β-particles are negative, therefore they are attracted to lower plate which is positive.
   (b) both α- and β-particles will be stopped by the aluminium
12 (a) γ-rays can penetrate inside a person's body. α-rays and β-rays will not do so.
   (b) γ-rays can damage cells and body tissues. They are stopped by lead.
   (c) γ-rays sterilise the syringes after packaging. The syringes can become recontaminated during packing after steam sterilisation.
13 (a) background radiation
   (b) radiation from the Sun, radioactive isotopes in rocks or radioactive gases in the air.
   (c) a Geiger-Müller tube (Geiger counter)
14 protons and neutrons
15 27
16 55
17 *decay*: random and spontaneous break-up of radioactive atoms
   half-life: the time it takes for half of a sample of radioactive isotope to decay
18 because the half-life of Cs–137 is much longer than that of Co–60
19 In position A, γ-rays escape through the channel. In position B, any γ-rays emitted would hit the surrounding lead and be absorbed.
20 Keep exposure time as short as possible. Work behind lead or concrete shields. Use remote handling equipment from as far away as possible.

Quick test 27

1 The Sun is the odd one out because it is a star and all the others are planets.
2 year Moon Earth day planet Mercury Pluto
3 Moon, planet, solar system, galaxy, universe
4 (i) gravity (gravitational force)
   (ii) mass, distance
   (iii) movement of the tides
5 Relative mass is likely to be smaller than that of Mercury, the smallest planet.
   Surface gravity will be small (probably less than that on Venus) as this force increases with mass.
   Distance from the Sun will be between 250 and 750 million km as they orbit between Mars and Jupiter.
   Surface temperature will be about −70°C as they orbit between Mars and Jupiter.
6 The universe
7 Jupiter
8 Venus
9 Because it has the smallest mass, it has the weakest gravitational forces.
10 It is closest to the Sun.
   It has little or no atmosphere to absorb the Sun's radiation (heat).
11 Because the atmosphere is so thin, heat from the planet is easily lost to outer space.
12 Rivers, probably with water, once flowed on Mars.
13 Because its temperature is so low.
14 The Earth's axis is tilted. At Christmas time, the Northern hemisphere is tilted away from the Sun with cold, short winter days. At this time, the Southern hemisphere is tilted towards the Sun with warm, long summer days.

Coursework

During the GCSE course, your teacher will assess your scientific skills in carrying out experiments and investigations. This covers the assessment of Attainment Target 1 (Sc1; Experimental and Investigative Science) in the National Curriculum.

In England, Wales and Northern Ireland, this coursework component is the same for **all** science courses (double award, single award and separate sciences). It carries 25% of the overall assessment for GCSE.

In Scotland, coursework counts for 33% of the overall assessment in Standard Grade.

Your coursework assessment should be based on experiments and investigations which you carry out during the study of Attainment Targets 2, 3 and 4 (Sc2, Sc3 and Sc4).

The main aims of coursework are to assess the four key activities or skill areas in practical work, fieldwork and investigations during your GCSE Science course. These four activities or skill areas for assessment, with their mark ranges, are:

Skill area	Mark scale
P: Planning experimental procedures	0–8
O: Obtaining evidence	0–8
A: Analysing evidence and drawing conclusions	0–8
E: Evaluating evidence	0–6

One piece of experimental work can be used to assess one, two, three or all four skill areas. In the course of your GCSE studies, you should be assessed in each skill area on a number of occasions and your best mark in each skill area should count.

However, to satisfy the requirements of the exam:

● for double award at least one skill area mark must be obtained from work in each of Sc2, Sc3 and Sc4,

● for single award two of the skill area marks must be obtained from work in any two of Sc2, Sc3 and Sc4,

● for both double and single award at least one skill area mark must be obtained from a **whole** investigation (i.e. a piece of work which involves all four skill areas.

Awarding marks for coursework

There is a maximum of 8 marks for each of skill areas P, O and A and a maximum of 6 marks for skill area E. A single final total mark out of a maximum of 63 is obtained. This mark is calculated by adding together the best marks awarded for each of the four skill areas, doubling the total and then adding a further mark out of 3 for spelling, punctuation and grammar (SPaG).

For example, if you are awarded 4 marks for skill areas P and O, 3 marks for skill area A, 2 marks for skill area E and 2 marks for SPaG, your overall mark will be

$$2 \times (4 + 4 + 3 + 2) + 2 = 28$$

A total of 28 out of 63 is, therefore, obtained for the coursework assessment.

The marks awarded to you by your teacher, and samples of the work from your school or college, will be checked (moderated) by an expert from outside your school to make sure the marking is the same as in all other schools and colleges. The moderator may add marks to your total, if your teacher has been harsh, or deduct marks, if your teacher has been generous in the marking.

Finally, your mark out of 63 is 'scaled' to give a mark out of 25.

Skill area P: Planning experimental procedures

In this skill area, you will be expected to:

● Write down the factors (variables) which *might* affect a phenomenon.

e.g. Factors which might affect the rate of a reaction are temperature, concentration, catalysts, etc.; factors which might affect the time swing (period) of a pendulum are the length of the string, the weight of the bob, the angle of the swing, etc.

- Use your scientific knowledge and understanding to predict how the different factors (variables) might affect the phenomenon.

  e.g. How does temperature affect the rate of reaction? If the temperature rises, does the rate change? If so, does the reaction go faster or slower?
- Try to decide which factors (variables) will have the greater effect.

  e.g. Will increasing temperature or increasing concentration have the greater effect on reaction rates?
- Try to make *quantitative* predictions if possible. You need to say something like: 'I think that doubling the concentration of a reactant would double the rate of the reaction'. Alternatively, you could draw a graph of reaction rate (vertically) against concentration (horizontally) to show how you think the reaction rate will be affected by changes in concentration.

  After you have made a prediction, try to give a scientific reason for it. It does not matter if you are wrong. You could write something like: 'I think that this will happen because...'.
- Make a plan for your investigation. Say which factor you will vary, which factors you will keep constant and what results you will try to collect. You should vary only one factor at a time.

  e.g. If you are investigating the effect of concentration on a reaction, you will need to vary the concentration of only one substance, keep other concentrations constant and have some means of measuring the reaction rate (such as the volume of gas collected in a given time).
- Decide on the number of observations or measurements you should make and the range over which they will be made. Normally you would be expected to obtain measurements for five different values of a variable over a reasonable range.

  e.g. Five different concentrations of hydrochloric acid between 0 and 2 moles per dm^3 if you are investigating the effect of the concentration of the acid on its reaction with limestone (calcium carbonate); or five different lengths of a pendulum string between 0 and 100 cm if you are investigating the effect of the length of the string on the time swing (period) of a pendulum.
- In some cases, such as fieldwork, it will be difficult to control the variables and other conditions. This means that you will have to decide how much information you need or how many observations/measurements to make.
- Select apparatus, equipment and techniques, taking account of safety requirements.

  e.g. You should plan to wear safety spectacles if you are using chemicals.

Skill area O: Obtaining evidence

In this skill area you will be expected to:
- Use apparatus and equipment safely and with skill.
- Make observations and measurements to an appropriate degree of precision.

  e.g. If you are measuring the time swing (period) of a pendulum for different lengths of string, you should be able to measure the length of the string to the nearest centimetre but not to the nearest millimetre.
- Make sufficient measurements and observations to obtain reliable data.

  e.g. Measure the time period of a pendulum for at least 5 different lengths of string between 0 and 100 cm.
- Repeat your measurements, make additional observations or modify your experiment if your results seem uncertain, unreliable or inconclusive.
- Record your evidence (results, observations, measurements) clearly and appropriately as you carry out experiments and investigations. Sometimes it will be helpful to record your results in a table.

Skill area A: Analysing evidence and drawing conclusions

In this skill area you will be expected to:
- Describe what you have found out (results, observations, measurements, etc.).
- Present numerical data to an appropriate degree of accuracy.

  e.g. Measurements with a metre rule cannot be given to a greater accuracy than 0.1 cm, burette measurements can be given to the nearest 0.05 cm^3.

- Present data in graphs (using lines of best fit, where appropriate) or in diagrams.
- Identify trends or patterns in your results.
- Use graphs to identify the relationship between variables and draw conclusions.

    e.g. From a graph of the time swing (period) of a pendulum against the length of the string, you should be able to conclude that the period increases as the length increases.

- Say whether your results support or undermine your original prediction. Are your predictions correct, incorrect or inconclusive?
- Try to explain your conclusions using scientific knowledge and ideas.

    e.g. You could explain the effect of temperature or concentration on the rate of a reaction using the idea of moving particles and their collisions.

Skill area E: Evaluating evidence

In this skill area, you will be expected to:

- Decide whether your results, observations and/or measurements are sufficient to allow you to draw conclusions.
- Identify results that do not fit the main pattern or trend (anomalous results) and reject them where appropriate.
- Suggest reasons for anomalous results, if possible.
- Comment on the accuracy and reliability of your results bearing in mind possible errors in measurements and observations.
- Suggest improvements to the methods you have used.
- Suggest further investigations to test your conclusions.

Assessment of coursework

Your teacher will assess your practical skills in two ways:

- by watching how you follow instructions and carry out experiments,
- by assessing your written report of an experiment or investigation.

You should be assessed on more than one occasion, so don't worry if you do badly on one piece of work. Nevertheless, you should discuss your standards in coursework assessment with your teacher throughout KS4.

The following information should be included in your written coursework:

1. A **clear title** and an **introduction** saying what you are investigating.
2. A list of the **factors** (**variables**) you are investigating.
3. A **diagram** of your apparatus.
4. A **description** of what you will do and what **data** (**results**) you will collect.
5. **Tables of your results**, showing the units of different quantities.
6. **Graphs** which enable you to make concise **conclusions** about the effects of different variables. Try to make quantitative conclusions and compare the relative effects of variables.
7. Any **precautions** you take for safety reasons or to make your investigations more accurate.
8. **List the sources of error** in your experiments and indicate **uncertainties** in your conclusions.
9. An **explanation** of your results or conclusions using scientific laws, theories and models.

Index

acceleration 236
acid rain 176–7
acids 176–9
    metal reaction 153–4
active transport, cells 37
air 135
alimentary canal 54–5
alkali metals 218–19
alkalis 179–80
    industrial use 181
alkanes 202
alkenes 203–4
alloys 155–6
alpha rays 314–15
alternators 307–9
aluminium, manufacture 168–9
ammonia 187
    fertilisers 188–9
    manufacture 187–8
amplitude 261
arteries 60
atmosphere 120–1
atomic number 215
atoms 144–5, 147–8, 160
    structure 214

bases 179
beta rays 314–16
biomass, pyramid 27
blood
    circulation 60–2
    functions of 59–60
    glucose 89
blood cells 58–9
boiling 142
bonds 171–3, 203–4
    covalent 223–4
    ionic 223
Boyle's law 143
breadmaking 73–4, 77
breathing 67–71
breeding, selective 104
brewing 73–4
bronchitis 70
bronze 155
Brownian motion 140

cancer, lung 70
capillaries 60
carbohydrates 48
carbon cycles 30–1
catalysts 193
cells 35–7
    division 92, 93, 99
    respiration 71, 77
central nervous system 78–9, 83–4, 85–6
chlorophyll 39–40
chromatography 132
chromosomes 98–9
circuit breakers 292–3

circuits 281–3
cloning 92–3
combustion 197
comets 328
compounds 134
    formulas 146–7, 148–9
    ionic 169–71
    molecular 171–3
condensing 142
conduction, electrical 165
conductivity 161
coulombs 283–4

diet 50
diffraction 269
diffusion
    in cells 37
    particles 139–40
digestion 53–6
diseases
    emphysema 70–1
    heart 62–3
    hereditary 103–4
    thrombosis 63
displacement 233
distance–time graphs 234–5
distillation 131–2
    oil 201–2
drugs 84–5

ear 81
Earth, structure 120
earth science 120–6
earth wires 292
earthquakes 124, 267–8
ecology 24
ecosystems 24–6
    food production 29–30
elasticity 229
electric charges 283–4, 294–5
electric circuits 281–3
electric currents 164–6, 281–97
electric generator 307–9
electric motors 305–6
electrical power 293
electricity 281–97
    bills 294
    house wiring 289–91
electrolysis 159, 165–9
electromagnetic induction 306–7
electromagnets 304
electrons 160, 214
    shells 217–18
electroplating 169
electrostatic charges 295–6
elements 133–4
    metals 133, 152–62
    non-metals 133
    symbols 145–6
    trace 24

transition 212, 221–2
emphysema 70–1
energy
    conservation law 247
    conservation of 250–1
    conversion efficiency 247–8
    conversions 246–7, 249–50
    electrical 287–9
    forms of 245–7
    renewable sources 200
    uses 250–1
energy chains 30–1
enzymes 42, 193–4
essential elements 43–4
ethanol 207–8
evaporation 142
evolution 104–8
eye 79–80

fats 47, 48
fermentation 73
fertilisation 92, 94
fertilisers 113–14
    ammonia 188–9
    nitrogen 189
fibre optics 278–9
filtering 130
fission 318–19
food
    chains 25–7
    digestive system 53–6
    types 47
    webs 25–7
forces 226–41, 244
freezing 142
frequency 261
friction 229–30
fuels 197–9
    energy 199
    fossil 199–200
fuses 291–2
fusion 320

gamma rays 314–16
Geiger-Müller tubes 316
genes 101–4
genetics 98–109
gravity 226–7, 239–41, 325–6

Haber Process 188
habitats 24–5
halogens 219–20
heart 62–3
heat 251
    conductivity 252
    insulation 252–4
    transfer 251–2
homeostatic control 88–9
Hooke's law 228
hormones 86–8

hydraulics 233

indicators 177–8
industry, chemical 184–95
insulators, electrical 165
ions 166–8
iron extraction 156
isotopes 215–16

joules 244

kidneys 63–4
kilowatt hours 294
kinetic energy 245
kinetic theory 140–1

light 273–9
long sight 80
lungs 67–71

magnetic fields 301–2
    Earth's 302
    electric currents 303–4
magnetic poles 300
magnetism 300–4
magnets, types 301
mass 226–7
mass number 215
materials
    change of state 141–2
    classification 128–9
    properties 129
meiosis 100–1
melting 142
metal extraction 158–9
metal properties 160–1
metal structure 159–60
metalloids 212
metals 133, 152–62
minerals 49
mirrors 274–5
mitochondria 36
mitosis 92, 99–100
mixtures 135
    separation 130–2
molecules 144–5
moments 230–1
Moon 327–8

National Grid 289, 310
natural selection 106–8
nervous system 78–9, 83–4, 85–6
neutralisation, acids/alkalis 180
neutrons 160, 214
newtons 226
Newton's laws of motion 237–8
nitrogen
    cycle 189–90
    fertilisers 189
noble gases 222
nose 81–2
nuclear energy 318–20
nuclear reactions 315–16
nuclear reactors 320
nucleus, cells 24, 36
nutrients 47

Ohm's law 286–8
oil 201–8
organelles 36
organisms
    adaptation 107–8
    characteristics 22
    classification 22–4
    populations 28–30
    variety 21
osmosis 37
oxidation 157
oxygen 136
    metal reactions 153

periodic table 211–13
pesticides 114
pH scale 177–8
photosynthesis 39–40, 41–3
pitch 264
planets 325, 326–7
plasma 58–9
plastics 205–6
plate tectonics 123–5
platelets 58
plugs, electrical 292
pollution 114–15
populations 28–30
potential difference 284–5
power 248–9
power stations 249–50
pressure 231–2
    gas 142–3
    liquids 232–3
proteins 47, 48
protons 160, 214
pyramids of numbers 27

radioactivity 314
    dangers 318
    detection 316
    half-life 316–17
    uses 317–18
reaction rates
    governing factors 192–4
    industrial processes 190
    measurement 190–2
reactions 162
    acid/bases 179
    acid/carbonates 179
    acid/metal 178
    nuclear 315–16
reactivity, metals 153–5
reactivity series 152–3
redox reaction 157–8
reduction 157
reflection 264–5, 273–5, 277–9
reflex actions 84–5
refraction 264–5, 275–7
reproduction 92–6, 100–1
resistance 285–8
resistors 285–6
resonance 262
resources, natural 115–16
respiration 67–77
rocks, types 122–3, 125–6
rusting 157

senses 78–90
short sight 80
skin 82–3
solar system 325, 326–7
solutions 130–2
sound 256–8
    echoes 258–60
    loudness 263–4
    pitch 264
    quality 263
    speed 258–9
space exploration 329
specific heat capacity 251
speed 234, 235
speed–time graphs 236–7
starch 24, 39, 40–1
stars 323–4, 330
stimuli 78
substances 128
    purity 133
    structures 172–3
sulphuric acid
    manufacture 186
    uses 185
Sun 324–5

taste 81–2
temperature 251
tension 227–8
thermometers 251
tides 328
total internal reflection 277–9
trace elements 44
transformers 309–10
transition metals 221–2
transpiration 42–3
turning forces 230–1

ultrasound 259–60
universe 324–5, 330–2

vascular system 25, 43
veins 60
velocity 234
    terminal 241
vitamins 49
volcanoes 122, 124
voltage 284–5, 287–9

waste 112–15
water, metal reaction 153
wave equation 262
wavelength 261
waves 256, 260–2
    electromagnetic 268–70
    seismic 267–8
    speed 261–2
    types 265–7
weathering 121
weight 226–7, 240
wildlife 116
work 244

zygote 100–1